Kindergarten Handwriting for Young Catholics

by Seton Staff

Seton Press
Front Royal, Virginia

Executive Editor: Dr. Mary Kay Clark
Editors: Seton Staff

© 2012 Seton Home Study School
All rights reserved.
Printed in the United States of America

Seton Home Study School
1350 Progress Drive
Front Royal, VA 22630
Phone: (540) 636-9990
Fax: (540) 636-1602

For more information, visit us on the Web at: www.setonhome.org
Contact us by e-mail at: info@setonhome.org

ISBN: 978-1-60704-003-3

Cover: *Madonna and Child Amongst the Flowers*

Today is Monday.
I see and trace backward circles.

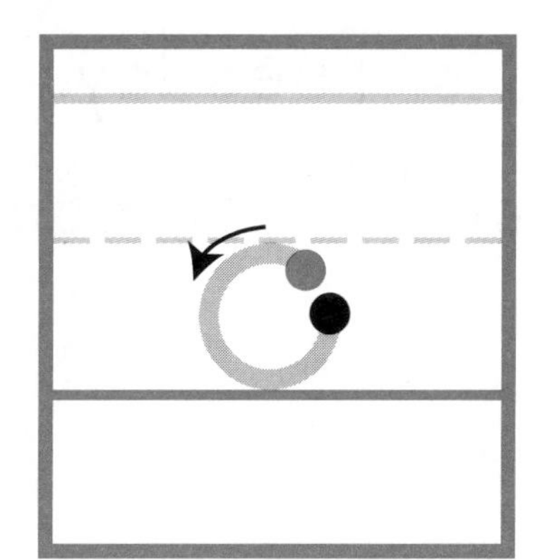

Stroke Refinement Exercises: Backward circles start at the top and stop almost at the beginning point of the circle. Have your child start at the blue dot and stop at the black dot, moving from top to bottom. Use a black crayon to trace the backward circles. Emphasize the movement from top to bottom. Note that when reading a book, our eyes move from the top of the page to the bottom of the page.

Today is Tuesday.

I see and trace backward circles.

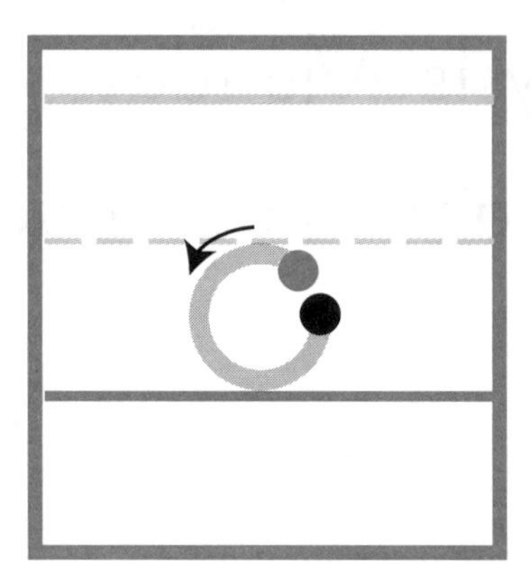

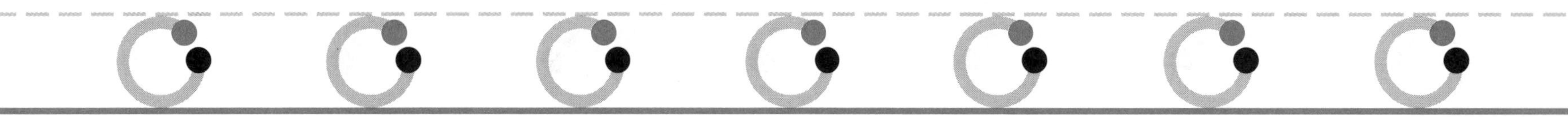

Stroke Refinement Exercises: Backward circles start at the top and stop almost at the beginning point of the circle. Have your child start at the blue dot and stop at the black dot, moving from top to bottom. Use a black crayon to trace the backward circles. Emphasize the movement from top to bottom. Note that when reading a book, our eyes move from the top of the page to the bottom of the page.

Today is Wednesday.
I write backward circles.

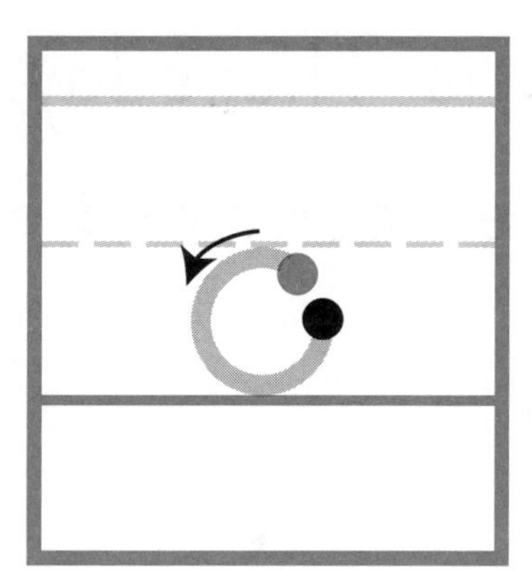

Stroke Refinement Exercises: Backward circles start at the top and stop at the beginning point of the circle. Have your child start at the blue dot and stop at the black dot, moving from top to bottom. Have your child write backward circles.

Today is Thursday.
I write backward circles.

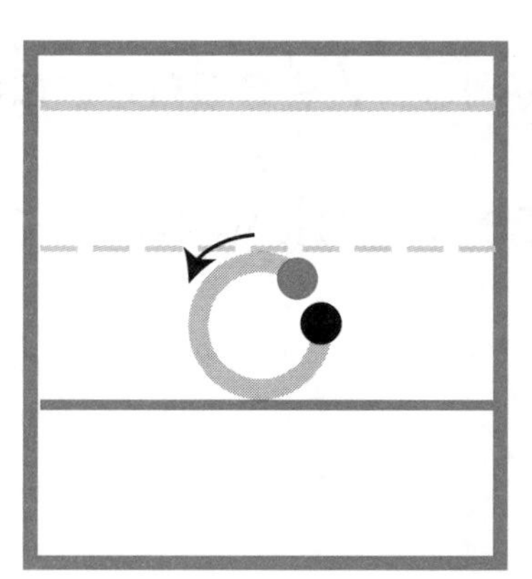

Stroke Refinement Exercises: Backward circles start at the top and stop at the beginning point of the circle. Have your child start at the blue dot and stop at the black dot, moving from top to bottom. Have your child write backward circles.

Today is Friday.
I see backward circles in letters.

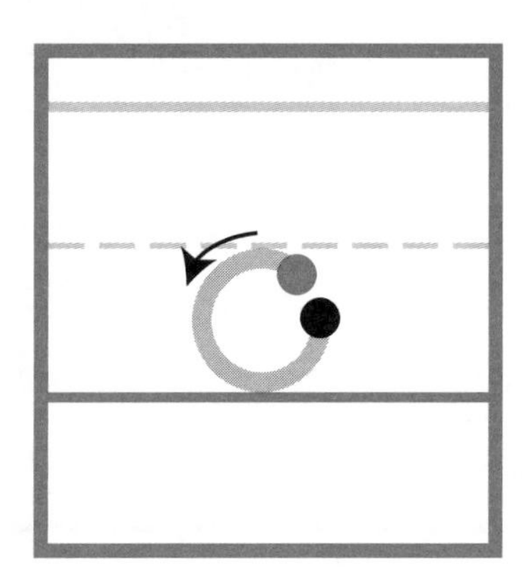

o c a d o c a d

o c a d o c a d

Stroke Refinement Exercises: Backward circles start at the top and stop at the beginning point of the circle. Have your child start at the blue dot and stop at the black dot, moving from top to bottom. Use a black crayon to trace the backward circles in the letters.

Close within thine arms enfold me.
Right beside thy Baby hold me.

Today is Monday.
I see and trace forward circles.

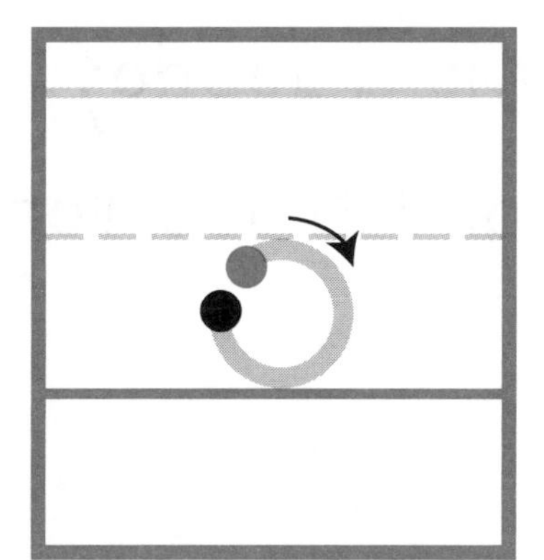

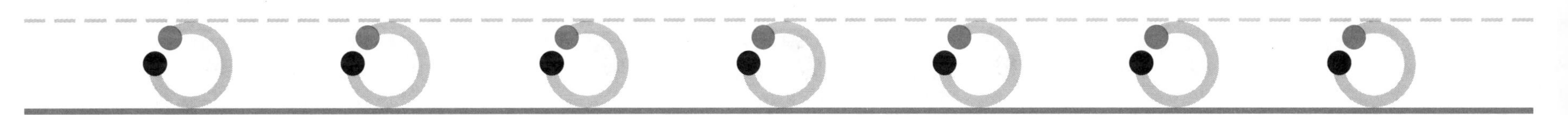

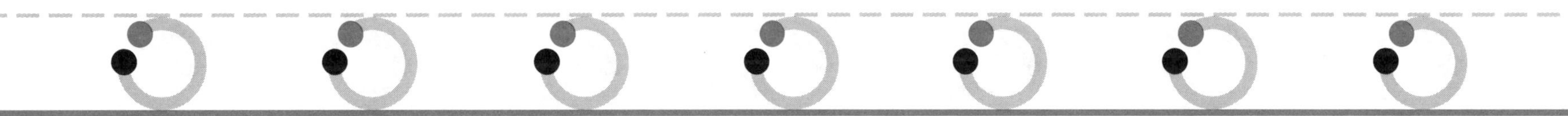

Stroke Refinement Exercises: Forward circles start at the top of the circle and move from left to right, stopping at the beginning point of the circle. Have your child start at the blue dot and stop at the black dot, moving from left to right. Use a black crayon to trace the forward circles. Emphasize the movement from left to right. Note that when reading a book, our eyes move from the left side of the each line to the right side of each line.

Today is Tuesday.

I see and trace forward circles.

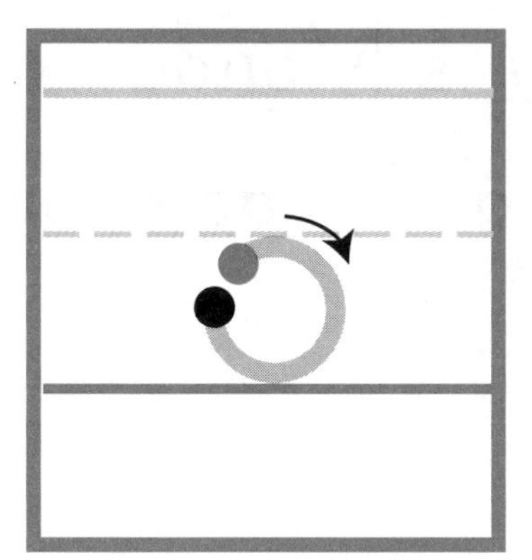

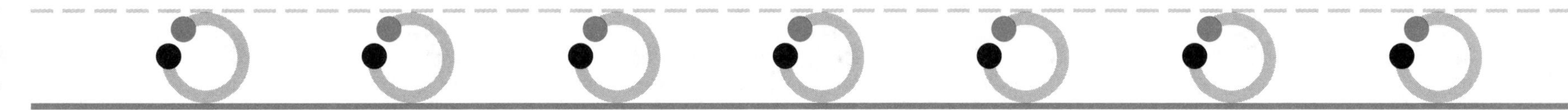

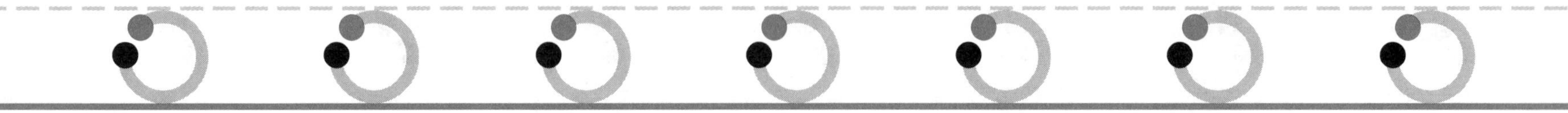

Stroke Refinement Exercises: Forward circles start at the top of the circle and move from left to right, stopping at the beginning point of the circle. Have your child start at the blue dot and stop at the black dot, moving from left to right. Use a black crayon to trace the forward circles. Emphasize the movement from left to right. Note that when reading a book, our eyes move from the left side of the each line to the right side of each line.

Today is Wednesday.
I write forward circles.

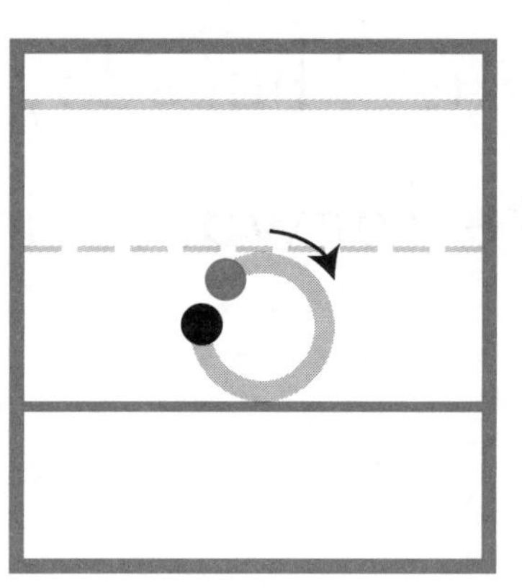

Stroke Refinement Exercises: Forward circles start at the top of the circle and move from left to right, stopping at the beginning point of the circle. Have your child start at the blue dot and stop at the black dot, moving from left to right. Have your child write forward circles.

Today is Thursday.
I write forward circles.

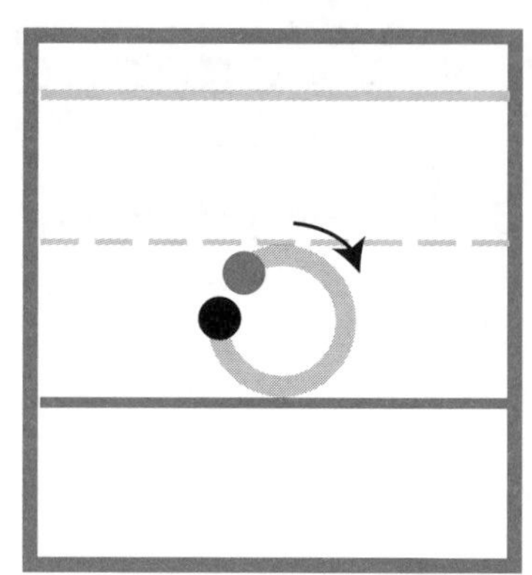

Stroke Refinement Exercises: Forward circles start at the top of the circle and move from left to right, stopping at the beginning point of the circle. Have your child start at the blue dot and stop at the black dot, moving from left to right. Have your child write forward circles.

Today is Friday.
I see forward circles in letters.

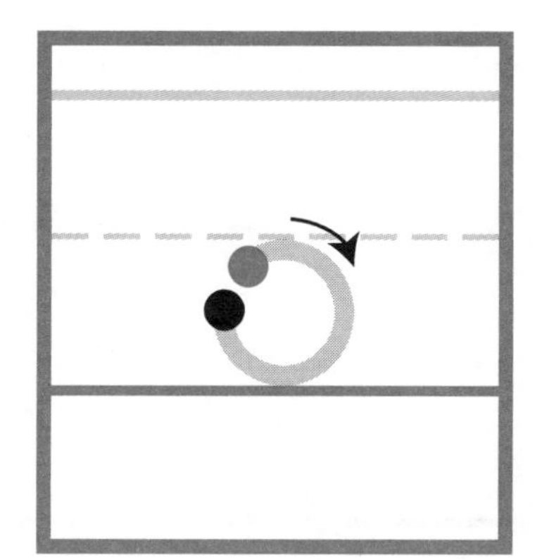

b p h n m r

b p h n m r

Stroke Refinement Exercises: Forward circles start at the top of the circle and move from left to right, stopping at the beginning point of the circle. Have your child start at the blue dot and stop at the black dot, moving from left to right. Use a black crayon to trace the forward circles in the letters.

Make me good and kind and fair,
Like thy little Jesus there.

Today is Monday.
I see and trace forward lines.

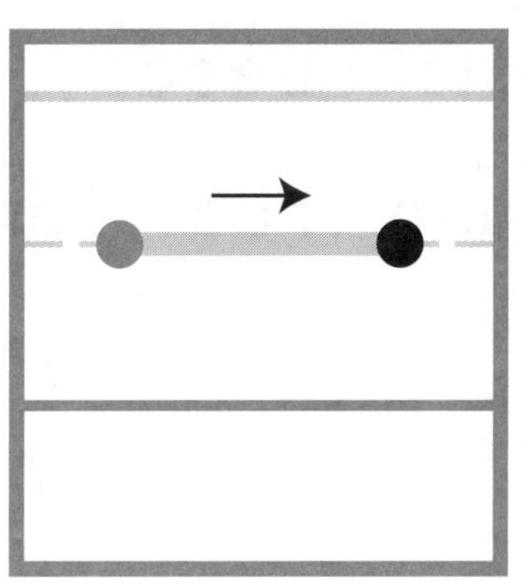

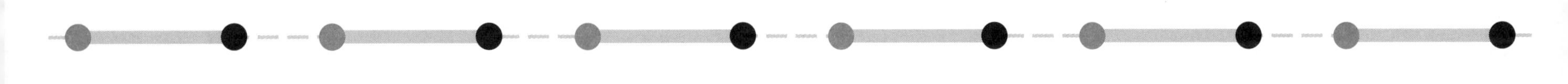

Stroke Refinement Exercises: Forward lines start at the left and stop at the right. Have your child start at the blue dot and stop at the black dot, moving from left to right. Use a black crayon to trace the forward lines. Emphasize the movement from left to right. Note that when reading a book, our eyes move from the left side of the each line to the right side of each line.

Today is Tuesday.
I see and trace forward lines.

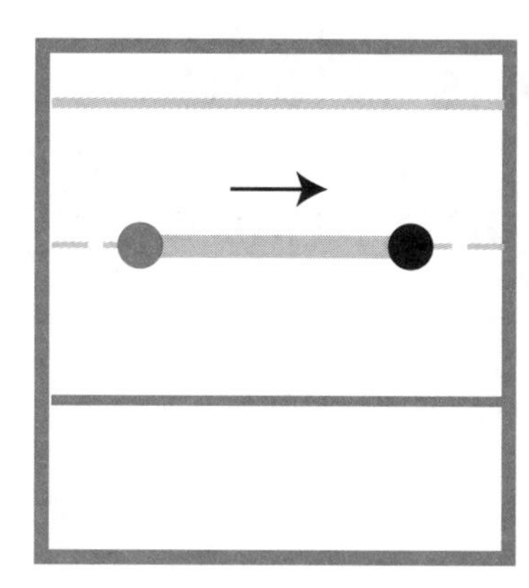

Stroke Refinement Exercises: Forward lines start at the left and stop at the right. Have your child start at the blue dot and stop at the black dot, moving from left to right. Use a black crayon to trace the forward lines. Emphasize the movement from left to right. Note that when reading a book, our eyes move from the left side of the each line to the right side of each line.

Today is Wednesday.
I write forward lines.

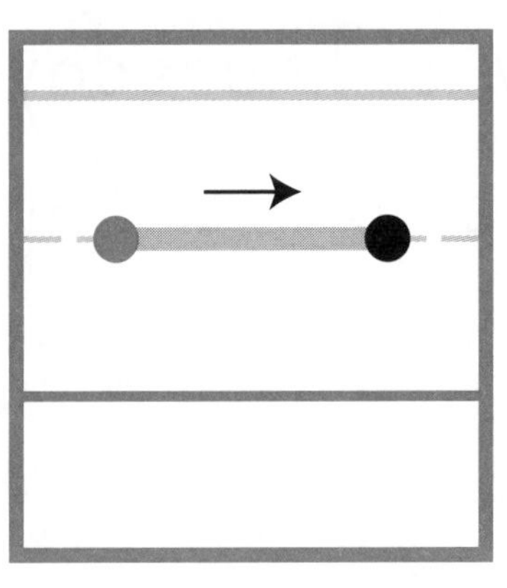

Stroke Refinement Exercises: Forward lines start at the left and stop at the right. Have your child start at the blue dot and stop at the black dot, moving from left to right. Have your child write forward lines.

Today is Thursday.
I write forward lines.

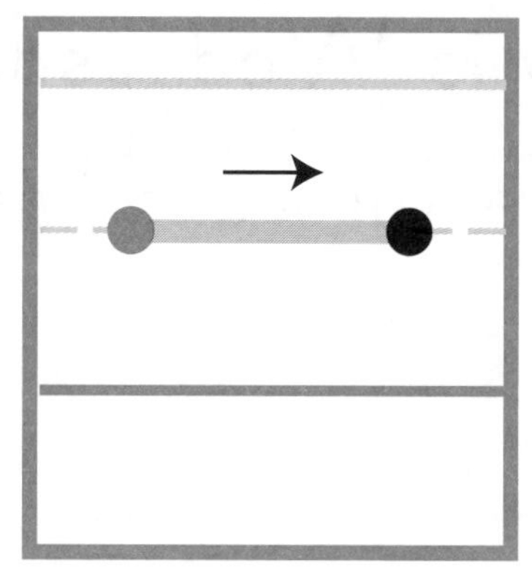

Stroke Refinement Exercises: Forward lines start at the left and stop at the right. Have your child start at the blue dot and stop at the black dot, moving from left to right. Have your child write forward lines.

Today is Friday.
I see forward lines in letters.

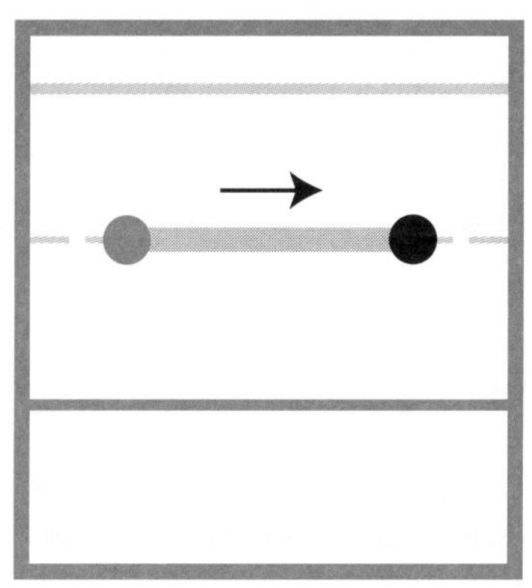

t e f t e f

t e f t e f

Stroke Refinement Exercises: Forward lines start at the left and stop at the right. Have your child start at the blue dot and stop at the black dot, moving from left to right. Use a black crayon to trace the forward lines in the letters.

Blessed Mother, pure and true,
Teach me how to pray with you.

Today is Monday.

I see and trace slant-stroke lines.

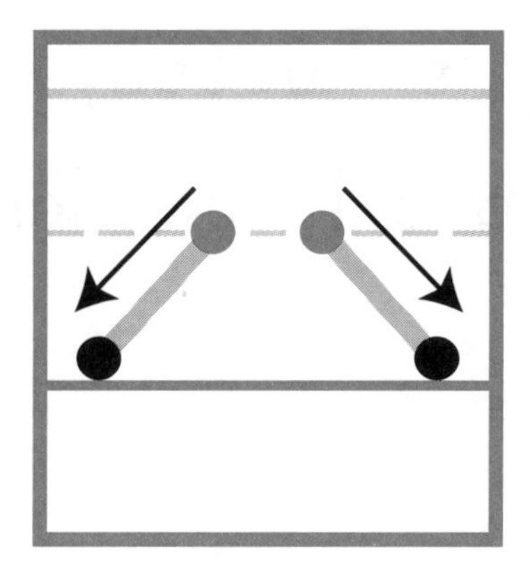

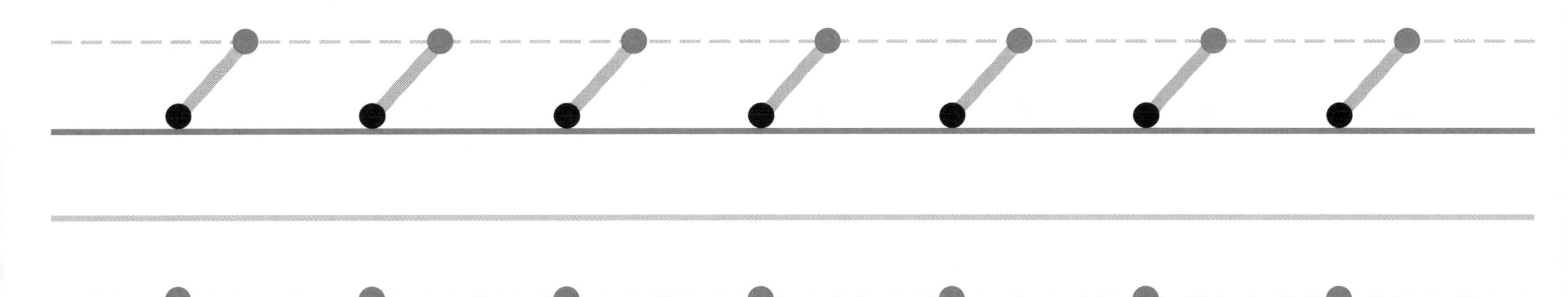

Stroke Refinement Exercises: Slant-stroke lines start at the top and stop at the bottom, moving in a slanted direction rather than straight down. Have your child start at the blue dot and stop at the black dot, moving from top to bottom in a slanted direction. Use a black crayon to trace the slant-stroke lines. Emphasize the movement from top to bottom. Note that when reading a book, our eyes move from the top of the page to the bottom of the page.

Today is Tuesday.

I see and trace slant-stroke lines.

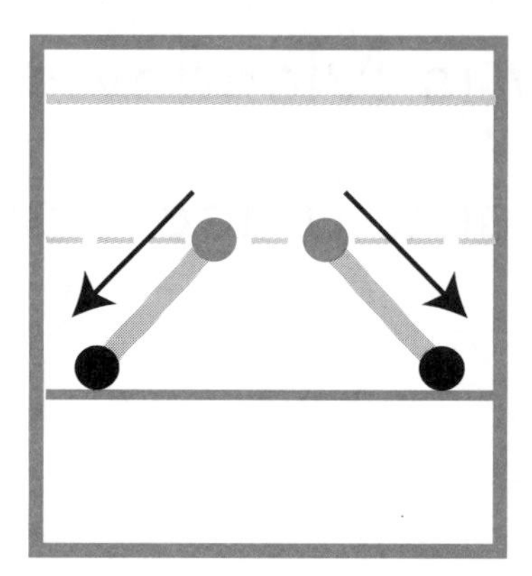

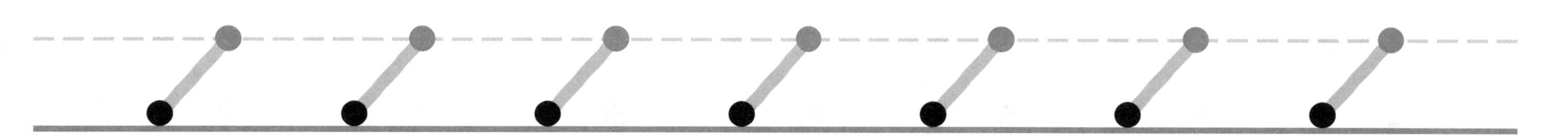

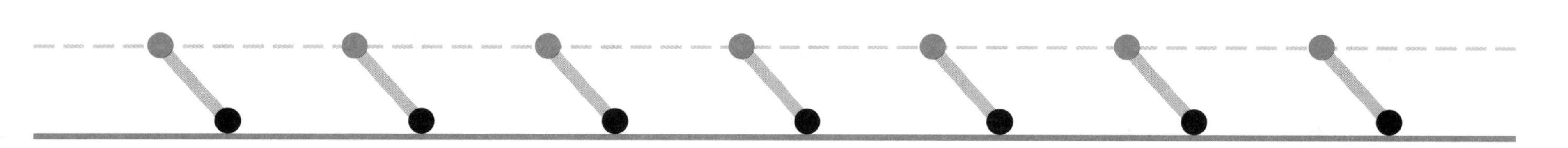

Stroke Refinement Exercises: Slant-stroke lines start at the top and stop at the bottom, moving in a slanted direction rather than straight down. Have your child start at the blue dot and stop at the black dot, moving from top to bottom in a slanted direction. Use a black crayon to trace the slant-stroke lines. Emphasize the movement from top to bottom. Note that when reading a book, our eyes move from the top of the page to the bottom of the page.

Today is Wednesday.
I write slant-stroke lines.

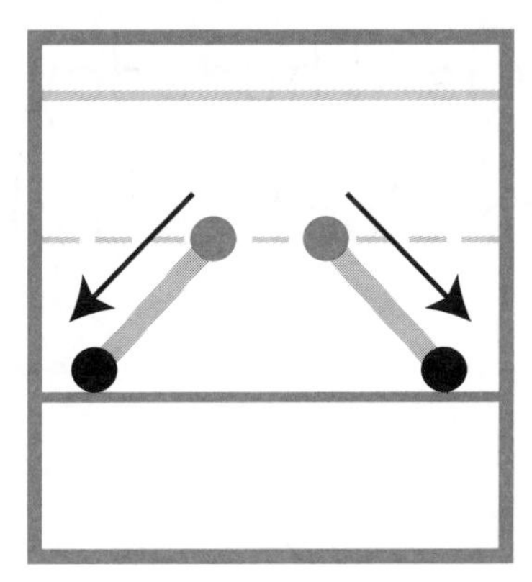

Stroke Refinement Exercises: Slant-stroke lines start at the top and stop at the bottom, moving in a slanted direction rather than straight down. Have your child start at the blue dot and stop at the black dot, moving from top to bottom in a slanted direction. Have your child write slant- stroke lines.

Today is Thursday.

I write slant-stroke lines.

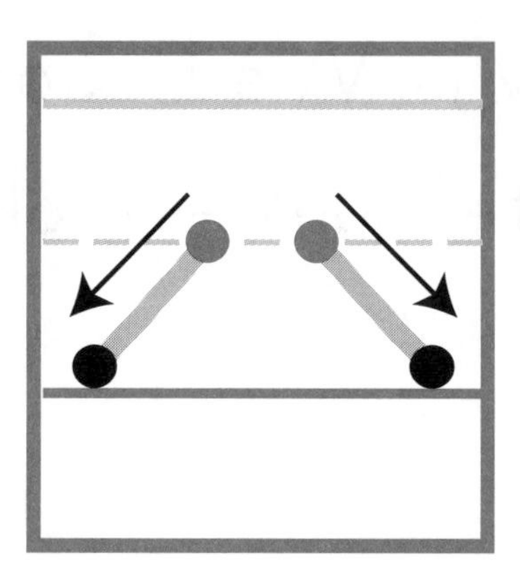

Stroke Refinement Exercises: Slant-stroke lines start at the top and stop at the bottom, moving in a slanted direction rather than straight down. Have your child start at the blue dot and stop at the black dot, moving from top to bottom in a slanted direction. Have your child write slant- stroke lines.

Today is Friday.

I see slant-stroke lines in letters.

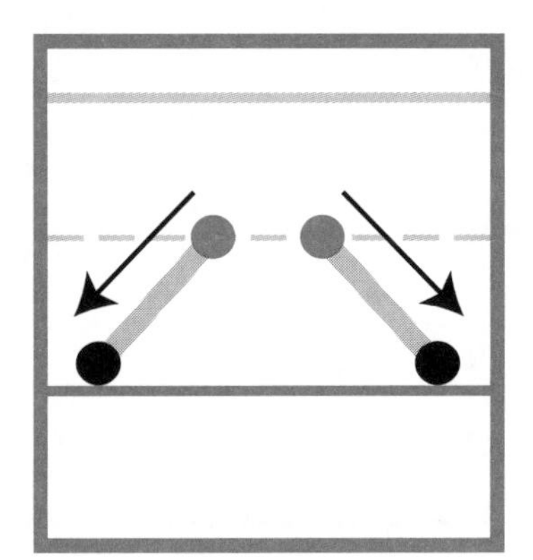

z k v w x y

z k v w x y

Stroke Refinement Exercises: Slant-stroke lines start at the top and stop at the bottom, moving in a slanted direction rather than straight down. Have your child start at the blue dot and stop at the black dot, moving from top to bottom in a slanted direction. Use a black crayon to trace the slant-stroke lines in the letters.

Jesus was your little Boy,
He filled your heart with joy.

Touch the blue dot on the headline; pull down straight to the black dot on the baseline. Lift.

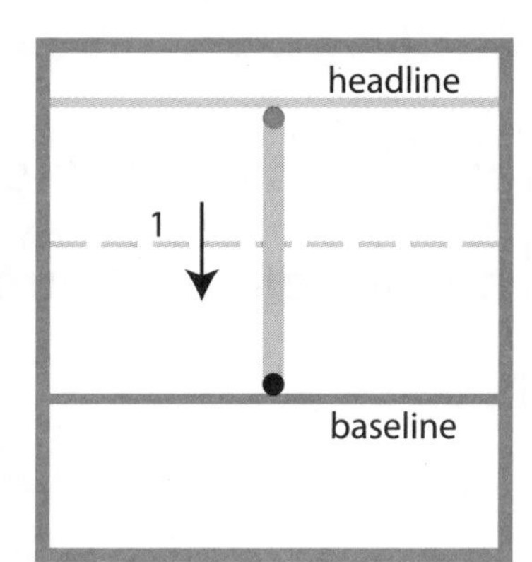

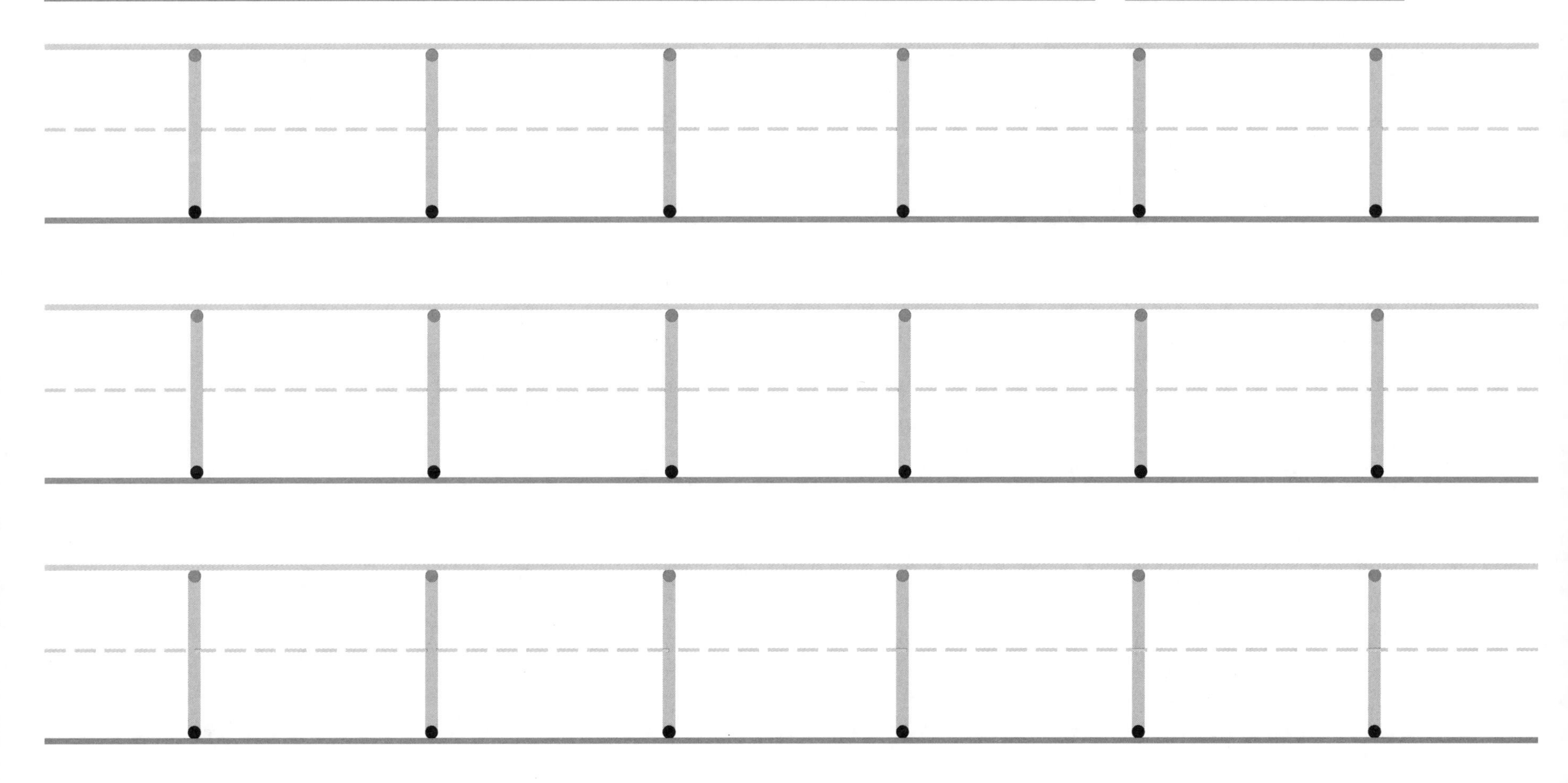

Touch the blue dot on the headline; pull down straight to the baseline. Pause; slide right to the black dot. Lift.

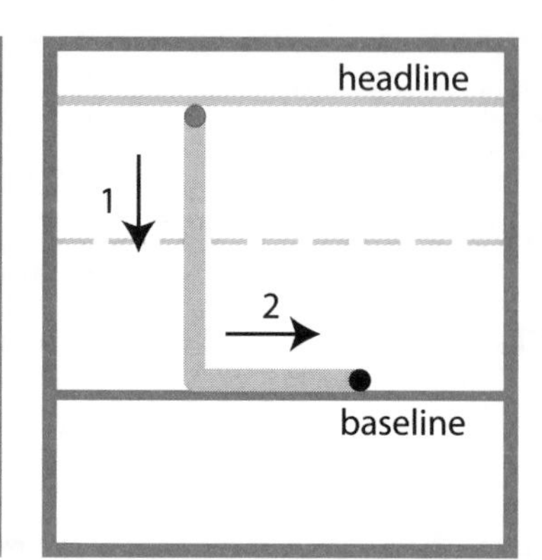

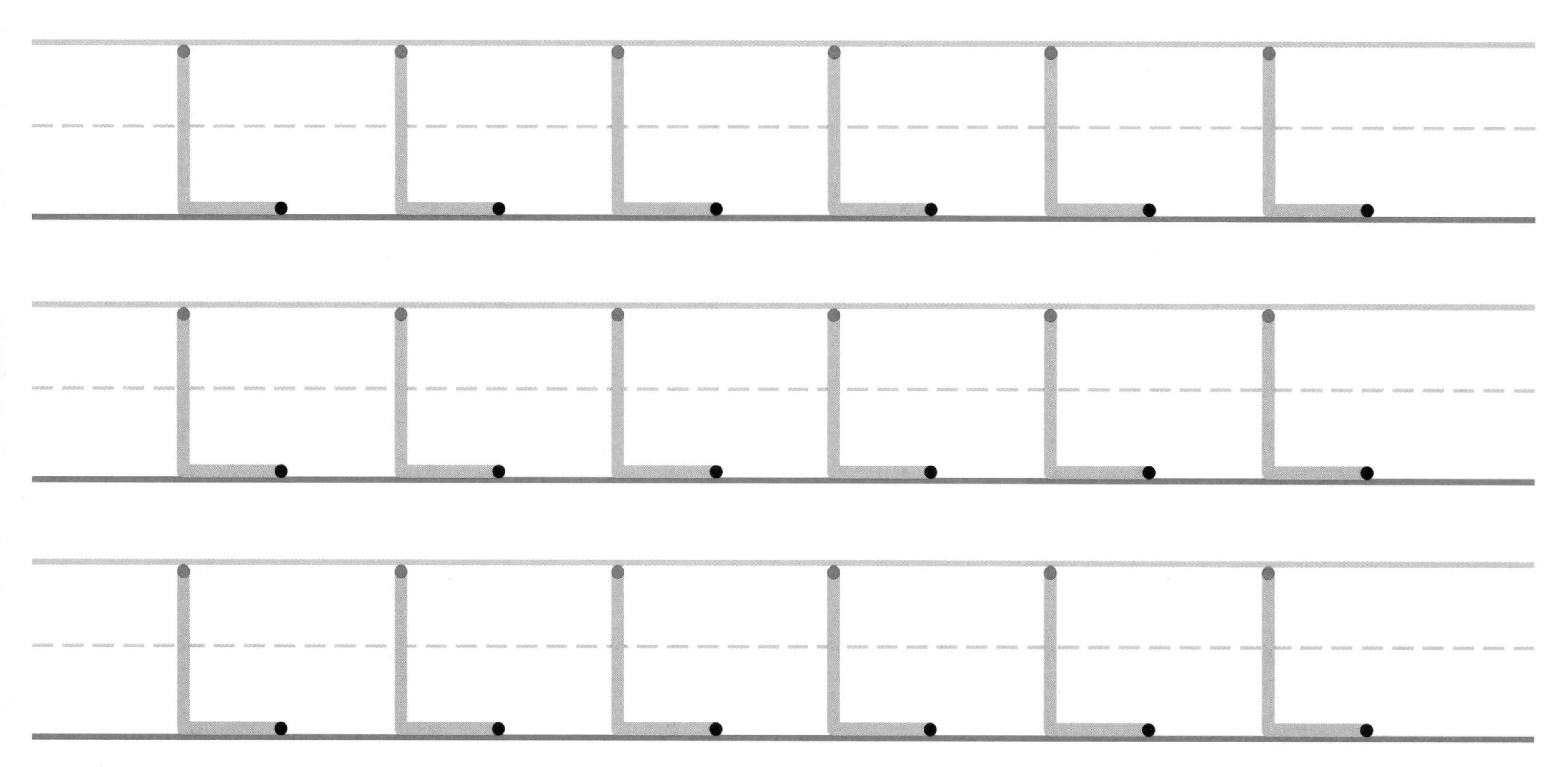

Today is Monday.

I see things that begin with the sound of l.

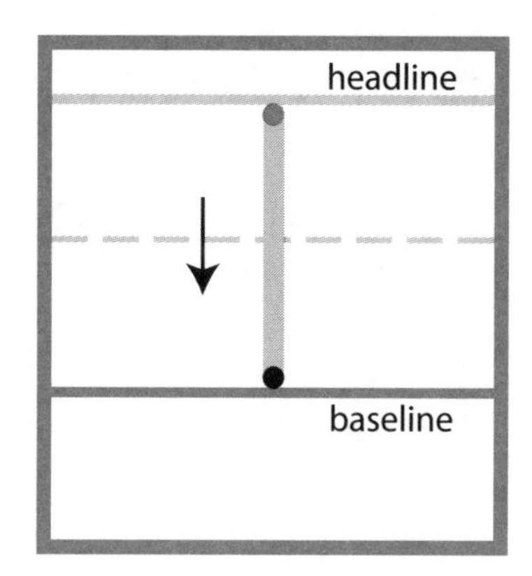

Attention Parent/Teacher: Using bright colored pencils, your child may draw pictures of today's items beginning with the sound of **l**. Emphasizing the sound of the letter, instruct your child to trace and write the letter. As your child writes, read the following Zaner-Bloser Stroke Descriptions: Touch the headline; pull down straight to the baseline.

Today is Tuesday.

I hear rhyming words that end with the sound of l.

bell	bill	full
fell	fill	gull
sell	sill	hull

Attention Parent/Teacher: Read the rhyming words to your child. Emphasizing the sound of the letter, instruct your child to trace and write the letter. As your child writes, read the following Zaner-Bloser Stroke Descriptions: Touch the headline; pull down straight to the baseline.

Today is Wednesday.

I taste things that begin with the sound of l.

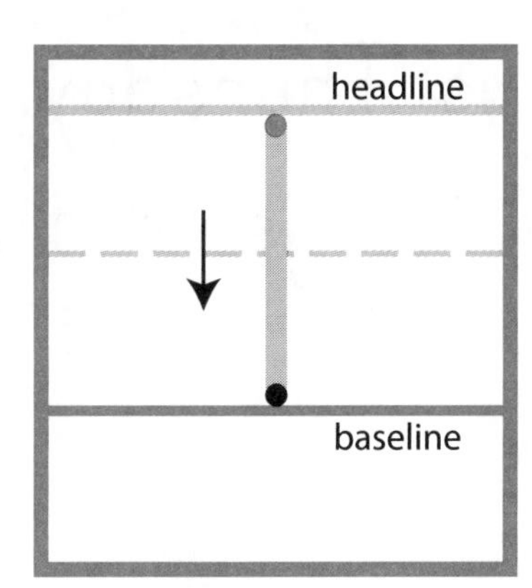

Attention Parent/Teacher: Using bright colored pencils, your child may draw pictures of today's items beginning with the sound of **l**. Emphasizing the sound of the letter, instruct your child to trace and write the letter. As your child writes, read the following Zaner-Bloser Stroke Descriptions: Touch the headline; pull down straight to the baseline.

Today is Thursday.

I smell things that begin with the sound of l.

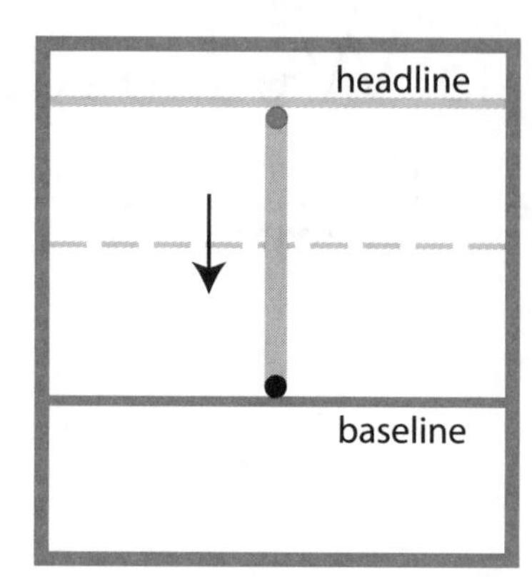

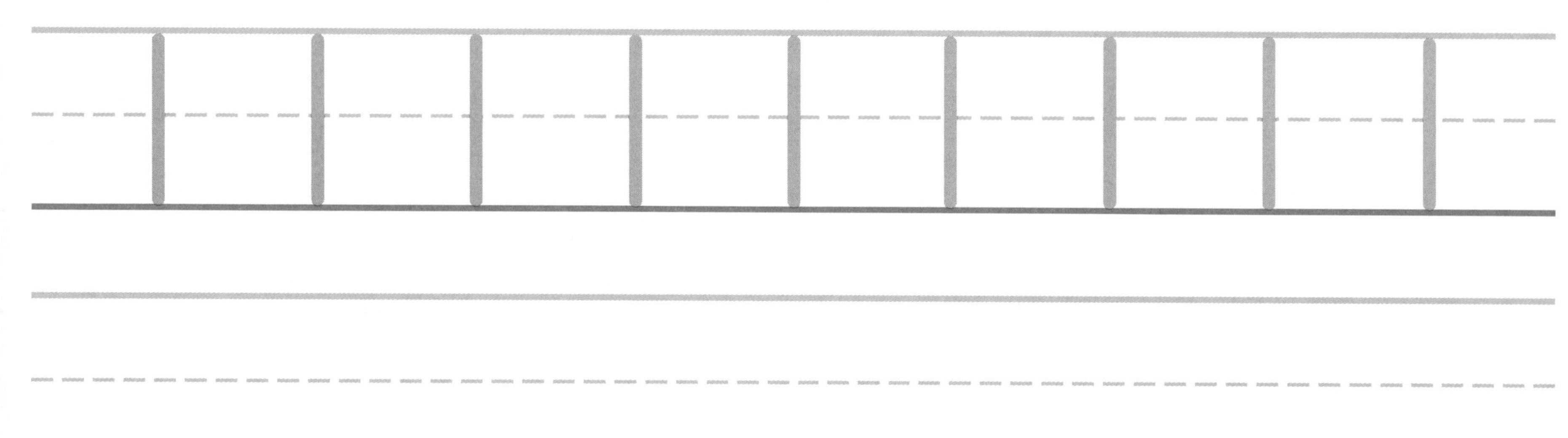

Attention Parent/Teacher: Using bright colored pencils, your child may draw pictures of today's items beginning with the sound of **l**. Emphasizing the sound of the letter, instruct your child to trace and write the letter. As your child writes, read the following Zaner-Bloser Stroke Descriptions: Touch the headline; pull down straight to the baseline.

Today is Friday.
I touch things that begin with the sound of l.

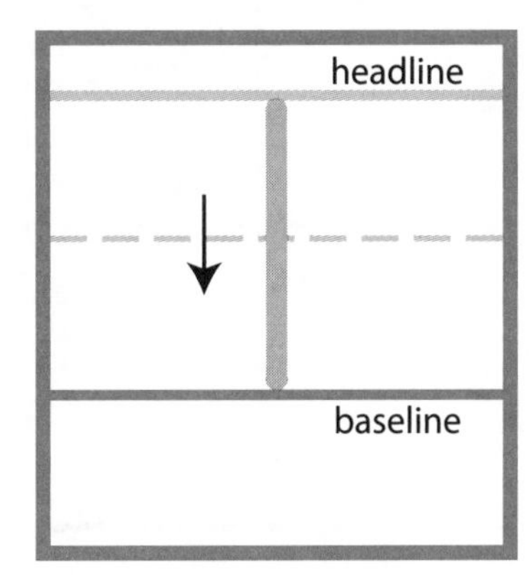

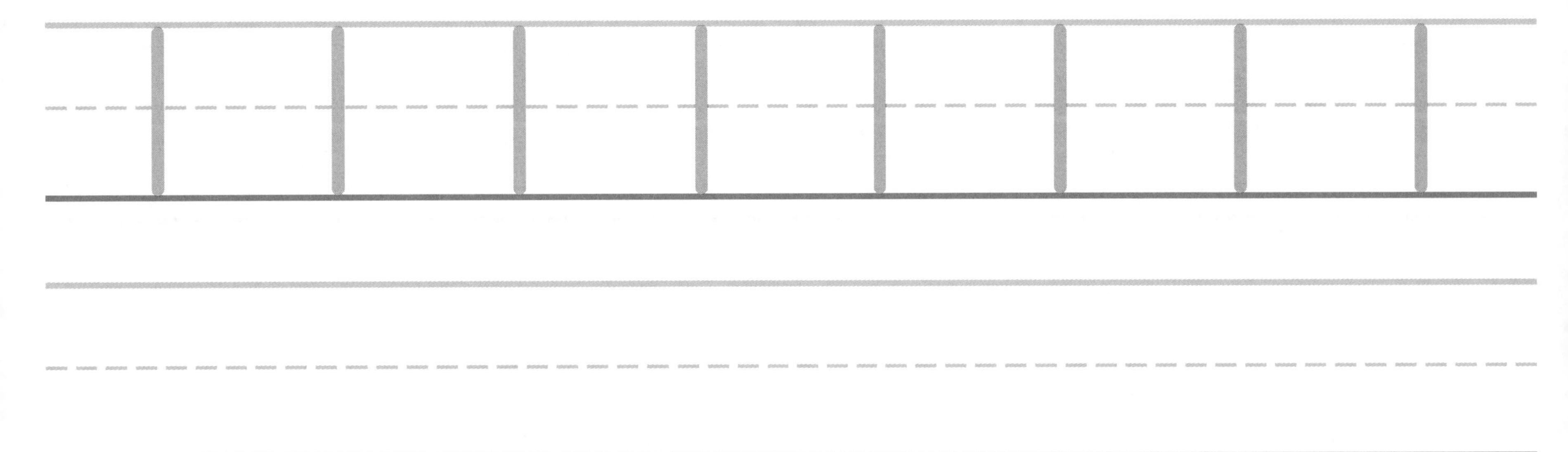

Attention Parent/Teacher: Using bright colored pencils, your child may draw pictures of today's items beginning with the sound of **l**. Emphasizing the sound of the letter, instruct your child to trace and write the letter. As your child writes, read the following Zaner-Bloser Stroke Descriptions: Touch the headline; pull down straight to the baseline.

Teach me what it means to pray
So that I may know the way.

1. Touch the blue dot on the midline; pull down straight to the black dot on the baseline. Lift.
2. Dot.

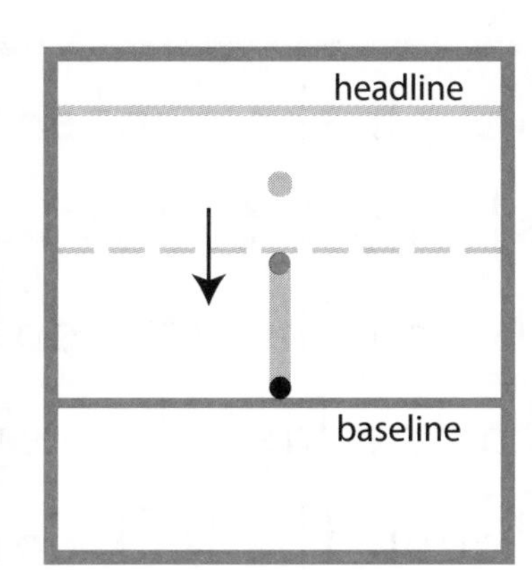

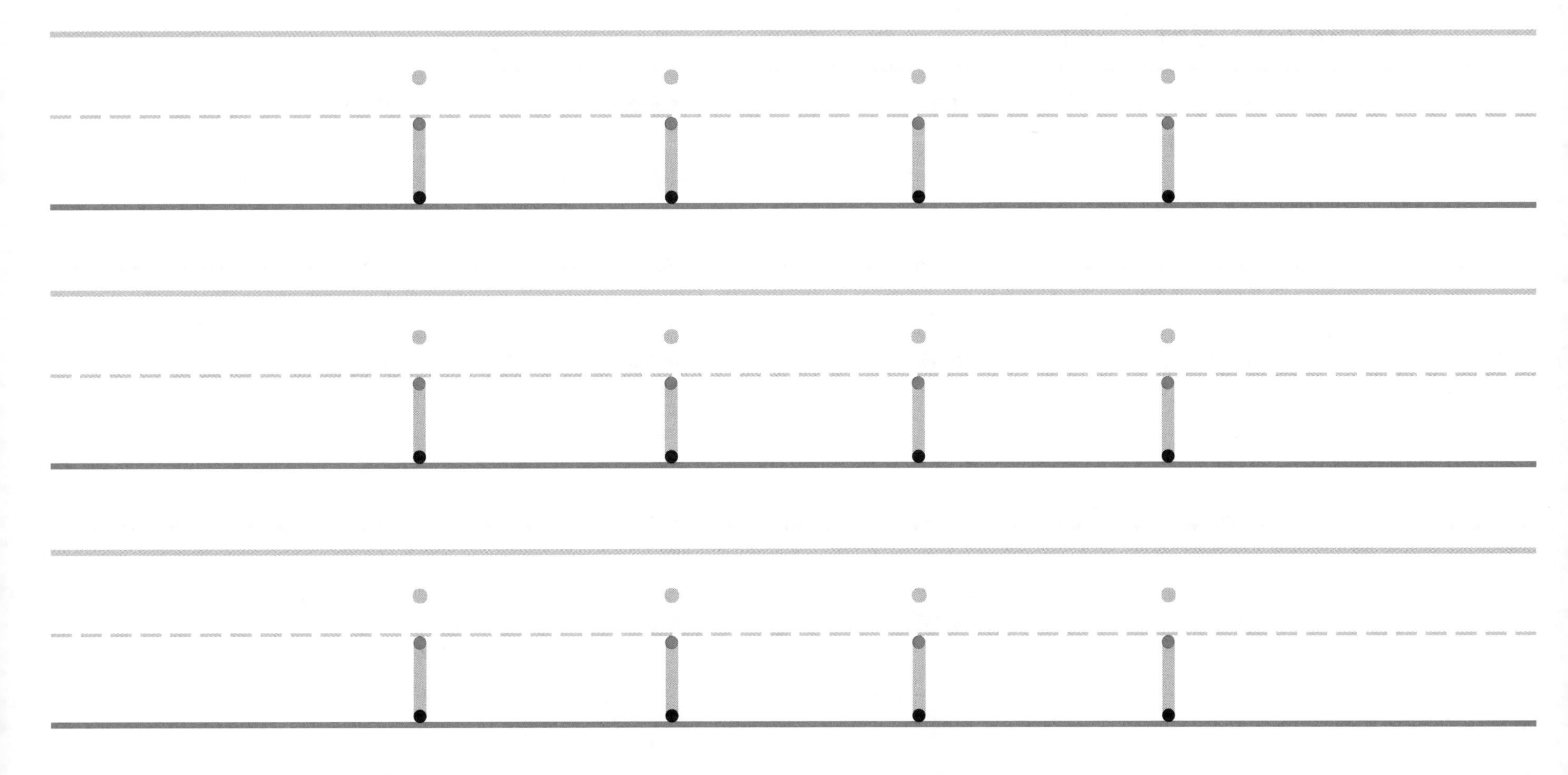

1. Touch the center blue dot on headline; pull down straight to the baseline dot. Lift.
2. Touch the left dot on the headline; slide right to the last dot. Lift.
3. Touch the left dot on the baseline; slide right to the last dot. Lift.

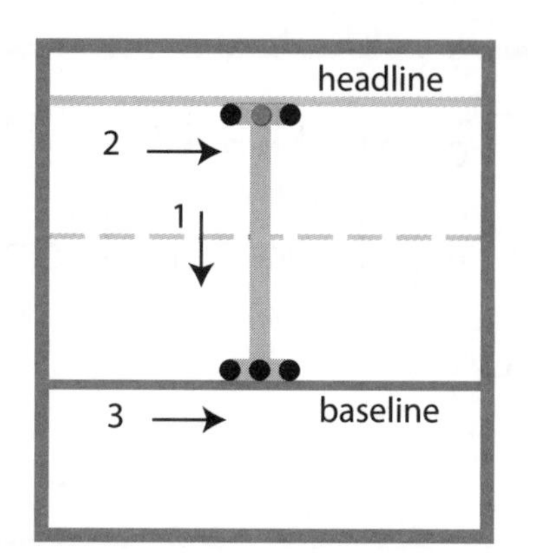

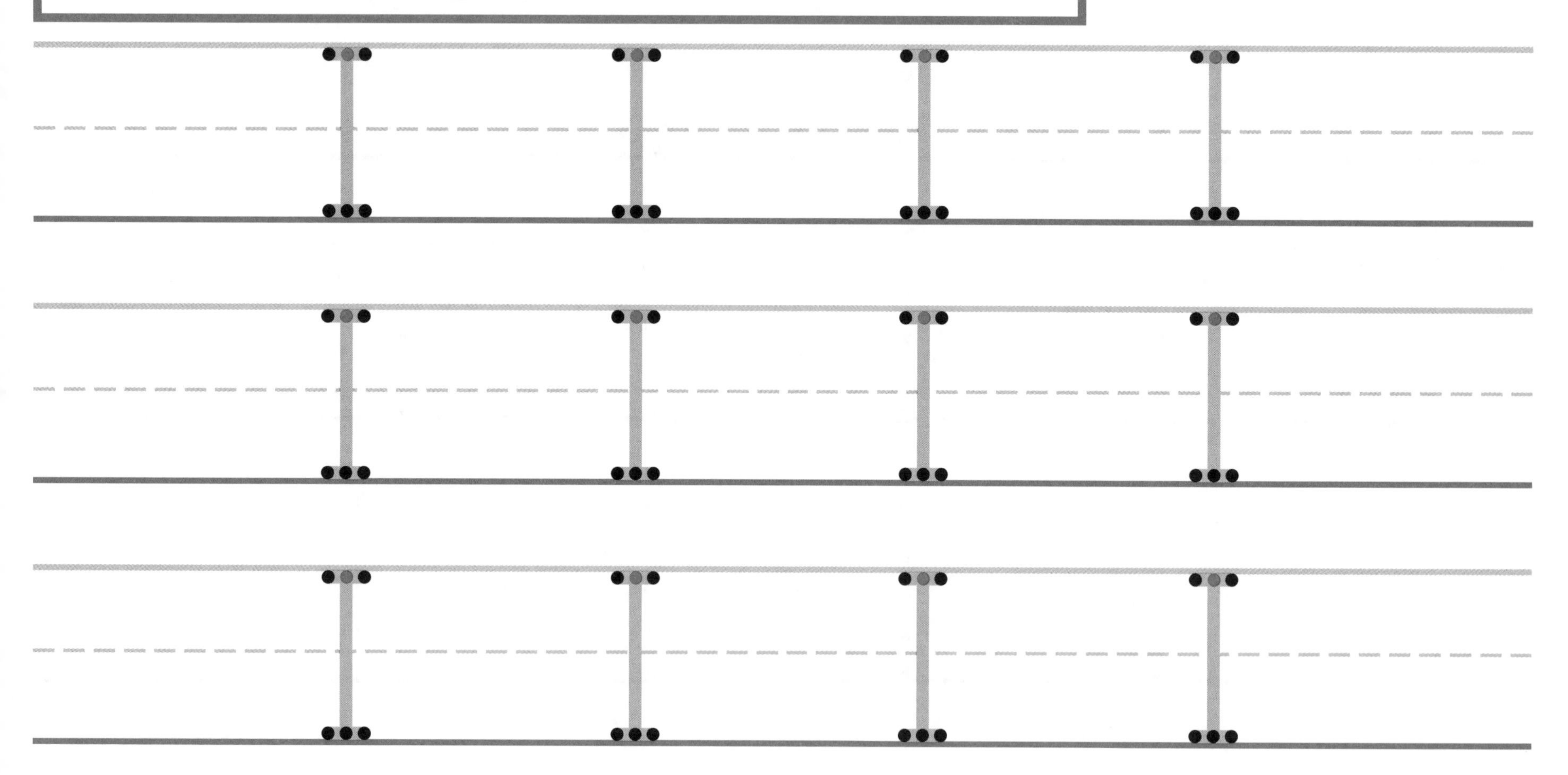

Today is Monday.

I see things that begin with the sound of i.

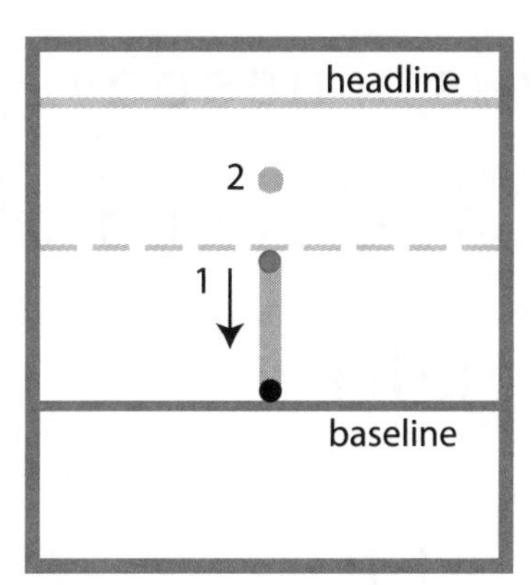

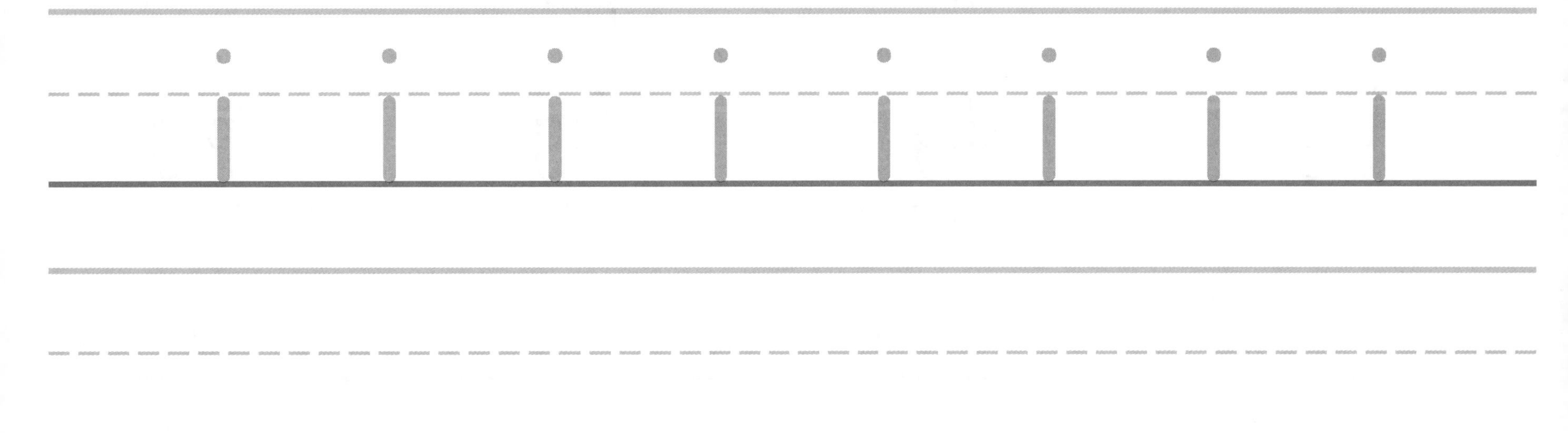

Attention Parent/Teacher: Using bright colored pencils, your child may draw pictures of today's items beginning with the sound of **i**. Emphasizing the sound of the letter, instruct your child to trace and write the letter. As your child writes, read the following Zaner-Bloser Stroke Descriptions: Touch the midline; pull down staight to the baseline. Lift. Dot.

Today is Tuesday.

I hear the sound of i in the middle of words.

bin	fin	pin	sin
dill	hill	pill	will
big	dig	fig	pig

i i i i i i i i

Attention Parent/Teacher: Read the words to your child. Emphasizing the sound of the letter, instruct your child to trace and write the letter. As your child writes, read the following Zaner-Bloser Stroke Descriptions: Touch the midline; pull down staight to the baseline. Lift. Dot.

Today is Wednesday.
I taste things that begin with the sound of i.

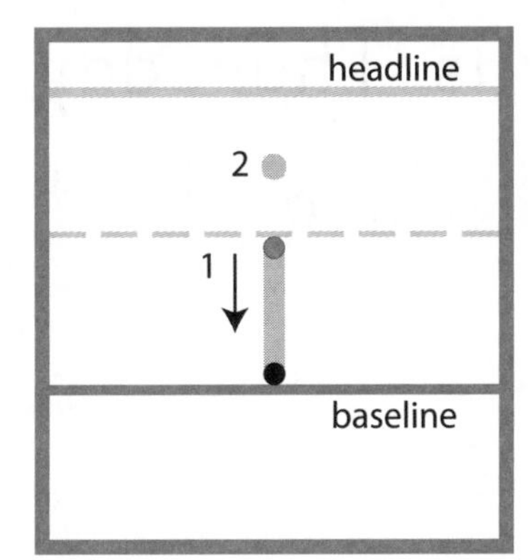

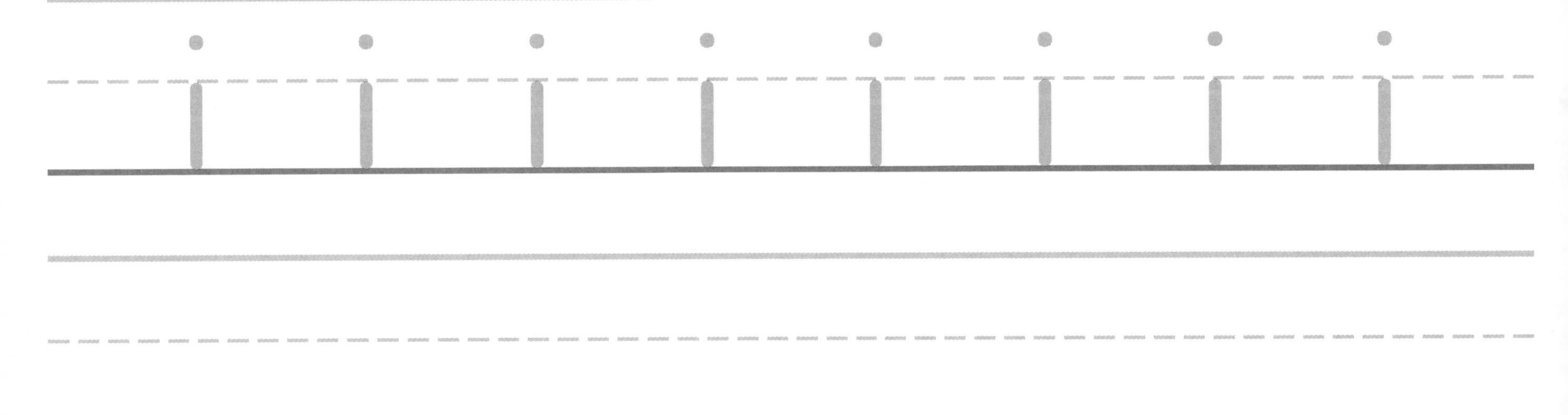

Attention Parent/Teacher: Using bright colored pencils, your child may draw pictures of today's items beginning with the sound of **i**. Emphasizing the sound of the letter, instruct your child to trace and write the letter. As your child writes, read the following Zaner-Bloser Stroke Descriptions: Touch the midline; pull down staight to the baseline. Lift. Dot.

Today is Thursday.

I smell things that begin with the sound of i.

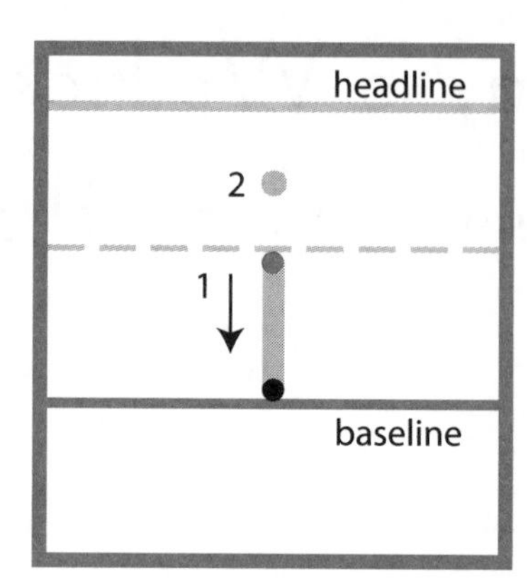

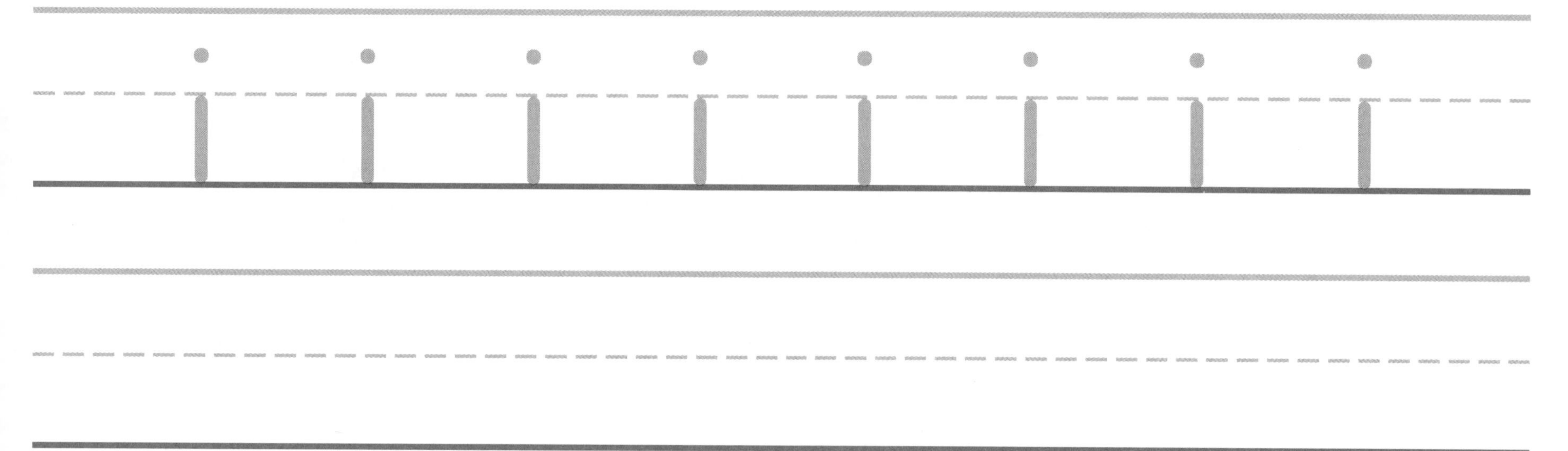

Attention Parent/Teacher: Using bright colored pencils, your child may draw pictures of today's items beginning with the sound of **i**. Emphasizing the sound of the letter, instruct your child to trace and write the letter. As your child writes, read the following Zaner-Bloser Stroke Descriptions: Touch the midline; pull down staight to the baseline. Lift. Dot.

Today is Friday.

I touch things that begin with the sound of i.

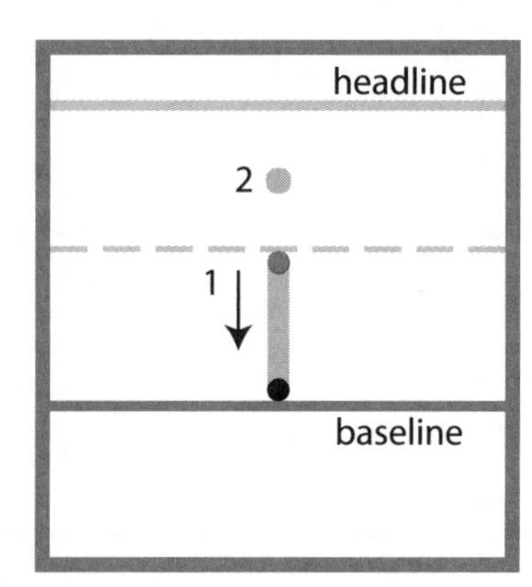

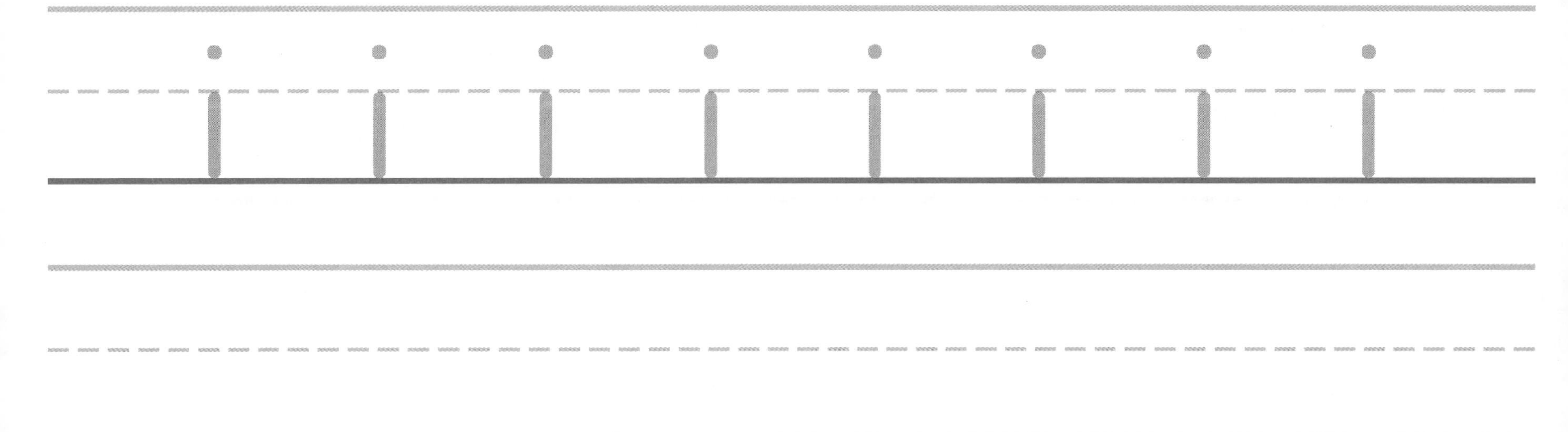

Attention Parent/Teacher: Using bright colored pencils, your child may draw pictures of today's items beginning with the sound of **i**. Emphasizing the sound of the letter, instruct your child to trace and write the letter. As your child writes, read the following Zaner-Bloser Stroke Descriptions: Touch the midline; pull down staight to the baseline. Lift. Dot.

May I love you night and day,
Oh, teach me how to pray.

1. Touch the blue dot on the midline; pull down straight to the black dot on the baseline. Lift.
2. Dot.

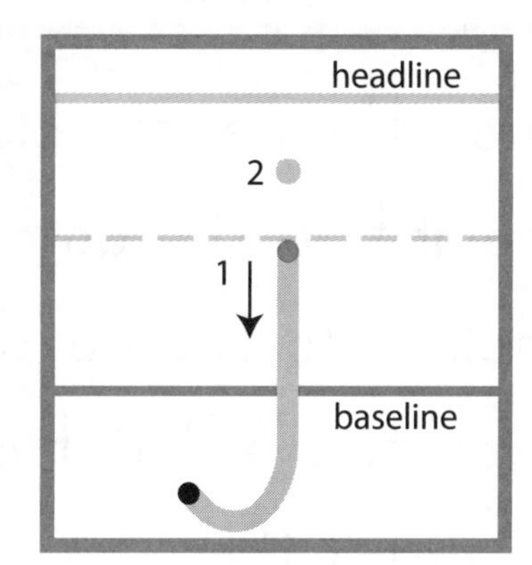

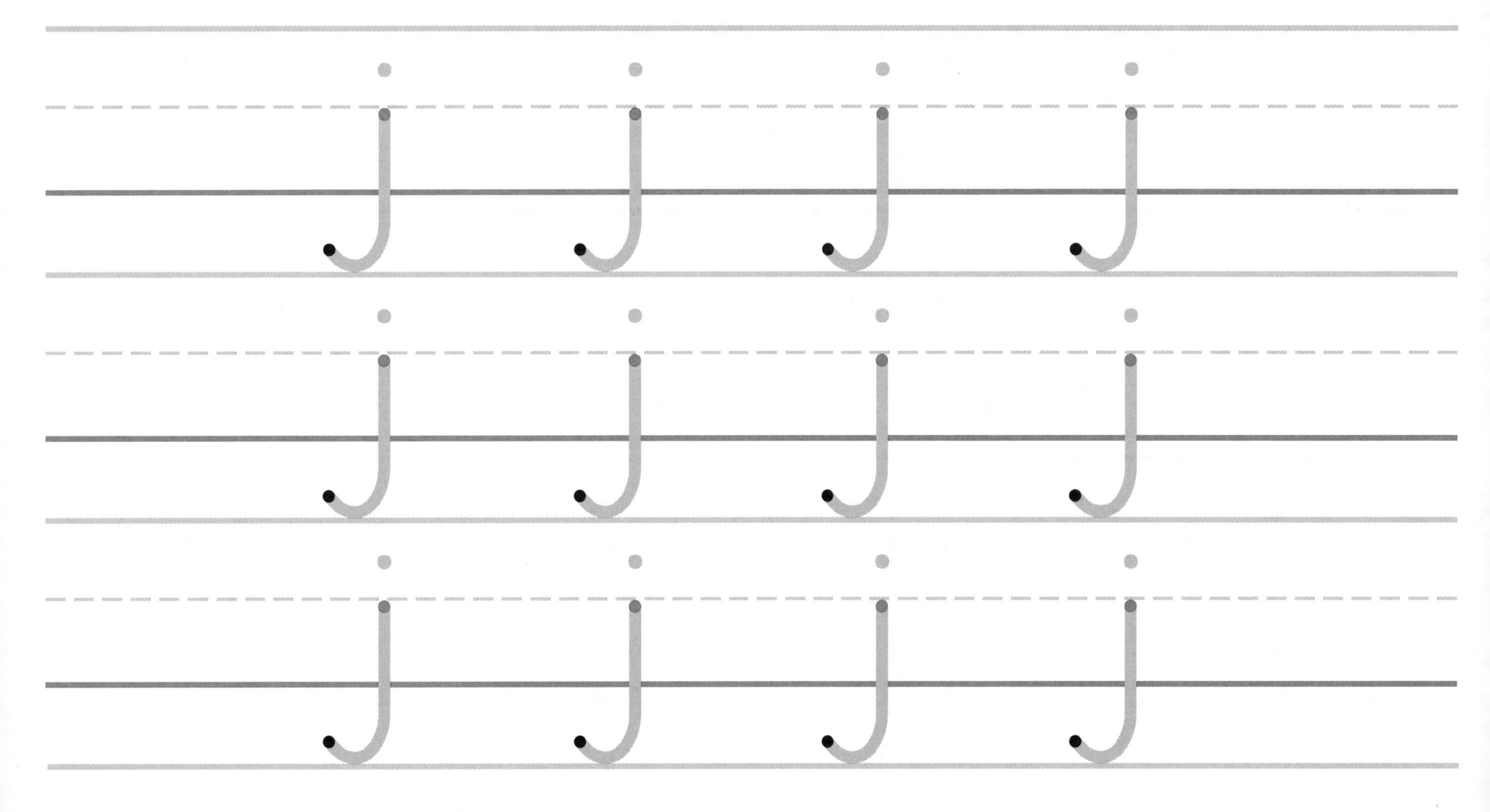

1. Touch the center blue dot on the headline; pull down straight to the dot; curve back left, touching the baseline, to the dot above the baseline. Lift.
2. Touch the left dot on the headline; slide right to the last dot. Lift.

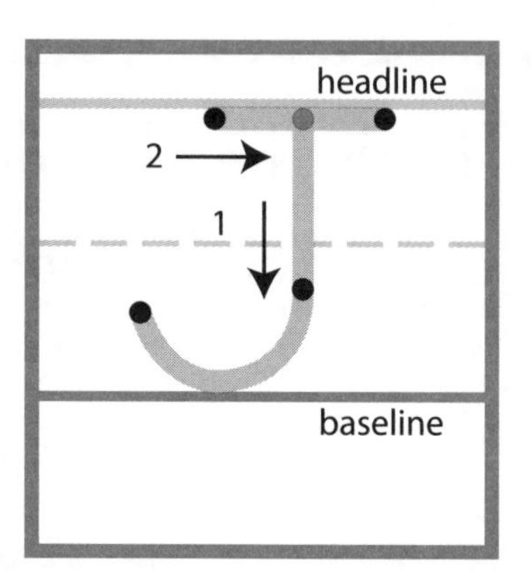

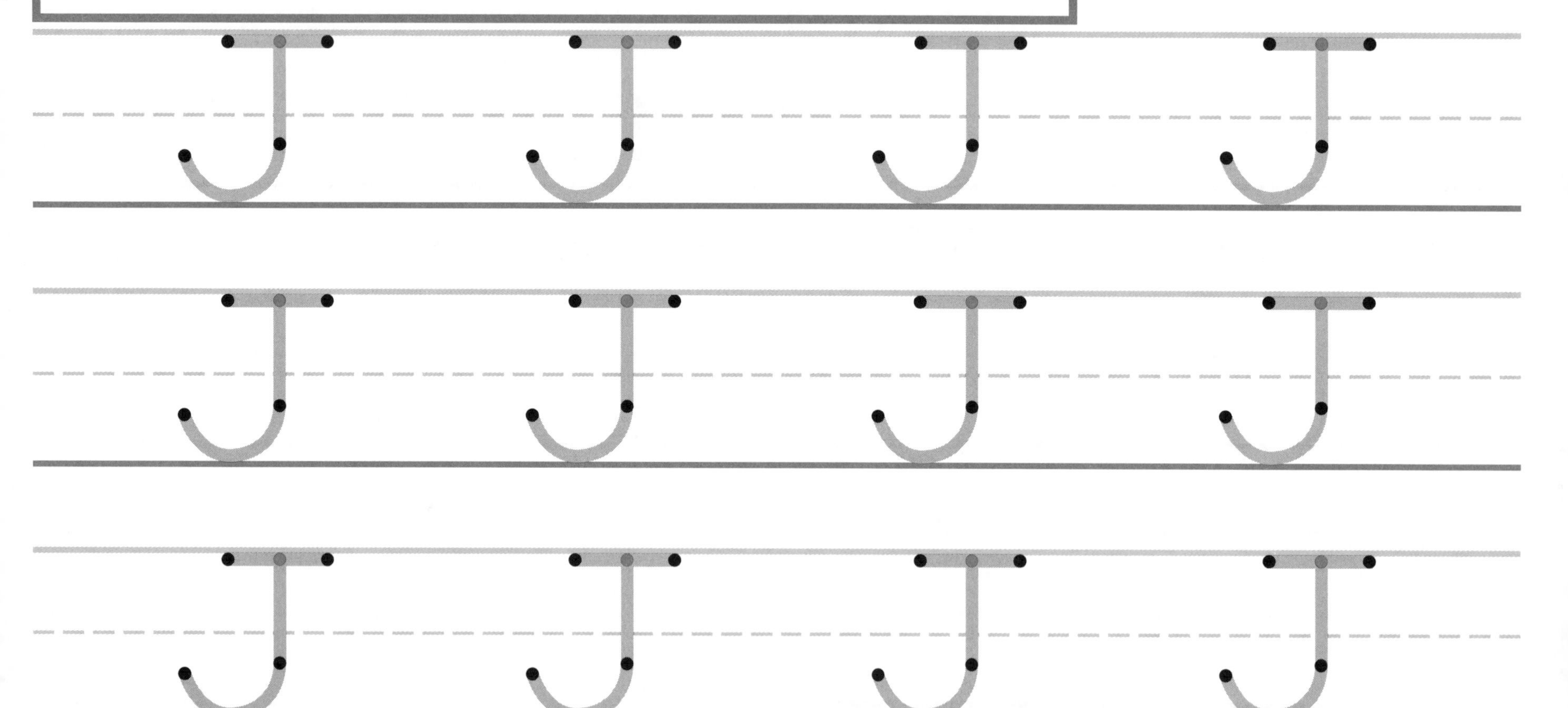

Today is Monday.

I see things that begin with the sound of j.

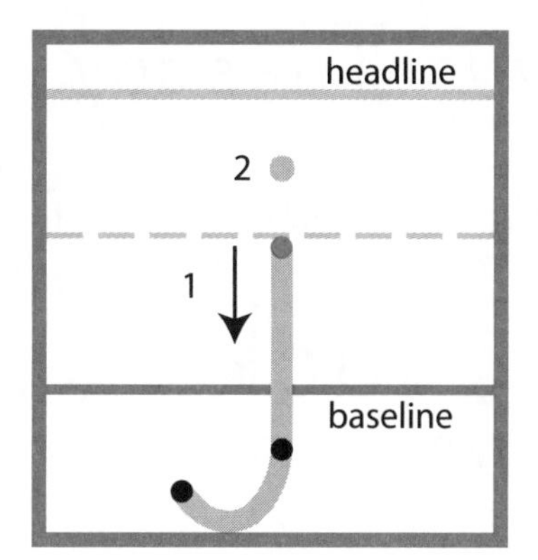

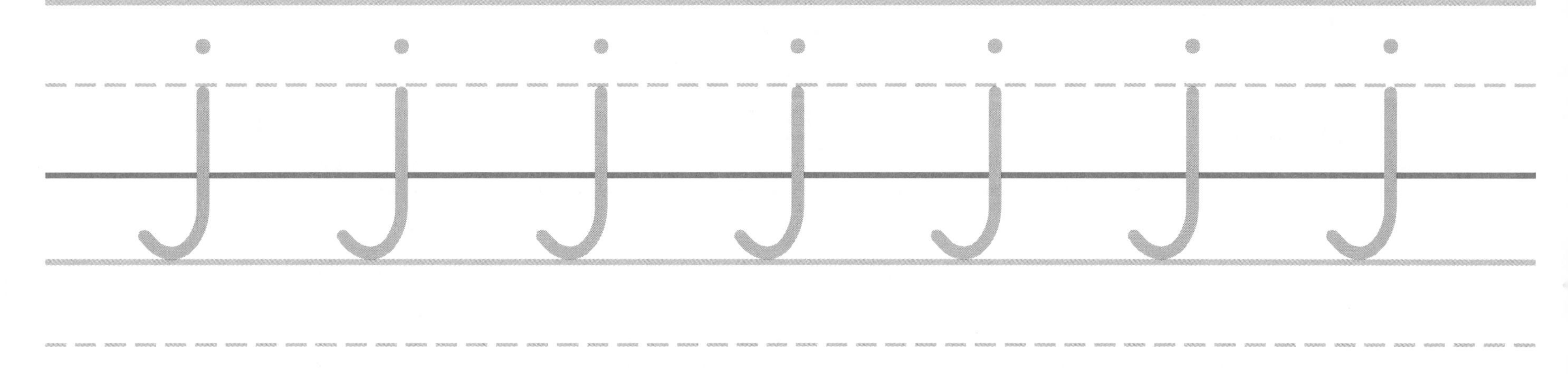

Attention Parent/Teacher: Using bright colored pencils, your child may draw pictures of today's items beginning with the sound of **j**. Emphasizing the sound of the letter, instruct your child to trace and write the letter. As your child writes, read the following Zaner-Bloser Stroke Descriptions: Touch the midline; pull down straight through the baseline; curve back (left). Lift. Dot.

Today is Tuesday.

I hear words that begin with the sound of j.

jack	jet	job
jam	jig	jog
jazz	jug	jot

j j j j j j j

Attention Parent/Teacher: Read the words to your child. Emphasizing the sound of the letter, instruct your child to trace and write the letter. As your child writes, read the following Zaner-Bloser Stroke Descriptions: Touch the midline; pull down straight through the baseline; curve back (left). Lift. Dot.

Today is Wednesday.

I taste things that begin with the sound of j.

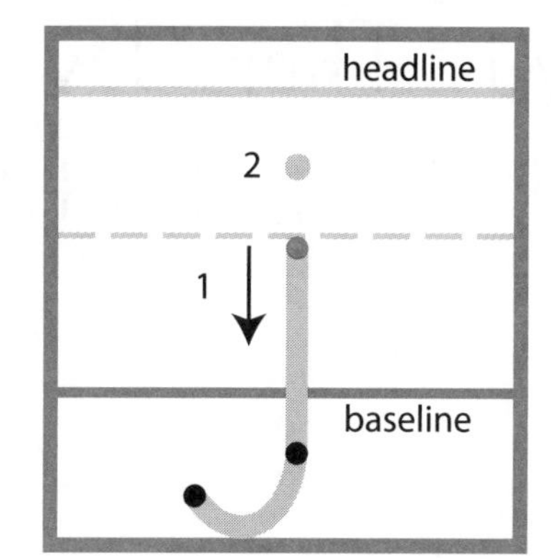

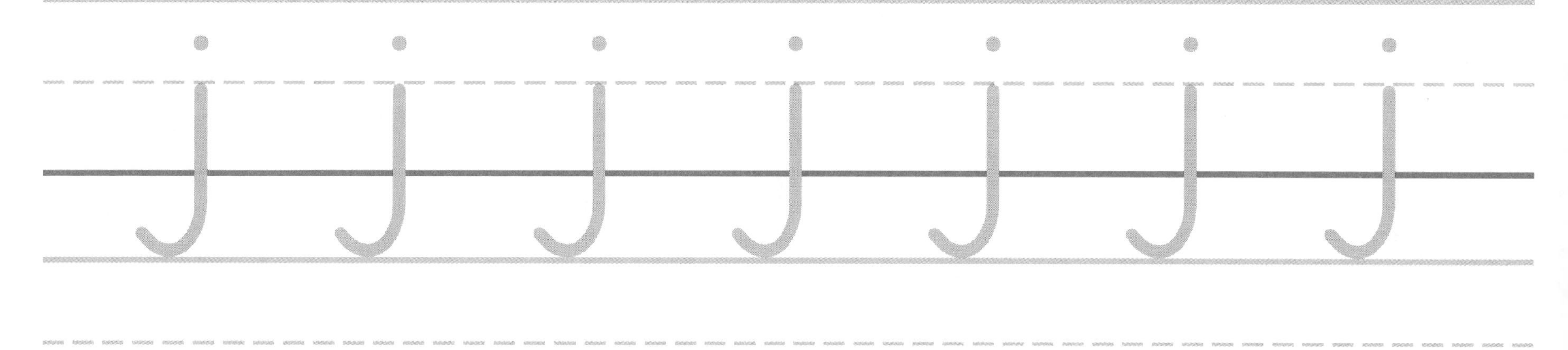

Attention Parent/Teacher: Using bright colored pencils, your child may draw pictures of today's items beginning with the sound of **j**. Emphasizing the sound of the letter, instruct your child to trace and write the letter. As your child writes, read the following Zaner-Bloser Stroke Descriptions: Touch the midline; pull down straight through the baseline; curve back (left). Lift. Dot.

Today is Thursday.

I smell things that begin with the sound of j.

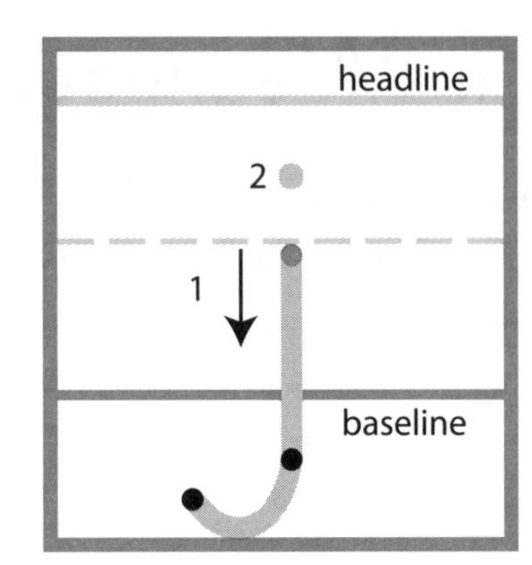

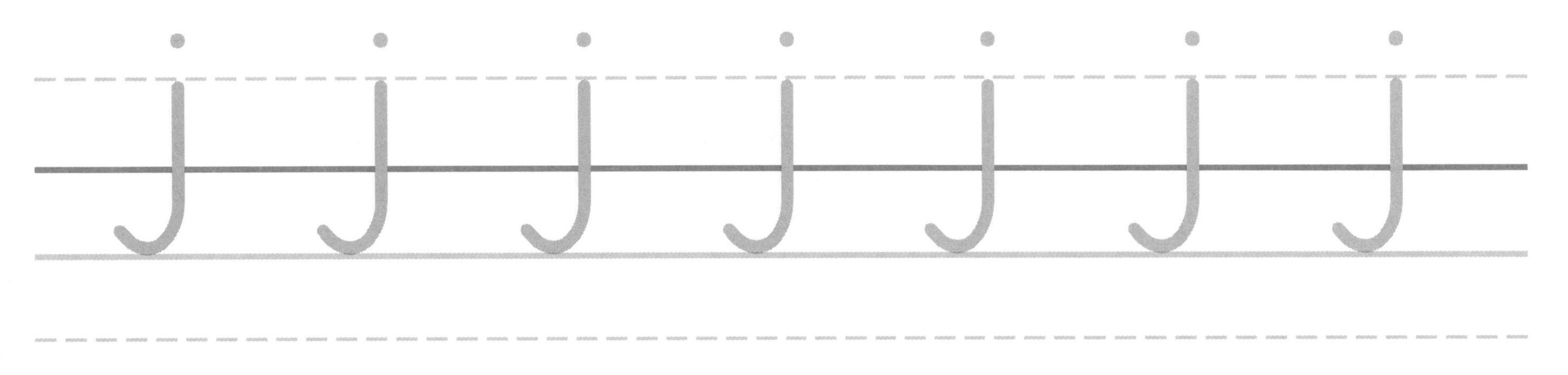

Attention Parent/Teacher: Using bright colored pencils, your child may draw pictures of today's items beginning with the sound of **j**. Emphasizing the sound of the letter, instruct your child to trace and write the letter. As your child writes, read the following Zaner-Bloser Stroke Descriptions: Touch the midline; pull down straight through the baseline; curve back (left). Lift. Dot.

Today is Friday.
I touch things that begin with the sound of j.

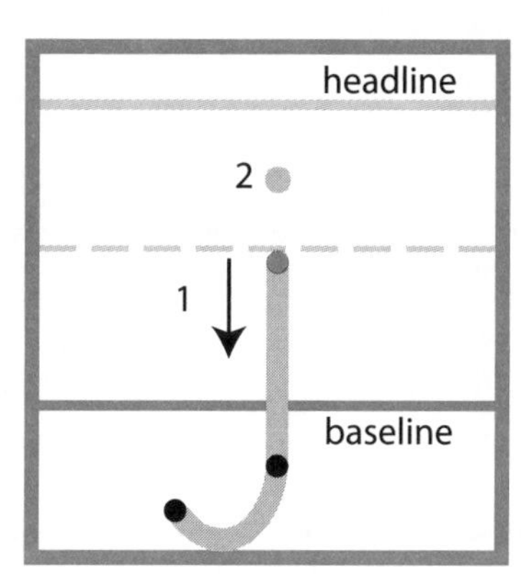

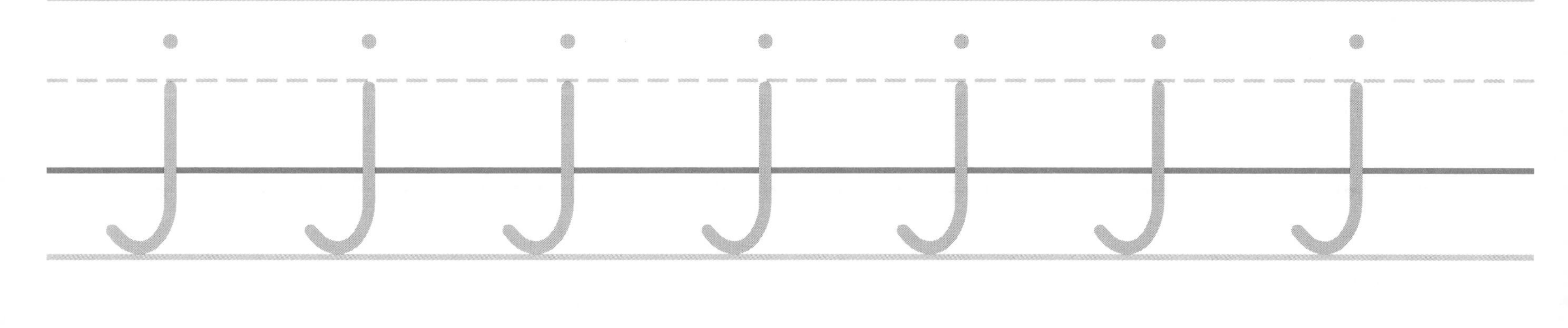

Attention Parent/Teacher: Using bright colored pencils, your child may draw pictures of today's items beginning with the sound of **j**. Emphasizing the sound of the letter, instruct your child to trace and write the letter. As your child writes, read the following Zaner-Bloser Stroke Descriptions: Touch the midline; pull down straight through the baseline; curve back (left). Lift. Dot.

Maiden Mother, meek and mild,
Take, oh, take me for thy child.

Touch the blue dot below the midline; circle back counterclockwise, touching the guidelines and back to the same dot. Lift.

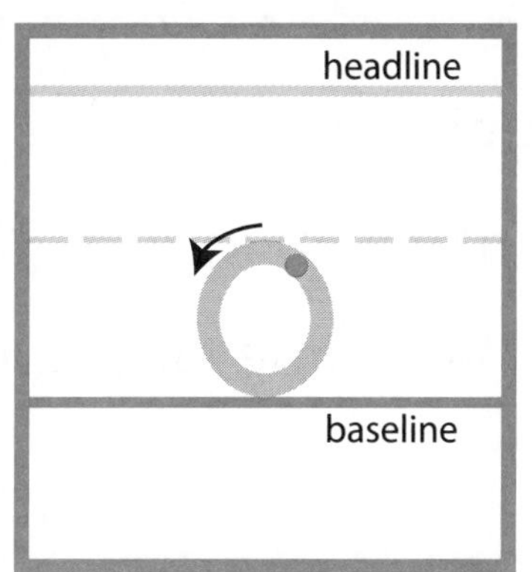

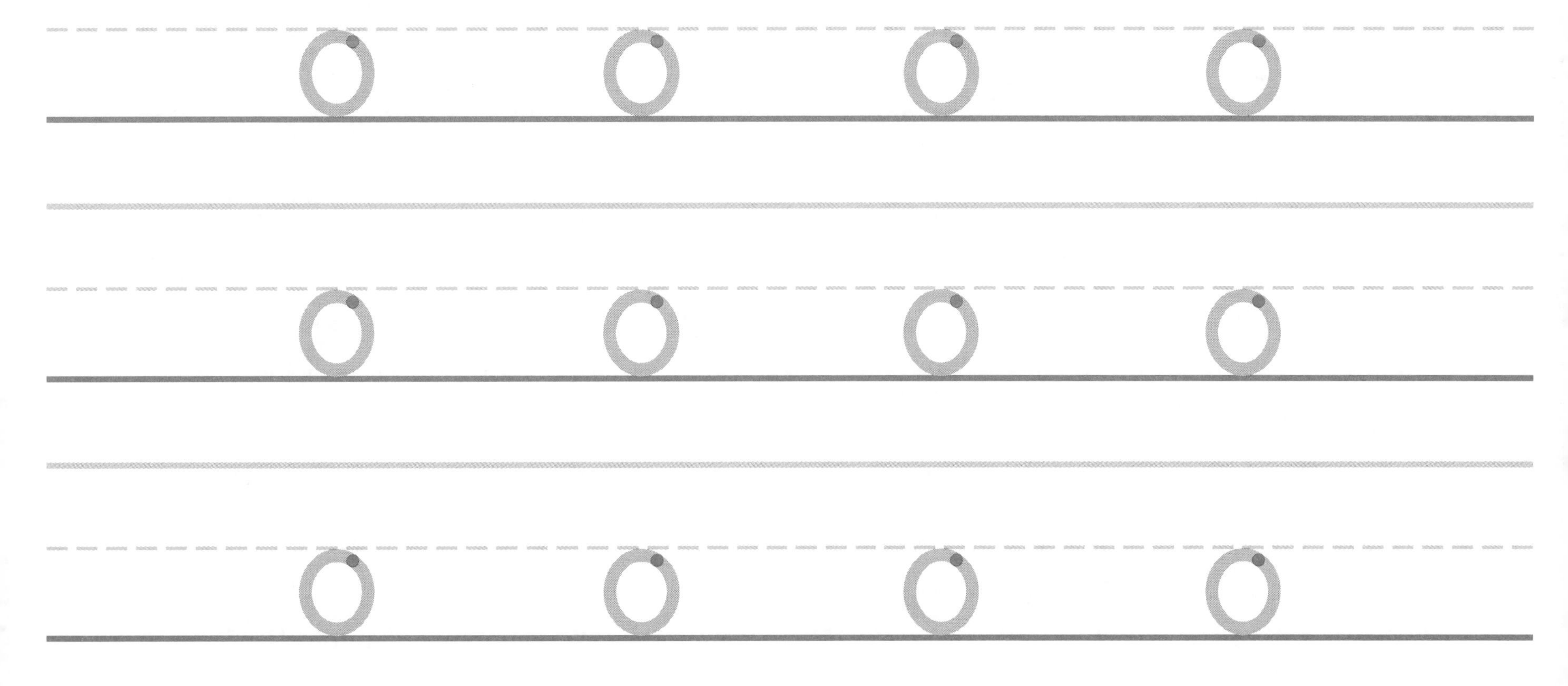

Touch the blue dot below the headline; circle back counterclockwise, touching the guidelines and back to the same dot. Lift.

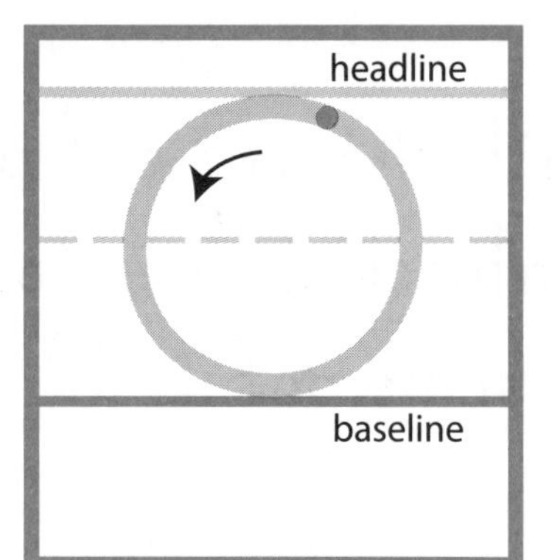

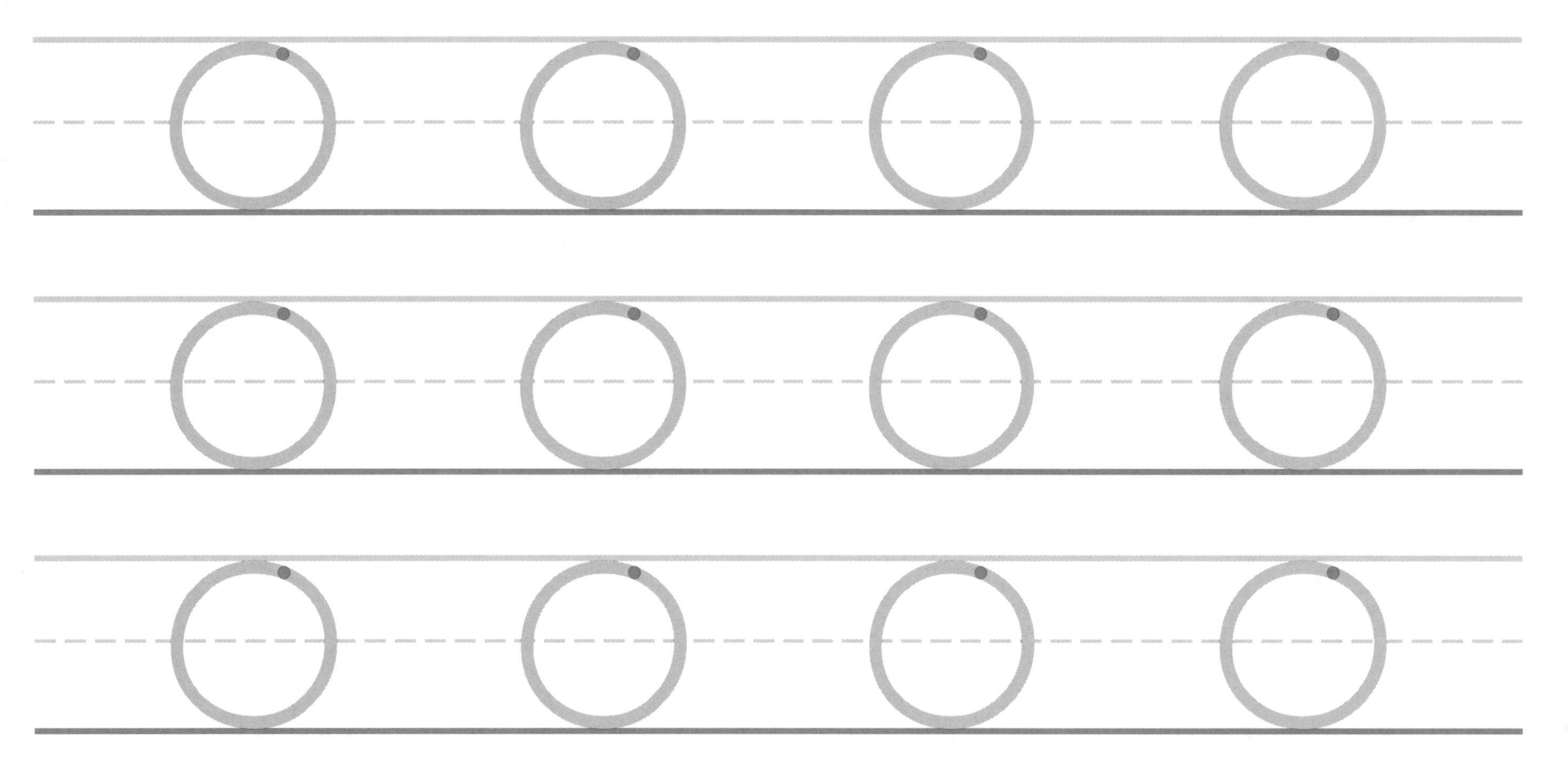

Today is Monday.

I see things that begin with the sound of o.

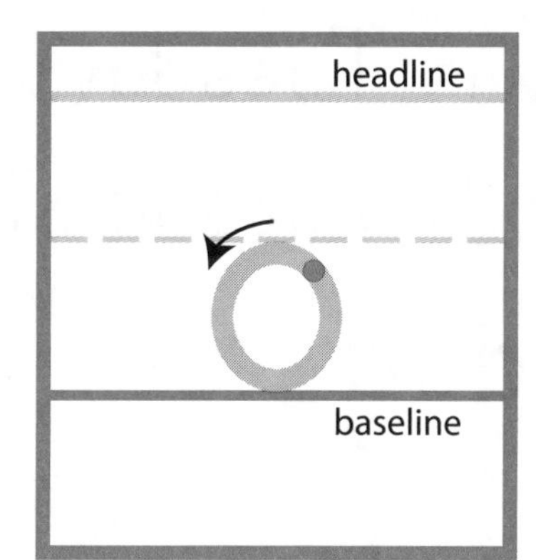

o o o o o o o

Attention Parent/Teacher: Using bright colored pencils, your child may draw pictures of today's items beginning with the sound of **o**. Emphasizing the sound of the letter, instruct your child to trace and write the letter. As your child writes, read the following Zaner-Bloser Stroke Descriptions: Touch below the midline; circle back (left) all the way around.

Today is Tuesday.

I hear the sound of o in the middle of words.

dog	fog	hog	log
got	hot	lot	tot
hop	mop	pop	stop

o o o o o o o

Attention Parent/Teacher: Read the words to your child. Emphasizing the sound of the letter, instruct your child to trace and write the letter. As your child writes, read the following Zaner-Bloser Stroke Descriptions: Touch below the midline; circle back (left) all the way around.

Today is Wednesday.

I taste things that begin with the sound of o.

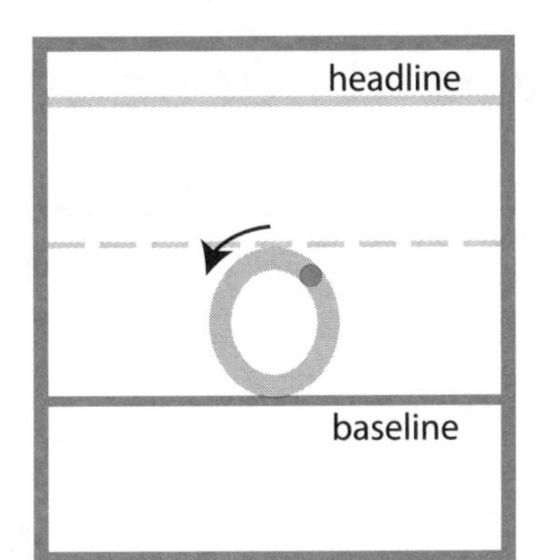

o o o o o o o

Attention Parent/Teacher: Using bright colored pencils, your child may draw pictures of today's items beginning with the sound of **o**. Emphasizing the sound of the letter, instruct your child to trace and write the letter. As your child writes, read the following Zaner-Bloser Stroke Descriptions: Touch below the midline; circle back (left) all the way around.

Today is Thursday.

I smell things that begin with the sound of o.

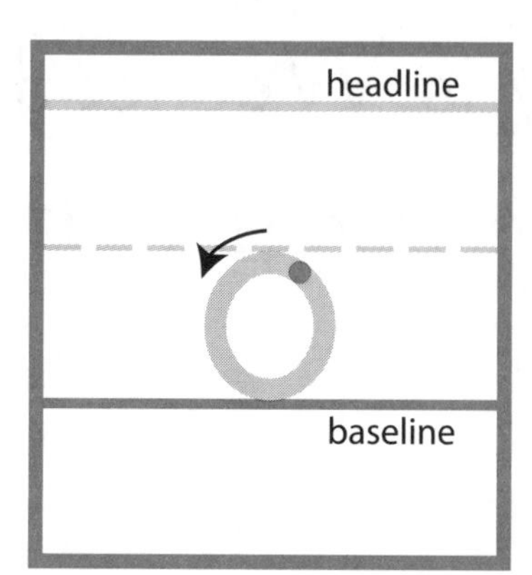

Attention Parent/Teacher: Using bright colored pencils, your child may draw pictures of today's items beginning with the sound of **o**. Emphasizing the sound of the letter, instruct your child to trace and write the letter. As your child writes, read the following Zaner-Bloser Stroke Descriptions: Touch below the midline; circle back (left) all the way around.

Today is Friday.

I touch things that begin with the sound of o.

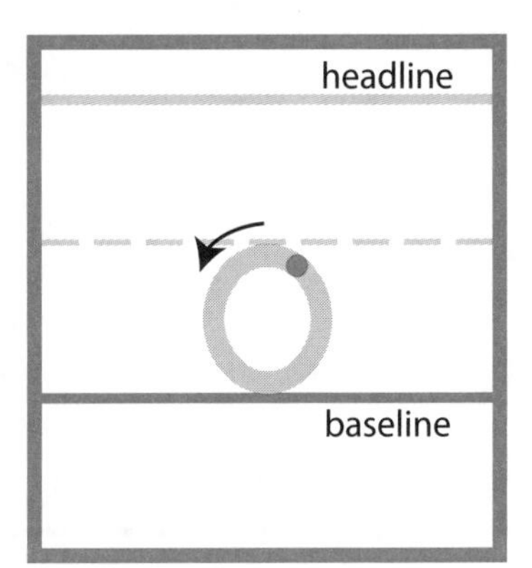

o o o o o o o

Attention Parent/Teacher: Using bright colored pencils, your child may draw pictures of today's items beginning with the sound of **o**. Emphasizing the sound of the letter, instruct your child to trace and write the letter. As your child writes, read the following Zaner-Bloser Stroke Descriptions: Touch below the midline; circle back (left) all the way around.

All my life, oh, let it be
My best joy to think of thee.

Touch the blue dot below the midline; circle back counterclockwise, touching the midline, and the baseline, and ending on the dot above the baseline. Lift.

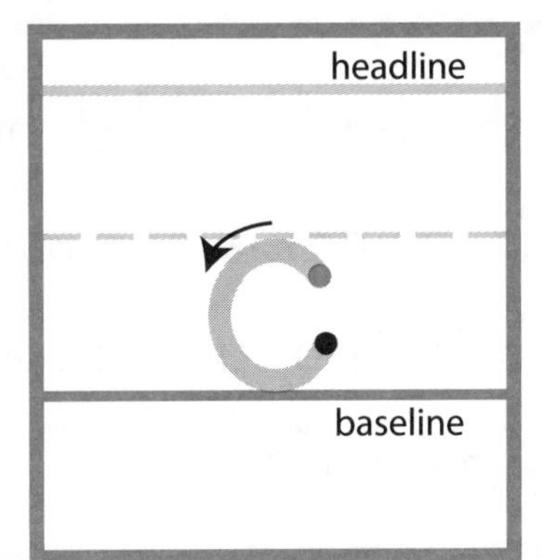

Touch the blue dot below the headline; circle back counterclockwise, touching the headline, midline, and baseline, and ending on the black dot above the baseline. Lift.

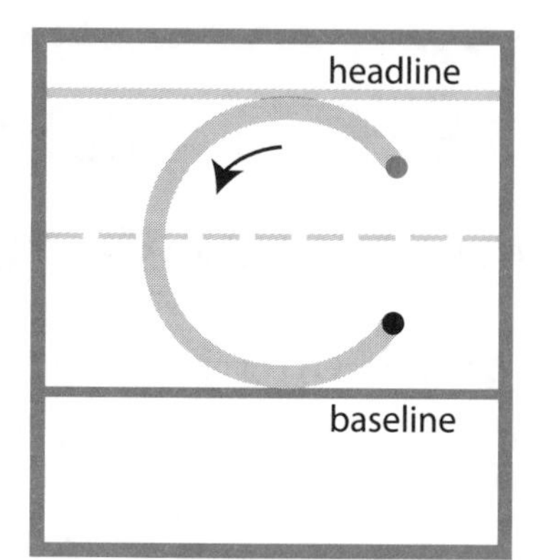

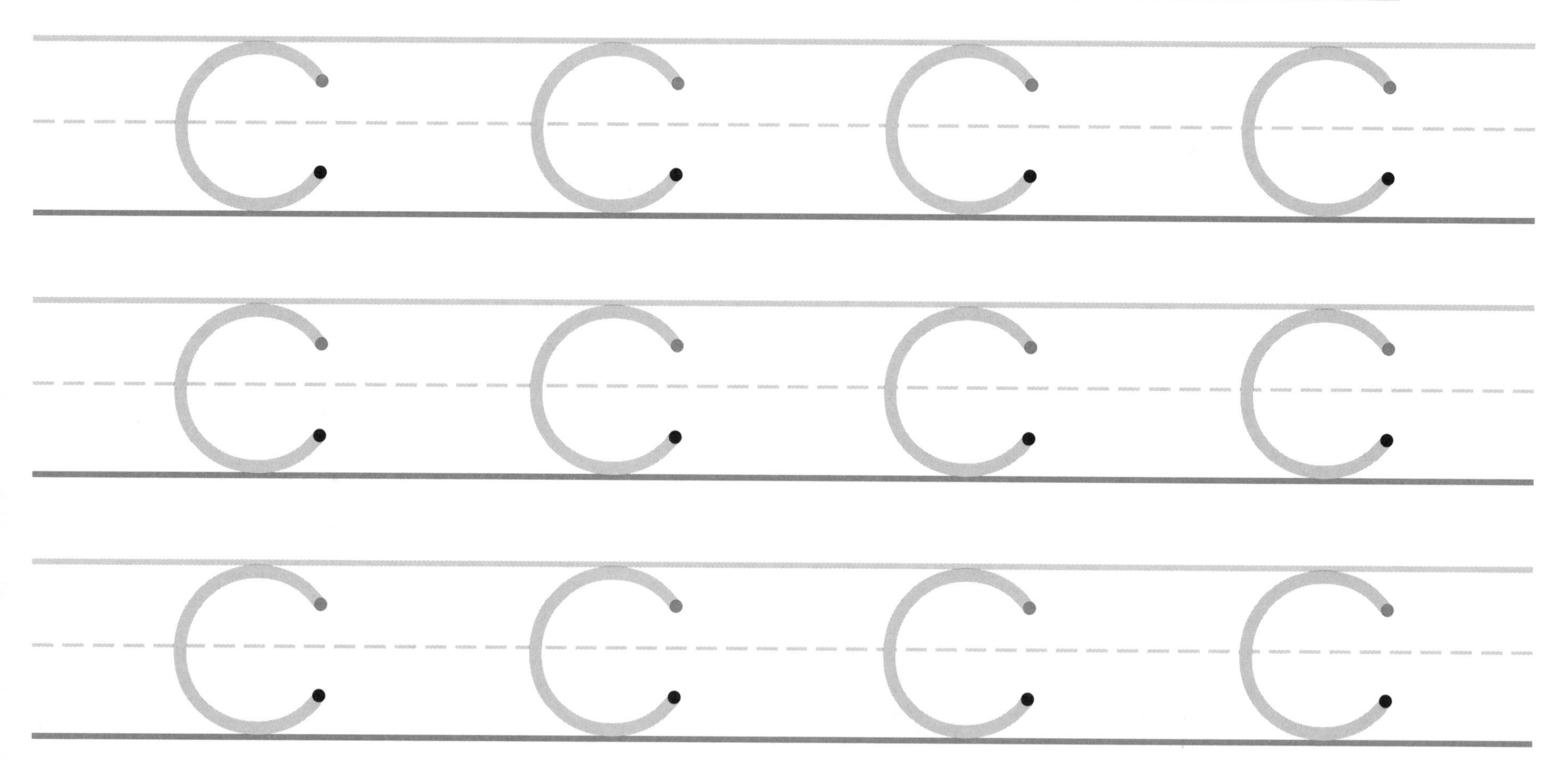

Today is Monday.
I see things that begin with the sound of c.

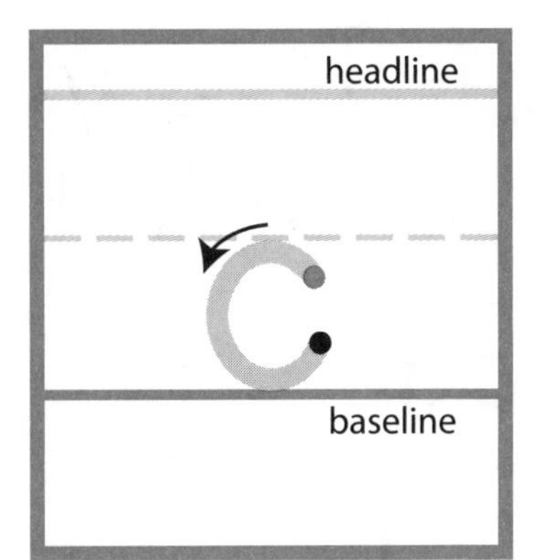

c c c c c c c

Attention Parent/Teacher: Using bright colored pencils, your child may draw pictures of today's items beginning with the sound of **c**. Emphasizing the sound of the letter, instruct your child to trace and write the letter. As your child writes, read the following Zaner-Bloser Stroke Descriptions: Touch below the midline; circle back (left), ending above the baseline.

Today is Tuesday.

I hear words that begin with the sound of c.

cab	can	cap	cat
cob	cod	cop	cot
cub	cuff	cup	cut

c c c c c c c

Attention Parent/Teacher: Read the words to your child. Emphasizing the sound of the letter, instruct your child to trace and write the letter. As your child writes, read the following Zaner-Bloser Stroke Descriptions: Touch below the midline; circle back (left), ending above the baseline.

Today is Wednesday.

I taste things that begin with the sound of c.

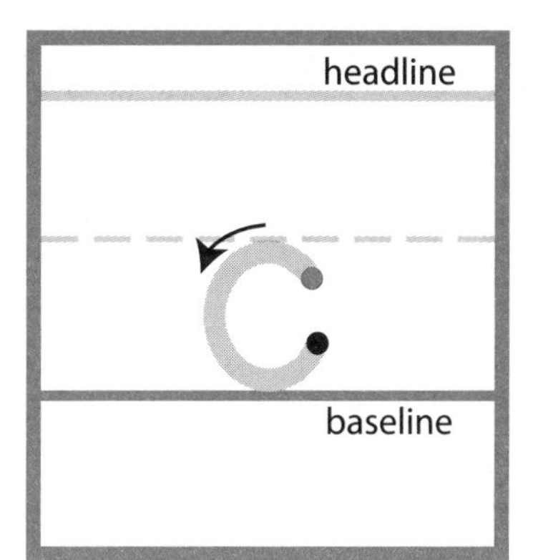

c c c c c c c

Attention Parent/Teacher: Using bright colored pencils, your child may draw pictures of today's items beginning with the sound of **c**. Emphasizing the sound of the letter, instruct your child to trace and write the letter. As your child writes, read the following Zaner-Bloser Stroke Descriptions: Touch below the midline; circle back (left), ending above the baseline.

Today is Thursday.

I smell things that begin with the sound of c.

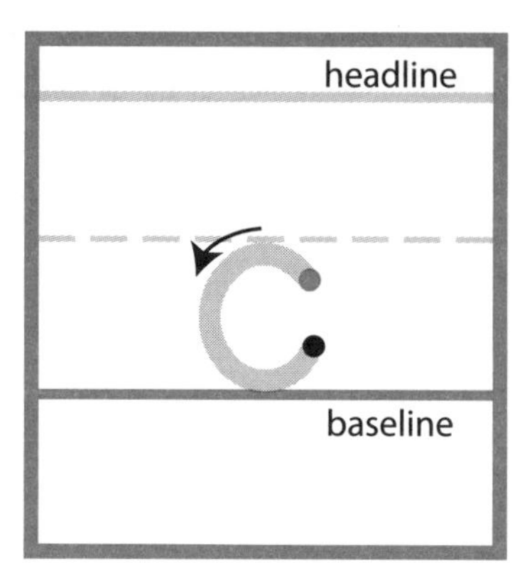

c c c c c c c

Attention Parent/Teacher: Using bright colored pencils, your child may draw pictures of today's items beginning with the sound of **c**. Emphasizing the sound of the letter, instruct your child to trace and write the letter. As your child writes, read the following Zaner-Bloser Stroke Descriptions: Touch below the midline; circle back (left), ending above the baseline.

Today is Friday.

I touch things that begin with the sound of c.

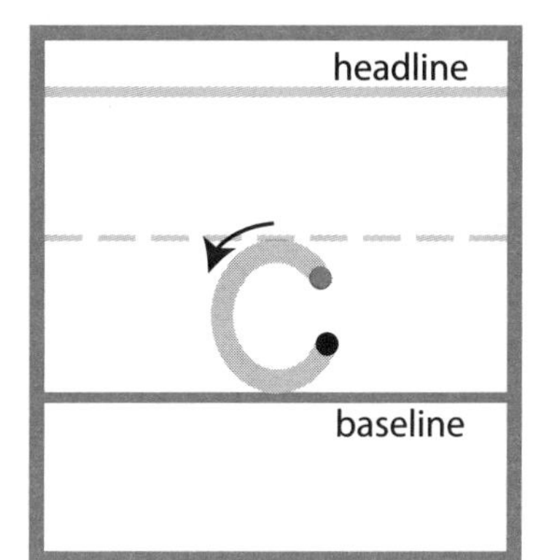

c c c c c c c

Attention Parent/Teacher: Using bright colored pencils, your child may draw pictures of today's items beginning with the sound of **c**. Emphasizing the sound of the letter, instruct your child to trace and write the letter. As your child writes, read the following Zaner-Bloser Stroke Descriptions: Touch below the midline; circle back (left), ending above the baseline.

Teach me when the sunbeam bright
Calls me with its golden light.

Touch the blue dot below the midline; circle back counterclockwise all the way around. Push up straight to the black dot on the midline. Pause; pull down straight to the black dot on the baseline. Lift.

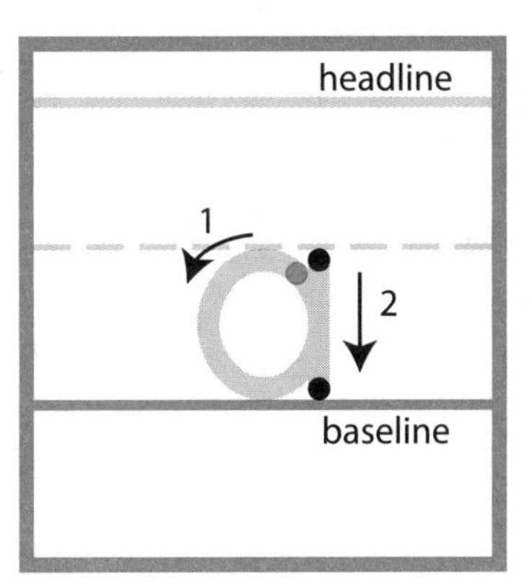

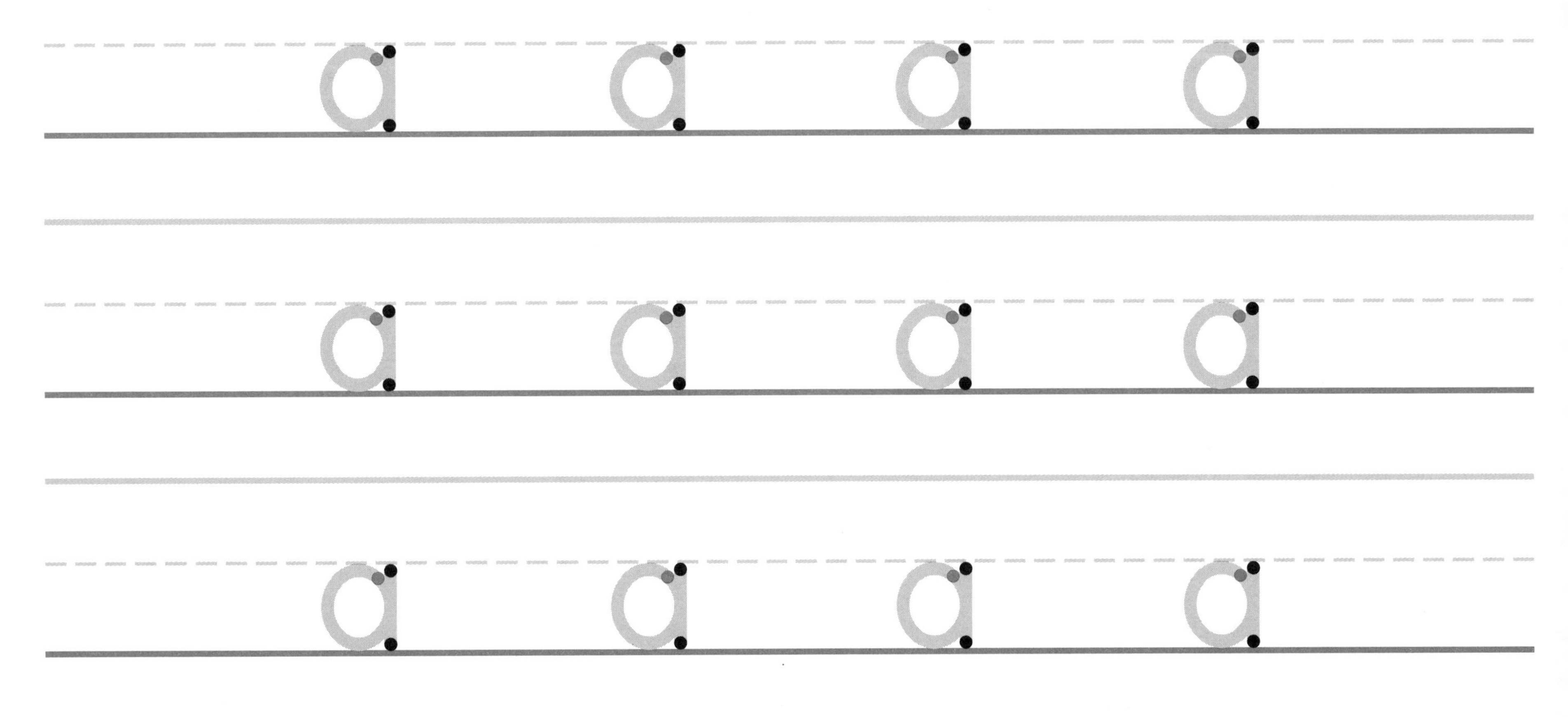

1. Touch the blue dot on the headline; slant left to the dot on the baseline; lift.
2. Touch the blue dot on the headline; slant right to the dot on the baseline; lift.
3. Touch the dot on the midline; slide right to the dot; lift.

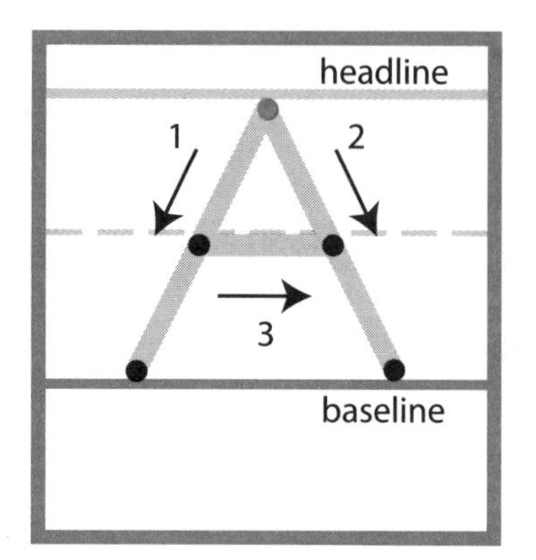

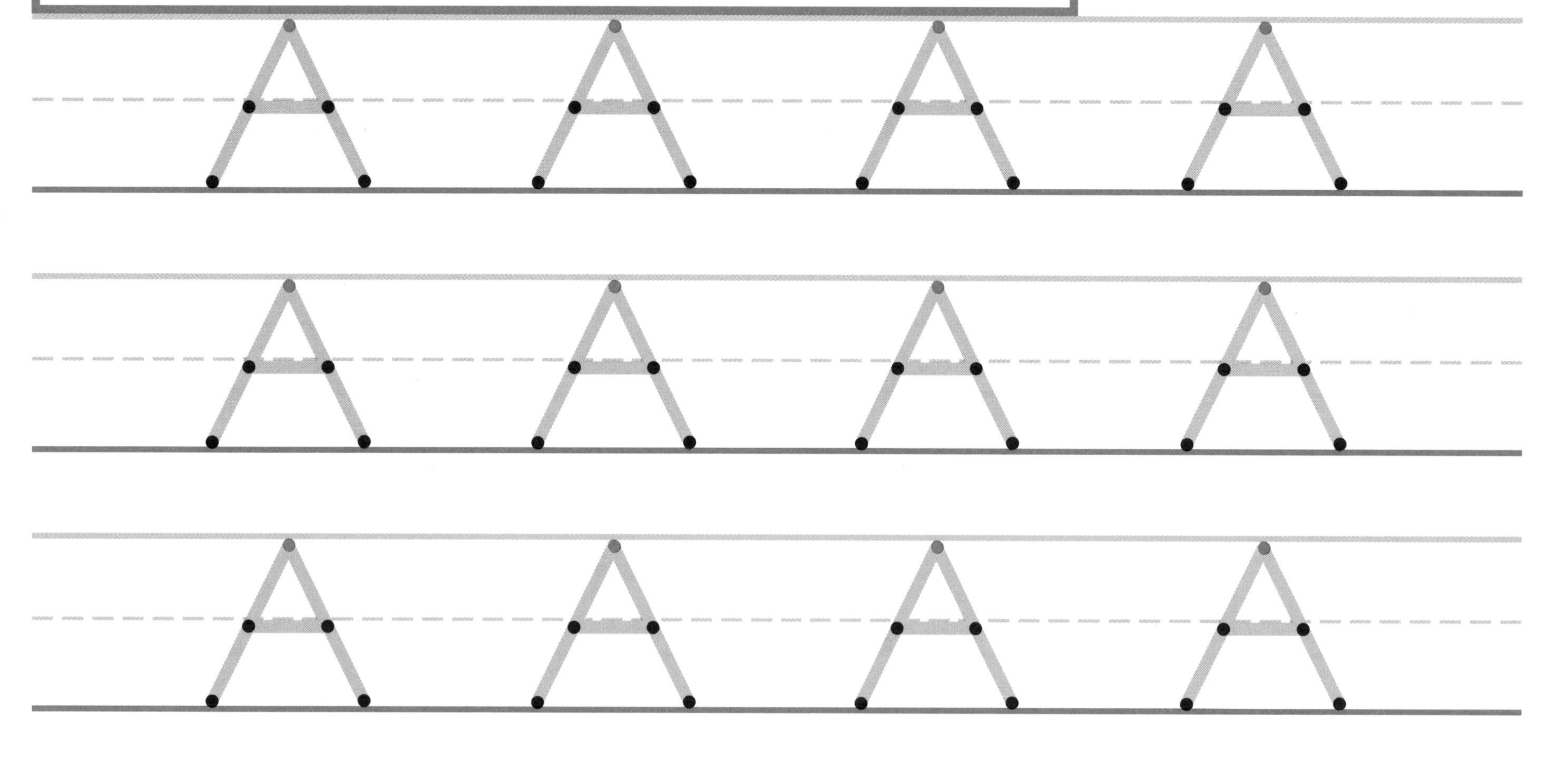

Today is Monday.

I see things that begin with the sound of a.

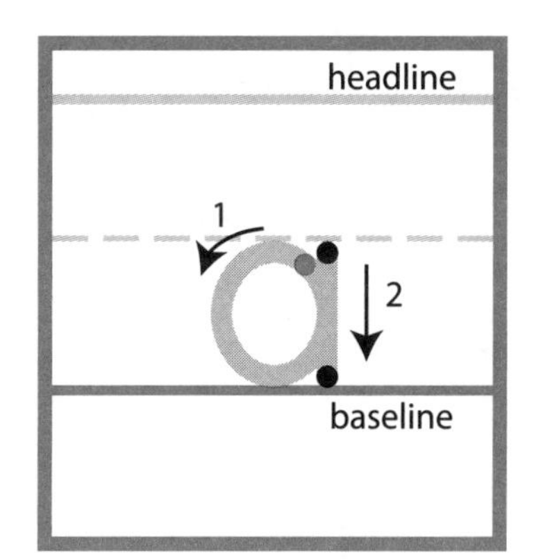

a a a a a a a

Attention Parent/Teacher: Using bright colored pencils, your child may draw pictures of today's items beginning with the sound of **a**. Emphasizing the sound of the letter, instruct your child to trace and write the letter. As your child writes, read the following Zaner-Bloser Stroke Descriptions: Touch below the midline; circle back (left) all the way around. Push up straight to the midline. Pull down straight to the baseline.

Today is Tuesday.

I hear the sound of a in the middle of words.

fat	cat	sat	mat
sad	dad	had	bad
man	can	fan	pan

a a a a a a a

Attention Parent/Teacher: Read the words to your child. Emphasizing the sound of the letter, instruct your child to trace and write the letter. As your child writes, read the following Zaner-Bloser Stroke Descriptions: Touch below the midline; circle back (left) all the way around. Push up straight to the midline. Pull down straight to the baseline.

Today is Wednesday.

I taste things that begin with the sound of a.

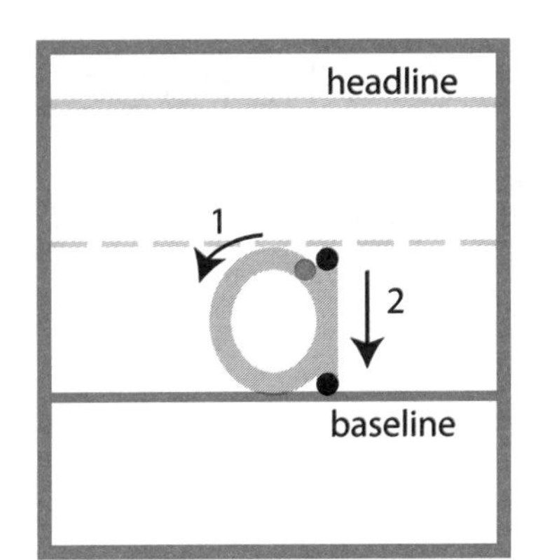

a a a a a a a

Attention Parent/Teacher: Using bright colored pencils, your child may draw pictures of today's items beginning with the sound of **a**. Emphasizing the sound of the letter, instruct your child to trace and write the letter. As your child writes, read the following Zaner-Bloser Stroke Descriptions: Touch below the midline; circle back (left) all the way around. Push up straight to the midline. Pull down straight to the baseline.

Today is Thursday.

I smell things that begin with the sound of a.

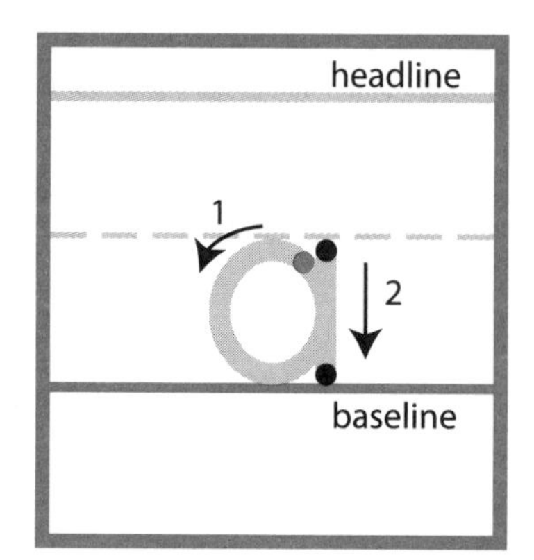

a a a a a a a

Attention Parent/Teacher: Using bright colored pencils, your child may draw pictures of today's items beginning with the sound of **a**. Emphasizing the sound of the letter, instruct your child to trace and write the letter. As your child writes, read the following Zaner-Bloser Stroke Descriptions: Touch below the midline; circle back (left) all the way around. Push up straight to the midline. Pull down straight to the baseline.

Today is Friday.

I touch things that begin with the sound of a.

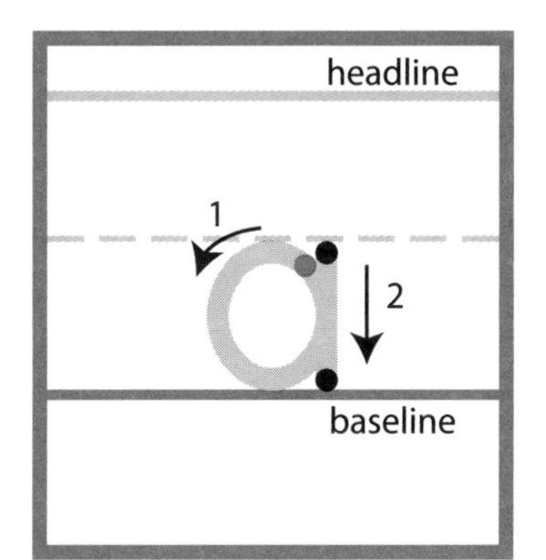

a a a a a a a

Attention Parent/Teacher: Using bright colored pencils, your child may draw pictures of today's items beginning with the sound of **a**. Emphasizing the sound of the letter, instruct your child to trace and write the letter. As your child writes, read the following Zaner-Bloser Stroke Descriptions: Touch below the midline; circle back (left) all the way around. Push up straight to the midline. Pull down straight to the baseline.

How my waking thoughts may be
Turned to Jesus and to thee.

Touch the blue dot below the midline; circle back counterclockwise all the way around. Push up straight to the dot on the headline. Pause; pull down straight to the dot on the baseline. Lift.

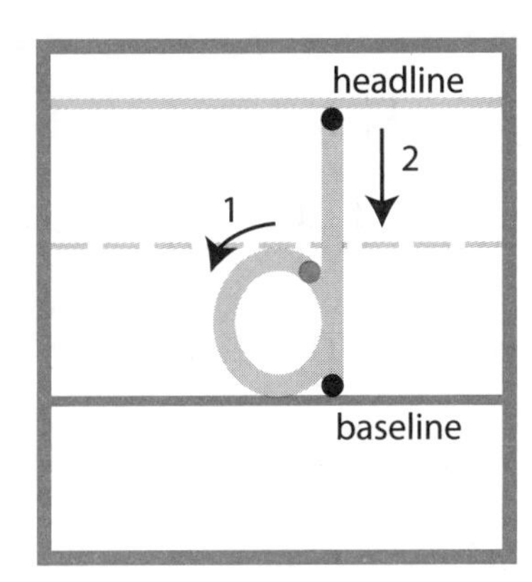

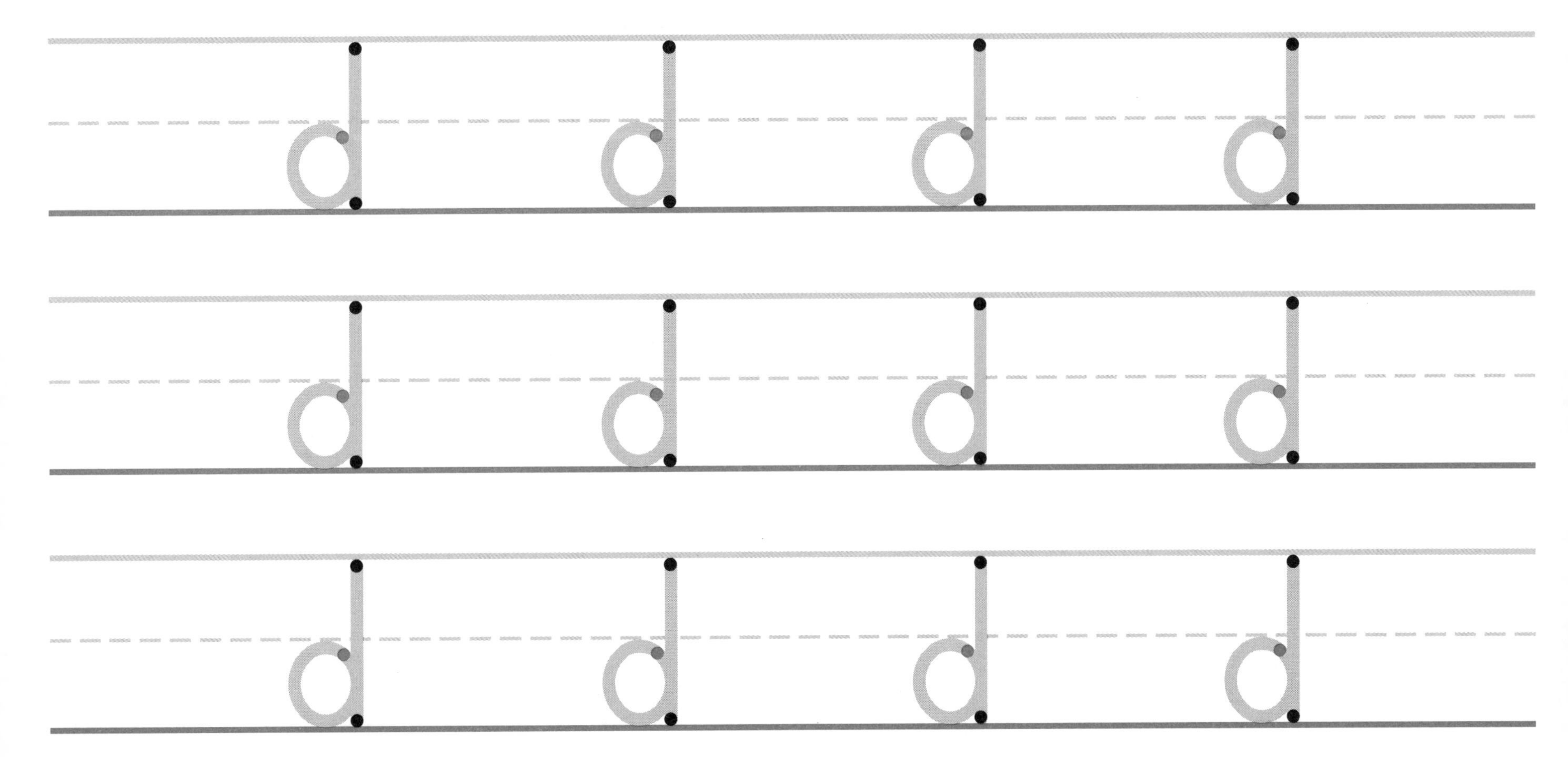

1. Touch the blue dot on the headline; pull down straight to the dot on the baseline. Lift.
2. Touch the blue dot on the headline; slide right; curve forward clockwise; slide left to the dot on the baseline. Lift.

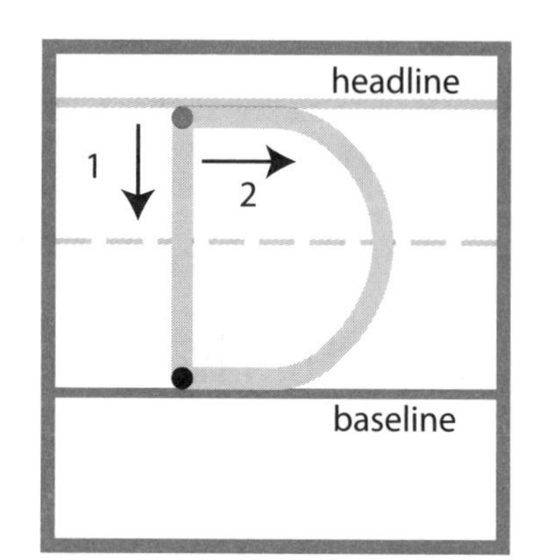

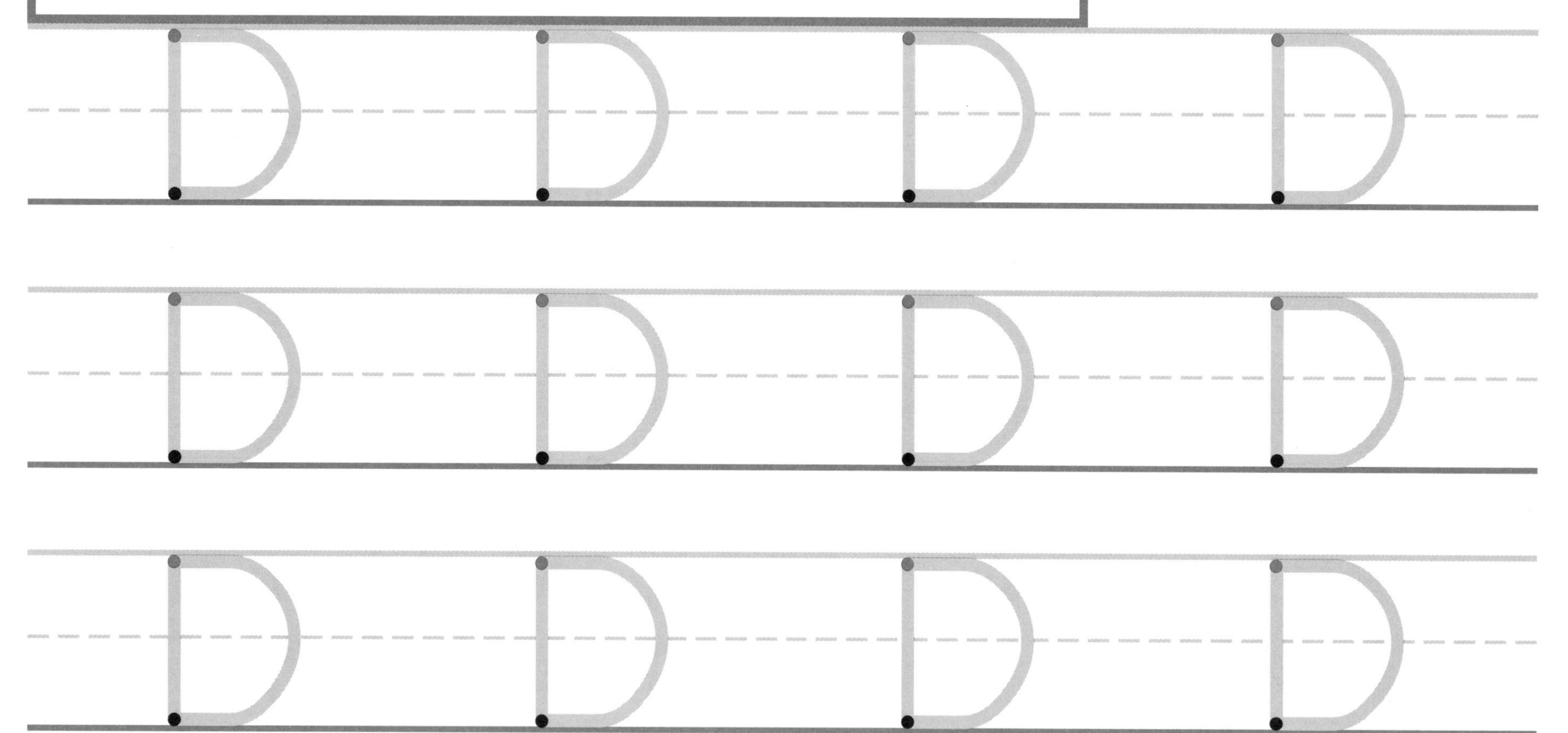

Today is Monday.

I see things that begin with the sound of d.

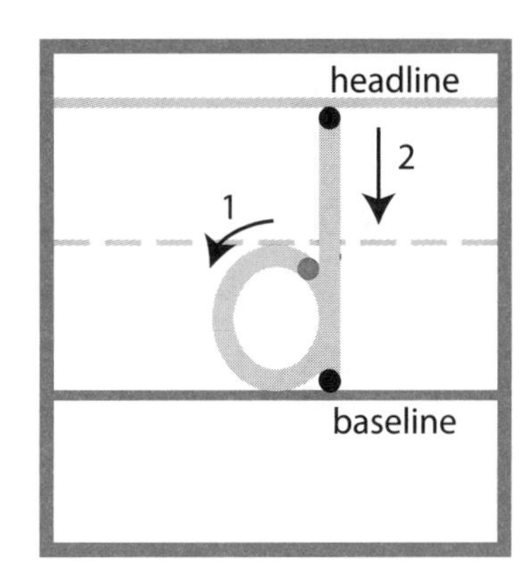

d d d d d d d

Attention Parent/Teacher: Using bright colored pencils, your child may draw pictures of today's items beginning with the sound of **d**. Emphasizing the sound of the letter, instruct your child to trace and write the letter. As your child writes, read the following Zaner-Bloser Stroke Descriptions: Touch below the midline; circle back (left) all the way around. Push up straight to the headline. Pull down straight to the baseline.

Today is Tuesday.

I hear rhyming words that end with the sound of d.

sad	dad	mad
bed	fed	red
bid	did	hid

d d d d d d d

Attention Parent/Teacher: Read the rhyming words to your child. Emphasizing the sound of the letter, instruct your child to trace and write the letter. As your child writes, read the following Zaner-Bloser Stroke Descriptions: Touch below the midline; circle back (left) all the way around. Push up straight to the headline. Pull down straight to the baseline.

Today is Wednesday.
I taste things that begin with the sound of d.

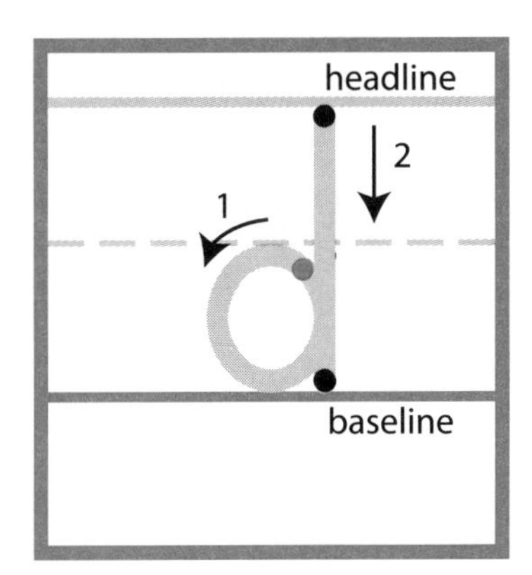

d d d d d d d

Attention Parent/Teacher: Using bright colored pencils, your child may draw pictures of today's items beginning with the sound of **d**. Emphasizing the sound of the letter, instruct your child to trace and write the letter. As your child writes, read the following Zaner-Bloser Stroke Descriptions: Touch below the midline; circle back (left) all the way around. Push up straight to the headline. Pull down straight to the baseline.

Today is Thursday.

I smell things that begin with the sound of d.

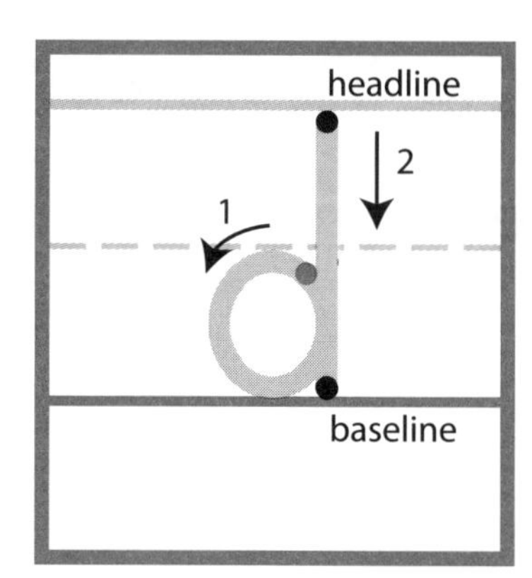

d d d d d d d

Attention Parent/Teacher: Using bright colored pencils, your child may draw pictures of today's items beginning with the sound of **d**. Emphasizing the sound of the letter, instruct your child to trace and write the letter. As your child writes, read the following Zaner-Bloser Stroke Descriptions: Touch below the midline; circle back (left) all the way around. Push up straight to the headline. Pull down straight to the baseline.

Today is Friday.

I touch things that begin with the sound of d.

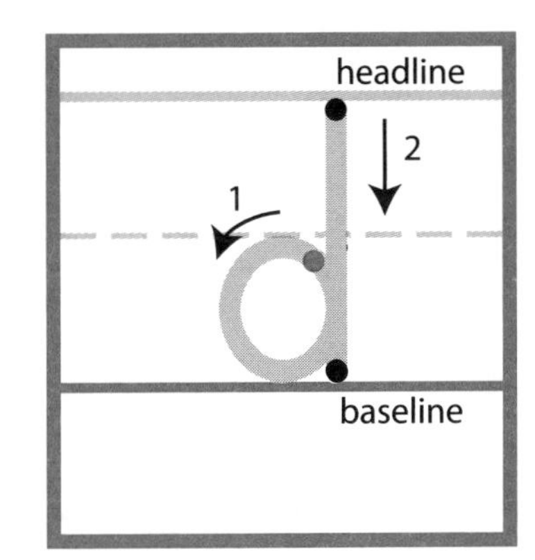

d d d d d d d

Attention Parent/Teacher: Using bright colored pencils, your child may draw pictures of today's items beginning with the sound of **d**. Emphasizing the sound of the letter, instruct your child to trace and write the letter. As your child writes, read the following Zaner-Bloser Stroke Descriptions: Touch below the midline; circle back (left) all the way around. Push up straight to the headline. Pull down straight to the baseline.

When my eyes are closed in sleep,
Through the night my slumbers keep.

Touch the blue dot below the midline; circle back counter clockwise all the way around. Push up straight to the dot on the midline. Pause; pull down straight through the baseline to the dot; curve back left, touching the baseline, to the dot above the baseline. Lift.

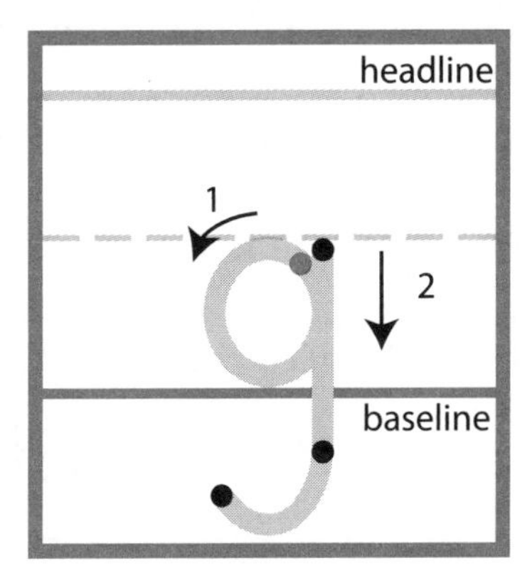

Touch the blue dot below the headline; circle back counterclockwise, touching the headline, midline, and baseline, and ending on the dot on the midline; slide left to the dot. Lift.

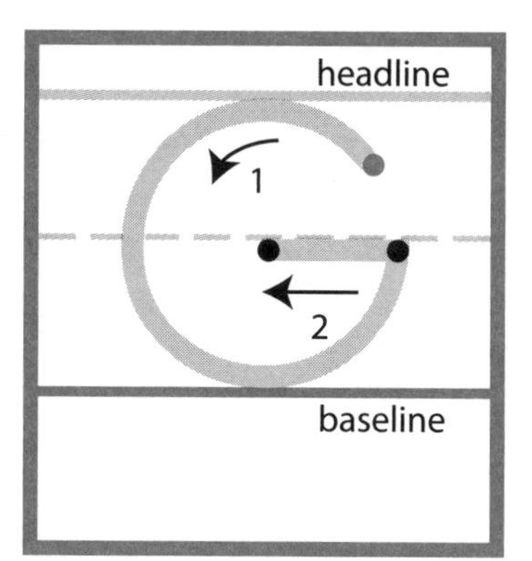

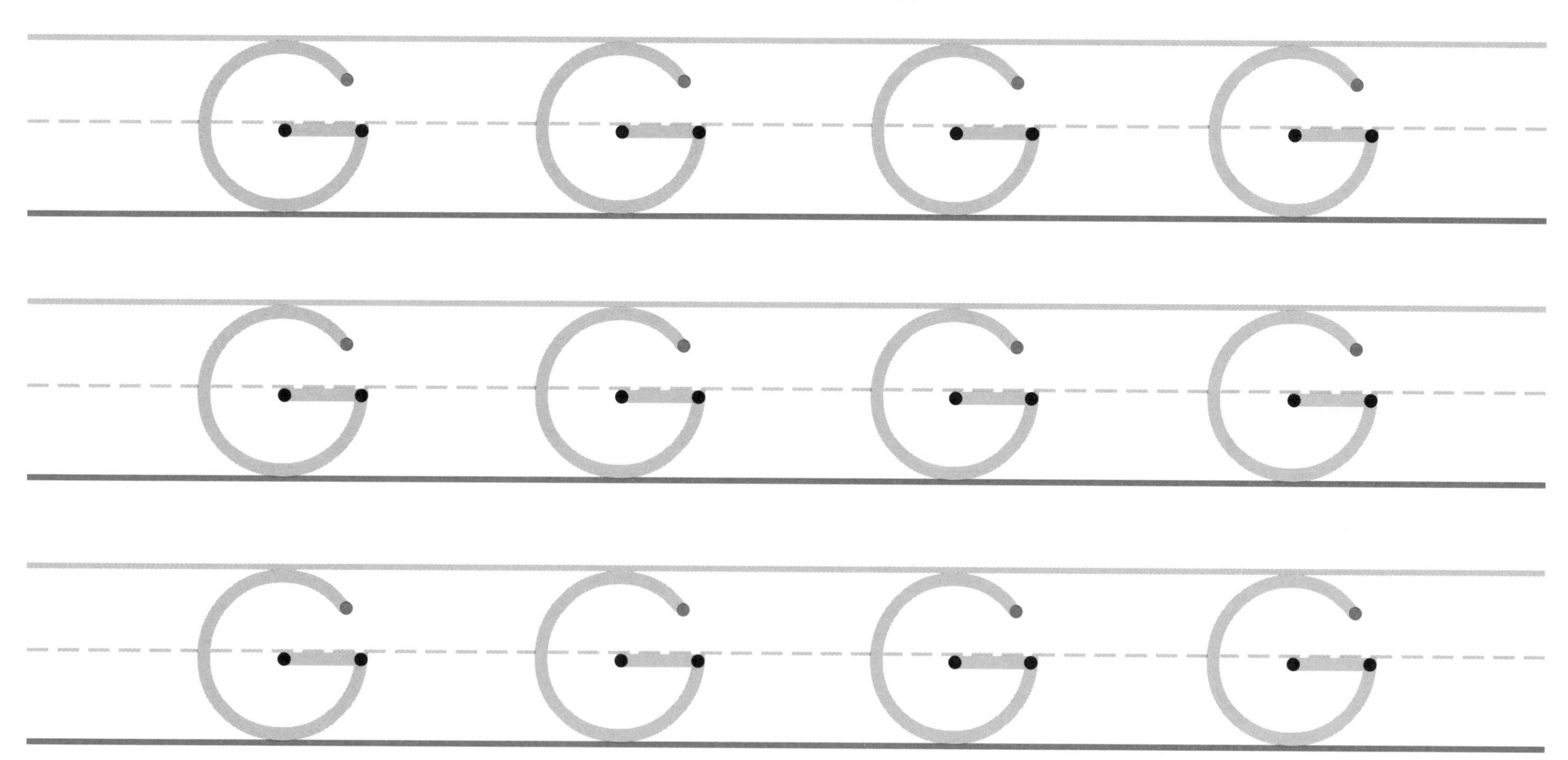

Today is Monday.

I see things that begin with the sound of g.

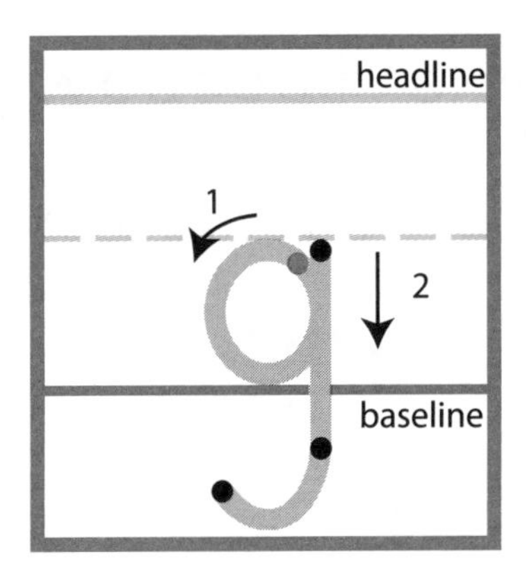

g g g g g g g

Attention Parent/Teacher: Using bright colored pencils, your child may draw pictures of today's items beginning with the sound of **g**. Emphasizing the sound of the letter, instruct your child to trace and write the letter. As your child writes, read the following Zaner-Bloser Stroke Descriptions: Touch below the midline; circle back (left), all the way around. Push up straight to the midline. Pull down straight through the baseline; curve back (left).

Today is Tuesday.

I hear rhyming words that end with the sound of g.

pig	jig	big
hog	jog	log
hug	jug	rug

g g g g g g g

Attention Parent/Teacher: Read the rhyming words to your child. Emphasizing the sound of the letter, instruct your child to trace and write the letter. As your child writes, read the following Zaner-Bloser Stroke Descriptions: Touch below the midline; circle back (left), all the way around. Push up straight to the midline. Pull down straight through the baseline; curve back (left).

Today is Wednesday.
I taste things that begin with the sound of g.

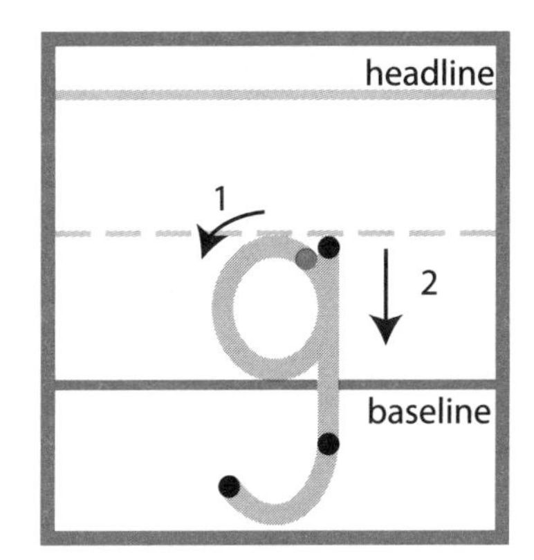

g g g g g g g

Attention Parent/Teacher: Using bright colored pencils, your child may draw pictures of today's items beginning with the sound of **g**. Emphasizing the sound of the letter, instruct your child to trace and write the letter. As your child writes, read the following Zaner-Bloser Stroke Descriptions: Touch below the midline; circle back (left), all the way around. Push up straight to the midline. Pull down straight through the baseline; curve back (left).

Today is Thursday.

I smell things that begin with the sound of g.

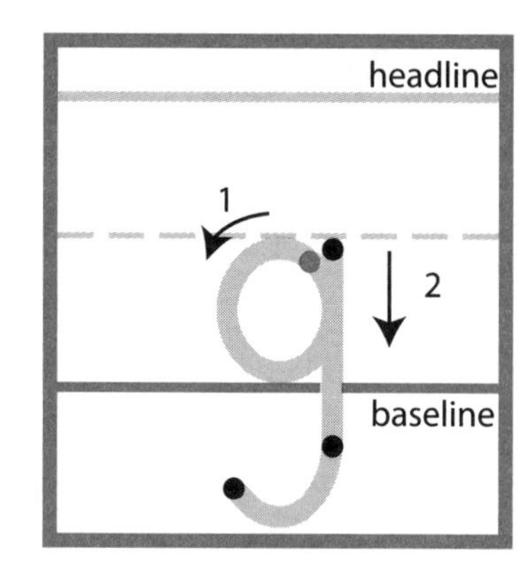

g g g g g g g

Attention Parent/Teacher: Using bright colored pencils, your child may draw pictures of today's items beginning with the sound of **g**. Emphasizing the sound of the letter, instruct your child to trace and write the letter. As your child writes, read the following Zaner-Bloser Stroke Descriptions: Touch below the midline; circle back (left), all the way around. Push up straight to the midline. Pull down straight through the baseline; curve back (left).

Today is Friday.

I touch things that begin with the sound of g.

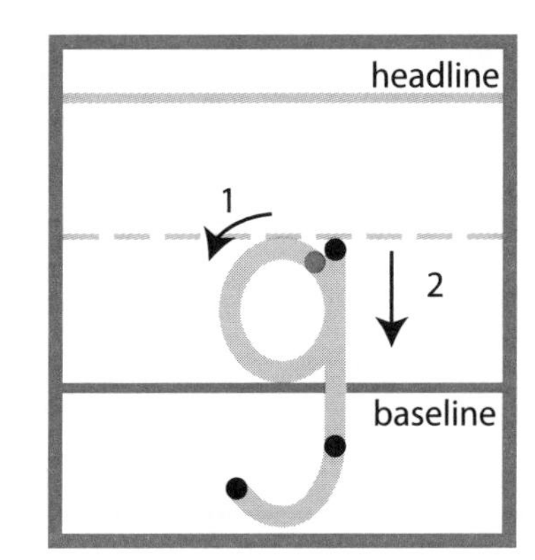

g g g g g g g

Attention Parent/Teacher: Using bright colored pencils, your child may draw pictures of today's items beginning with the sound of **g**. Emphasizing the sound of the letter, instruct your child to trace and write the letter. As your child writes, read the following Zaner-Bloser Stroke Descriptions: Touch below the midline; circle back (left), all the way around. Push up straight to the midline. Pull down straight through the baseline; curve back (left).

Make my latest thought to be
How to love thy Son and thee.

Touch the blue dot below the midline; circle back counterclockwise all the way around. Push up straight to the dot on the midline. Pause; pull down straight through the baseline; curve forward right, touching the next guideline, to the dot. Lift.

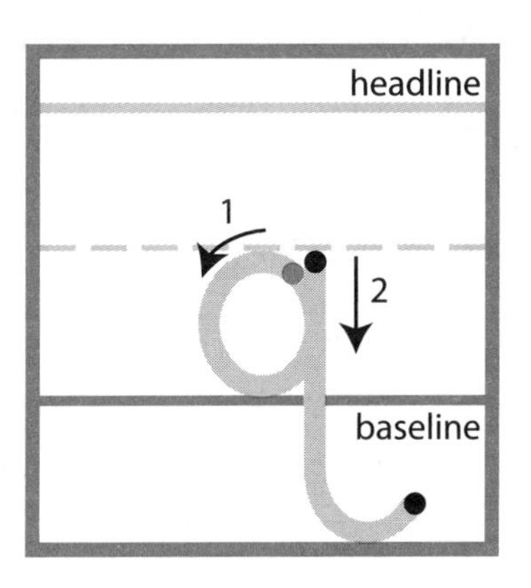

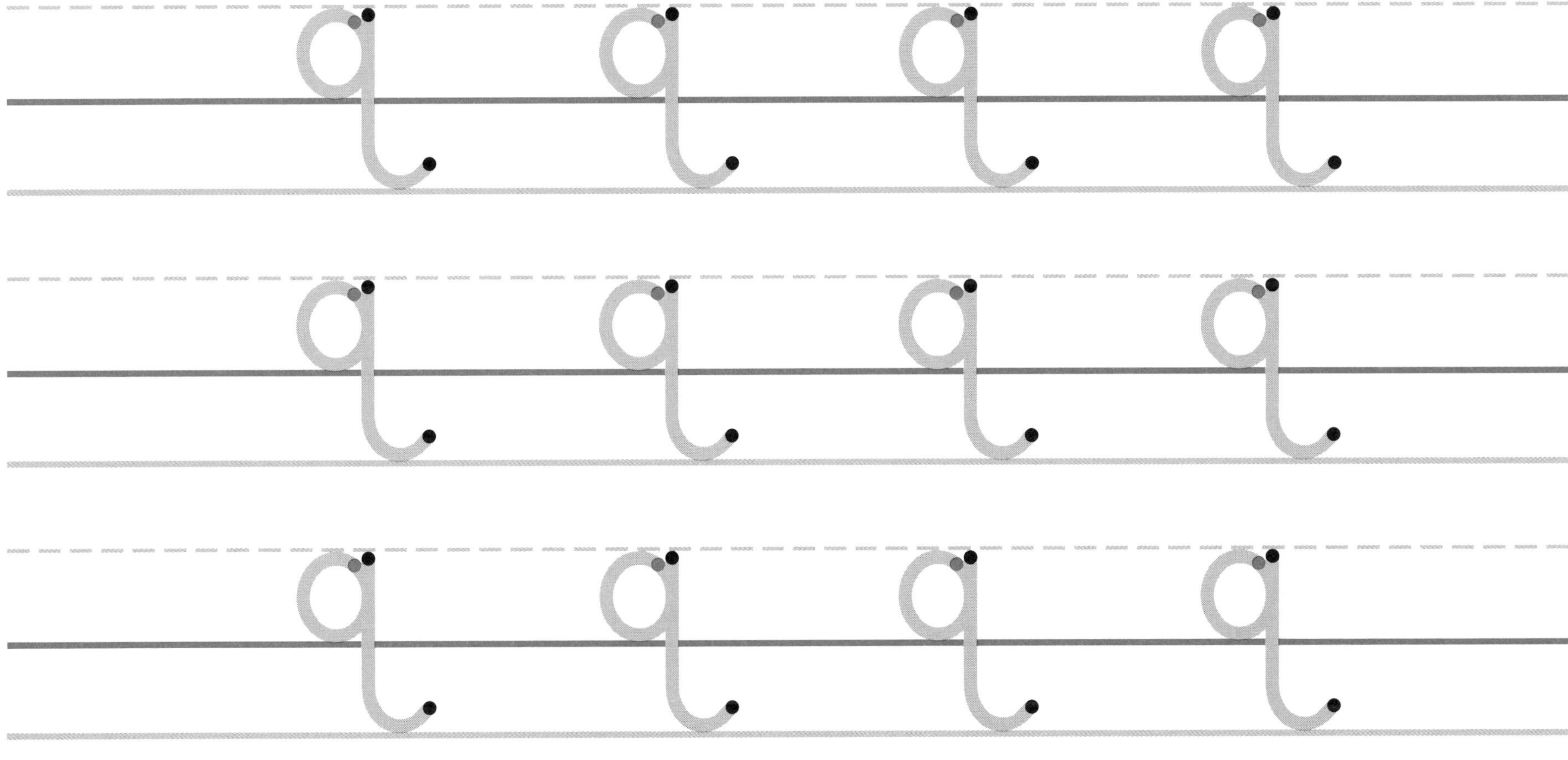

1. Touch the blue dot below the headline; circle back counterclockwise touching all the dots, back to the same dot. Lift.
2. Touch the dot between the midline and baseline; slant right to the dot on the baseline. Lift.

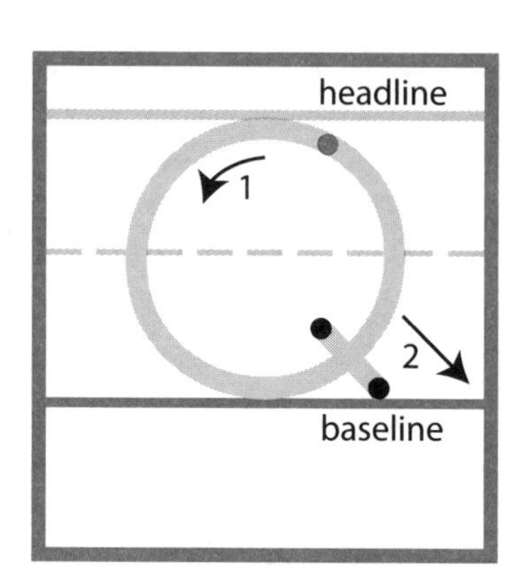

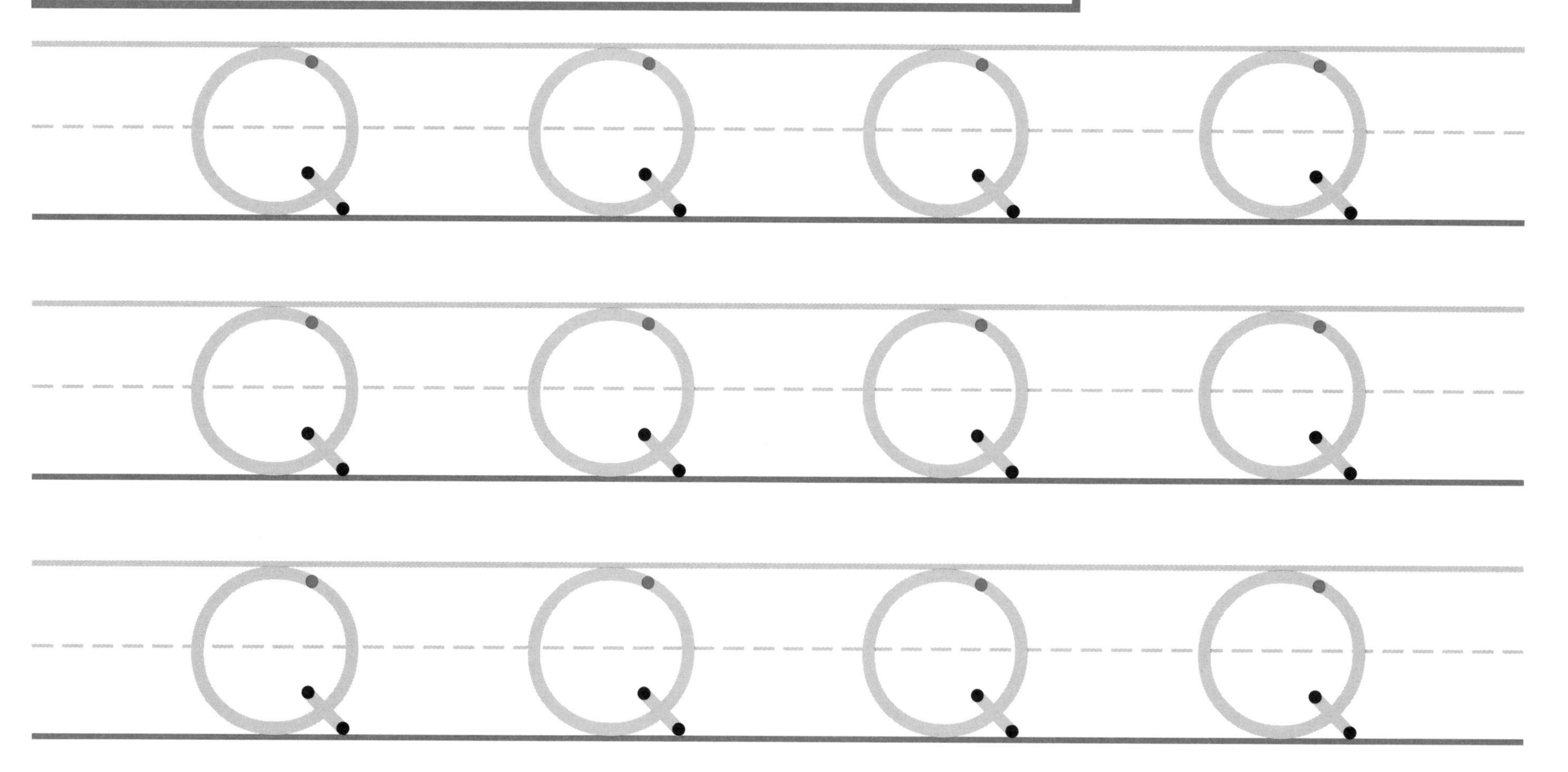

Today is Monday.

I see things that begin with the sound of q.

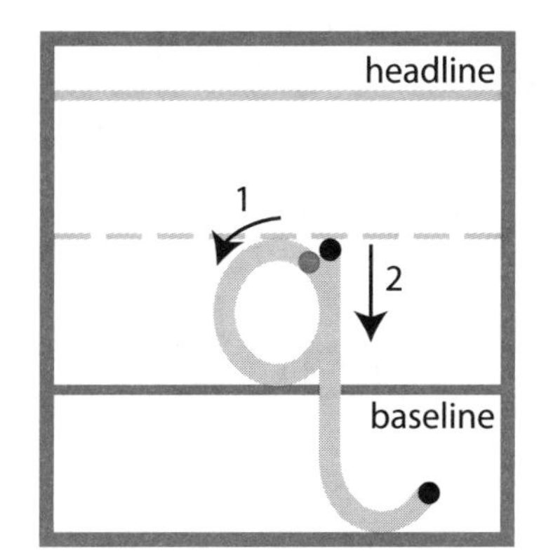

q q q q q q q

Attention Parent/Teacher: Using bright colored pencils, your child may draw pictures of today's items beginning with the sound of **q**. Emphasizing the sound of the letter, instruct your child to trace and write the letter. As your child writes, read the following Zaner-Bloser Stroke Descriptions: Touch below the midline; circle back (left) all the way around. Push up straight to the midline. Pull down straight through the baseline; curve forward (right).

Today is Tuesday.

I hear words that begin with the sound of q.

quack quilt quiz

quick quit quip

q q q q q q q

Attention Parent/Teacher: Read the words to your child. Emphasizing the sound of the letter, instruct your child to trace and write the letter. As your child writes, read the following Zaner-Bloser Stroke Descriptions: Touch below the midline; circle back (left) all the way around. Push up straight to the midline. Pull down straight through the baseline; curve forward (right).

Today is Wednesday.

I taste things that begin with the sound of q.

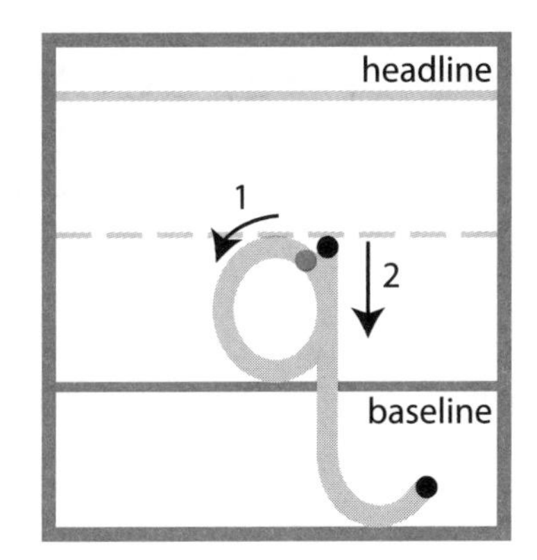

q q q q q q q

Attention Parent/Teacher: Using bright colored pencils, your child may draw pictures of today's items beginning with the sound of **q**. Emphasizing the sound of the letter, instruct your child to trace and write the letter. As your child writes, read the following Zaner-Bloser Stroke Descriptions: Touch below the midline; circle back (left) all the way around. Push up straight to the midline. Pull down straight through the baseline; curve forward (right).

Today is Thursday.

I smell things that begin with the sound of q.

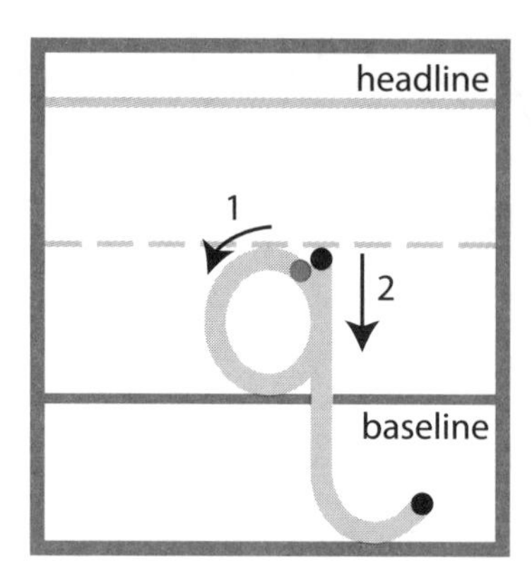

q q q q q q q

Attention Parent/Teacher: Using bright colored pencils, your child may draw pictures of today's items beginning with the sound of **q**. Emphasizing the sound of the letter, instruct your child to trace and write the letter. As your child writes, read the following Zaner-Bloser Stroke Descriptions: Touch below the midline; circle back (left) all the way around. Push up straight to the midline. Pull down straight through the baseline; curve forward (right).

Today is Friday.

I touch things that begin with the sound of q.

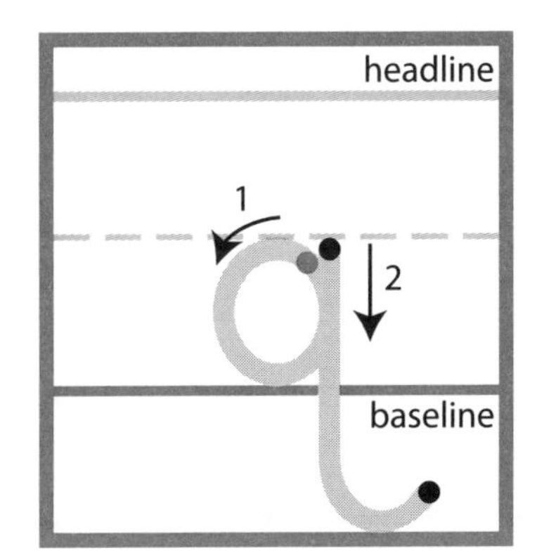

q q q q q q q

Attention Parent/Teacher: Using bright colored pencils, your child may draw pictures of today's items beginning with the sound of **q**. Emphasizing the sound of the letter, instruct your child to trace and write the letter. As your child writes, read the following Zaner-Bloser Stroke Descriptions: Touch below the midline; circle back (left) all the way around. Push up straight to the midline. Pull down straight through the baseline; curve forward (right).

Oh! Wake me up tomorrow morn,
So early, Mother dear.
Tomorrow will be May Day,
The gladdest of the year!

Touch the blue dot on the midline; pull down straight; curve forward right, touching the baseline. Push up to the dot on the midline. Pause; pull down straight to the dot on the baseline. Lift.

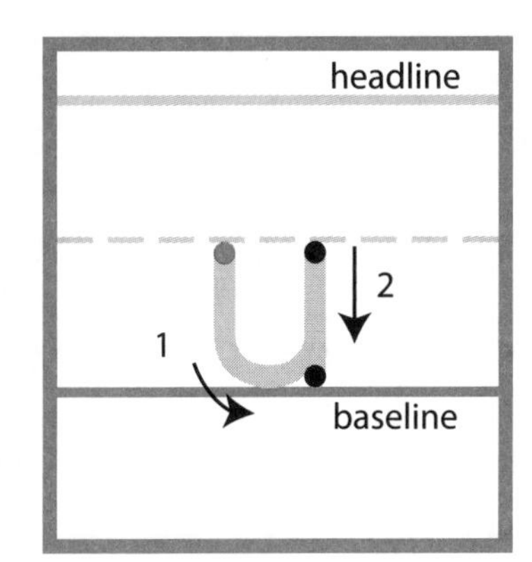

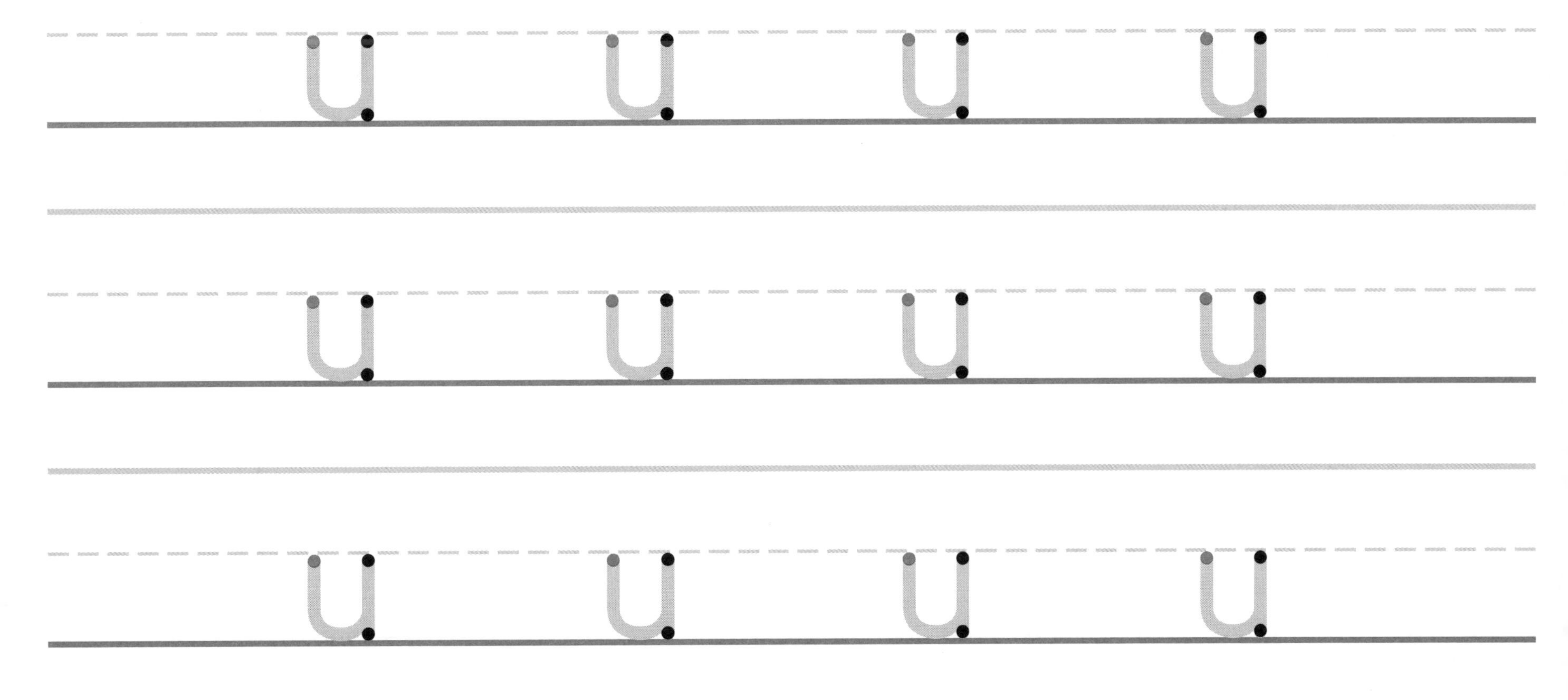

Touch the blue dot on the headline; pull down straight to the dot below the midline; curve forward right, touching the baseline, to the dot below the midline; push up to the dot on the headline. Lift.

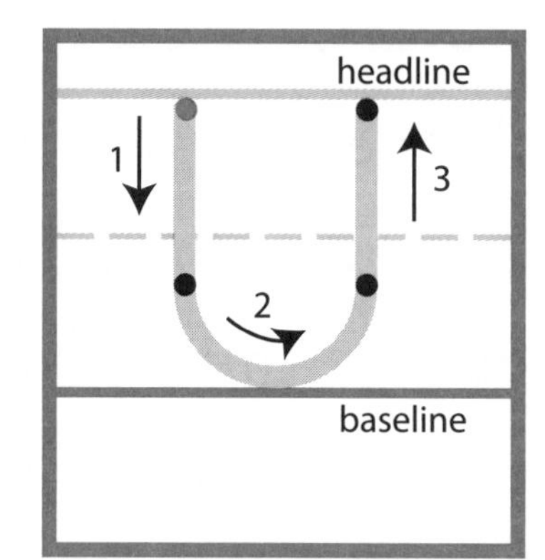

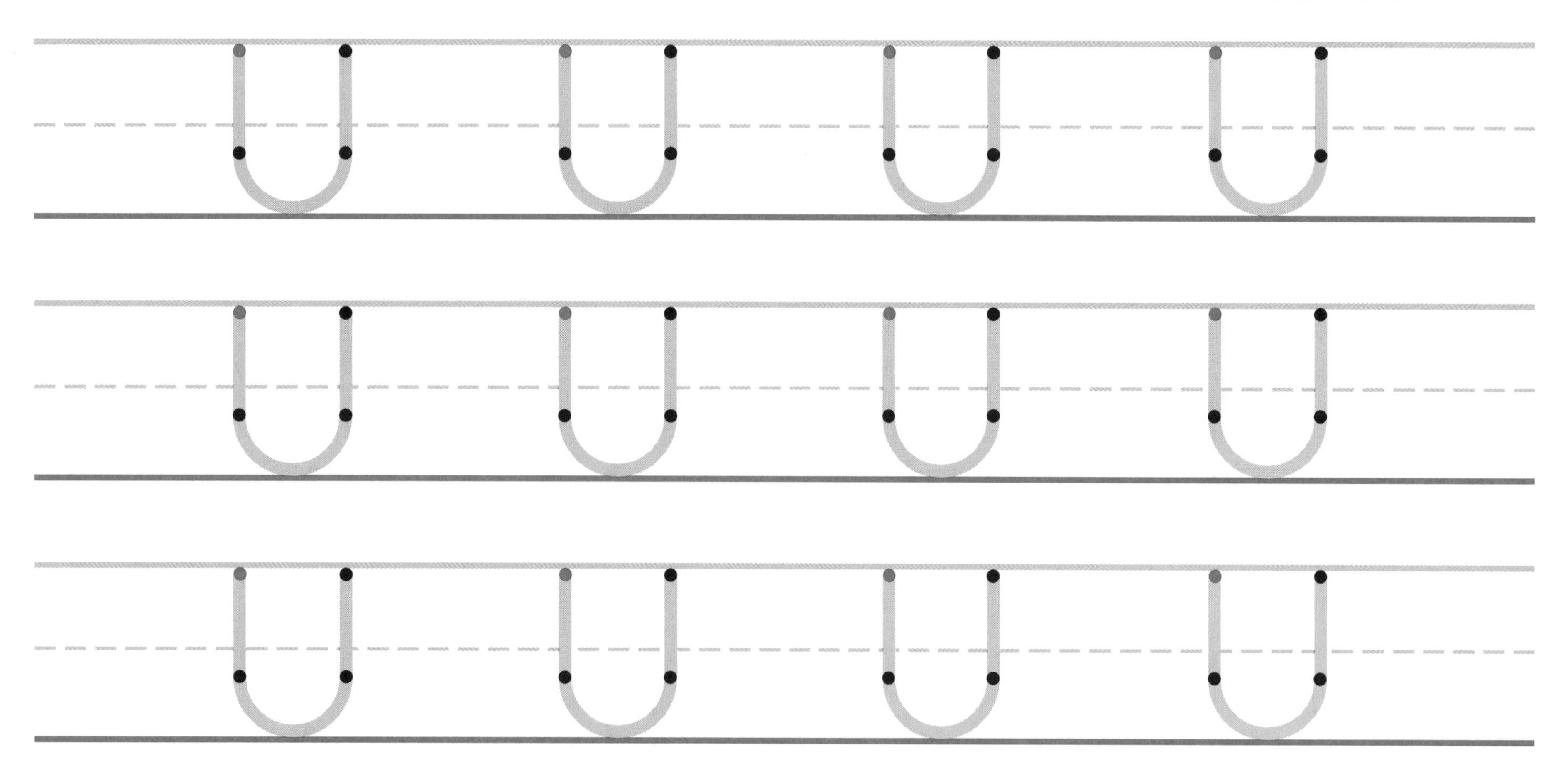

Today is Monday.
I see things that begin with the sound of u.

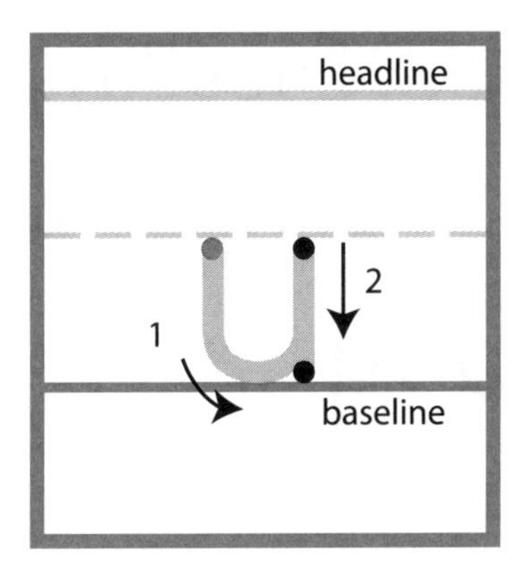

u u u u u u u

Attention Parent/Teacher: Using bright colored pencils, your child may draw pictures of today's items beginning with the sound of **u**. Emphasizing the sound of the letter, instruct your child to trace and write the letter. As your child writes, read the following Zaner-Bloser Stroke Descriptions: Touch the midline; pull down straight; curve forward (right); push up to the midline. Pull down straight to the baseline.

Today is Tuesday.

I hear the sound of u in the middle of words.

bug	hug	rug	tug
bun	fun	nun	sun
cub	hub	sub	tub

u u u u u u u

Attention Parent/Teacher: Read the words to your child. Emphasizing the sound of the letter, instruct your child to trace and write the letter. As your child writes, read the following Zaner-Bloser Stroke Descriptions: Touch the midline; pull down straight; curve forward (right); push up to the midline. Pull down straight to the baseline.

Today is Wednesday.

I taste things that begin with the sound of u.

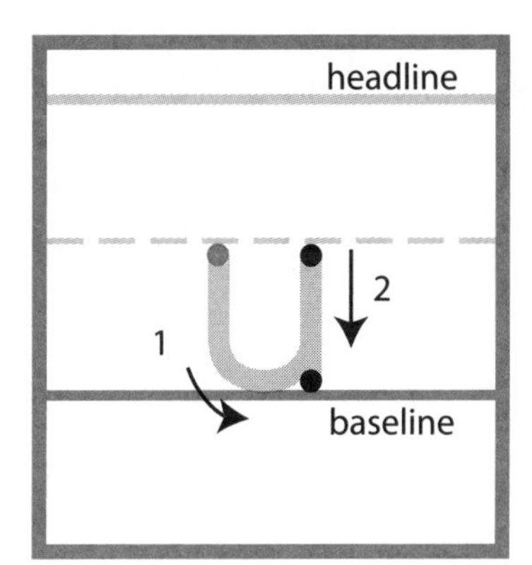

u u u u u u u

Attention Parent/Teacher: Using bright colored pencils, your child may draw pictures of today's items beginning with the sound of **u**. Emphasizing the sound of the letter, instruct your child to trace and write the letter. As your child writes, read the following Zaner-Bloser Stroke Descriptions: Touch the midline; pull down straight; curve forward (right); push up to the midline. Pull down straight to the baseline.

Today is Thursday.

I smell things that begin with the sound of u.

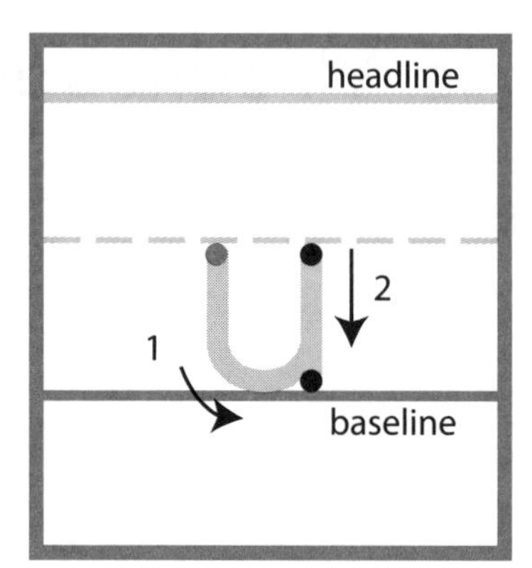

u u u u u u u

Attention Parent/Teacher: Using bright colored pencils, your child may draw pictures of today's items beginning with the sound of **u**. Emphasizing the sound of the letter, instruct your child to trace and write the letter. As your child writes, read the following Zaner-Bloser Stroke Descriptions: Touch the midline; pull down straight; curve forward (right); push up to the midline. Pull down straight to the baseline.

Today is Friday.

I touch things that begin with the sound of u.

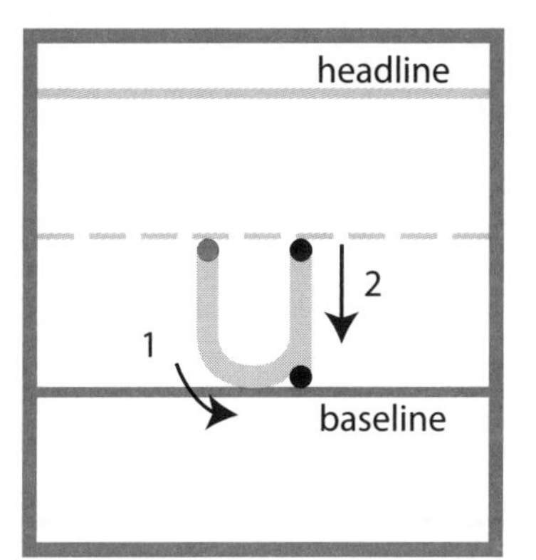

u u u u u u u

Attention Parent/Teacher: Using bright colored pencils, your child may draw pictures of today's items beginning with the sound of **u**. Emphasizing the sound of the letter, instruct your child to trace and write the letter. As your child writes, read the following Zaner-Bloser Stroke Descriptions: Touch the midline; pull down straight; curve forward (right); push up to the midline. Pull down straight to the baseline.

At early Mass we'll welcome in
The summer's brightest day,
For Mary is the Queen of Heaven,
And also Queen of May!

Touch the blue dot below the midline; curve back left; curve forward right, ending on the dot just above the baseline. Lift.

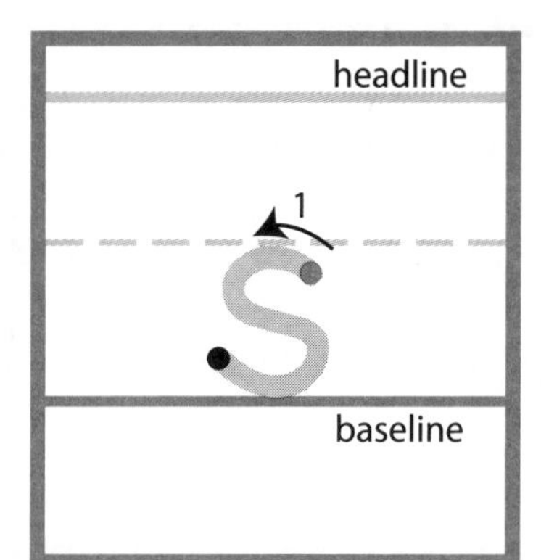

s s s s

s s s s

s s s s

Touch the blue dot below the headline; curve back left; curve forward right, ending on the dot just above the baseline. Lift.

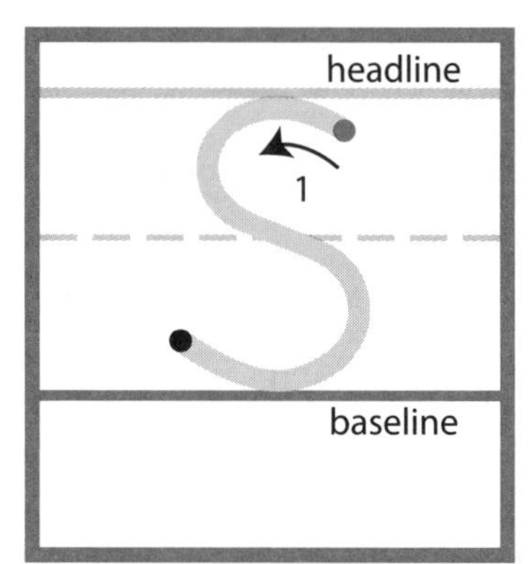

Today is Monday.

I see things that begin with the sound of s.

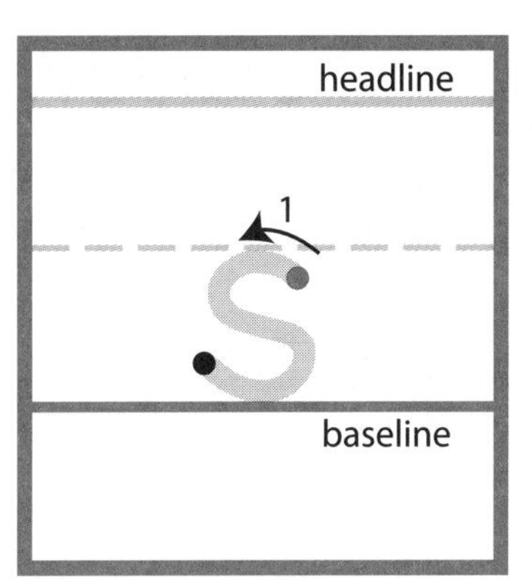

s s s s s s s

Attention Parent/Teacher: Using bright colored pencils, your child may draw pictures of today's items beginning with the sound of **s.** Emphasizing the sound of the letter, instruct your child to trace and write the letter. As your child writes, read the following Zaner-Bloser Stroke Descriptions: Touch below the midline curve back (left); curve forward (right), ending above the baseline.

Today is Tuesday.

I hear rhyming words that end with the sound of s.

pass	Mass	gas
loss	moss	toss
hiss	miss	kiss

Attention Parent/Teacher: Read the rhyming words to your child. Emphasizing the sound of the letter, instruct your child to trace and write the letter. As your child writes, read the following Zaner-Bloser Stroke Descriptions: Touch below the midline curve back (left); curve forward (right), ending above the baseline.

Today is Wednesday.

I taste things that begin with the sound of s.

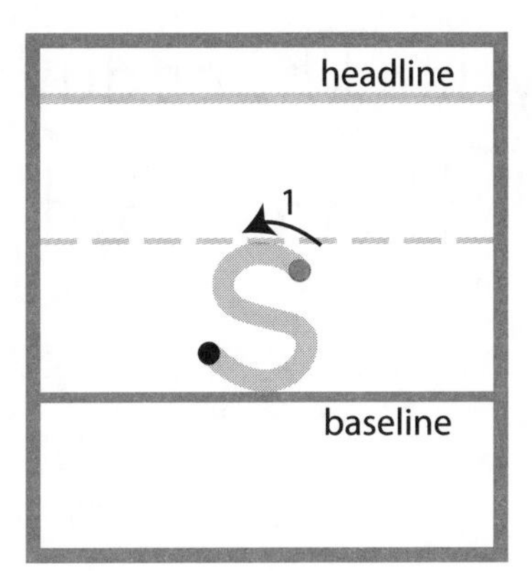

s s s s s s s

Attention Parent/Teacher: Using bright colored pencils, your child may draw pictures of today's items beginning with the sound of **s**. Emphasizing the sound of the letter, instruct your child to trace and write the letter. As your child writes, read the following Zaner-Bloser Stroke Descriptions: Touch below the midline curve back (left); curve forward (right), ending above the baseline.

Today is Thursday.

I smell things that begin with the sound of s.

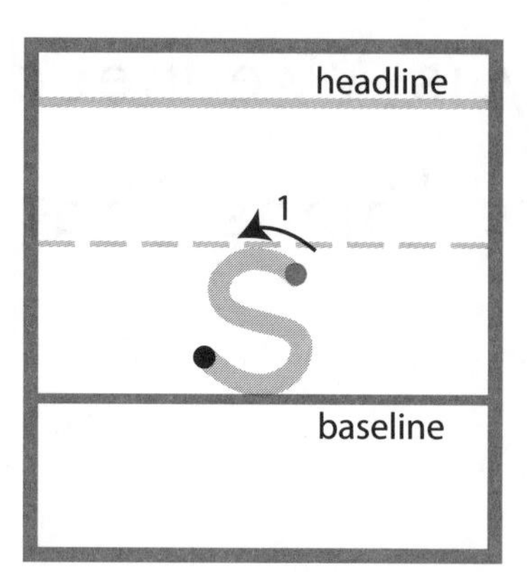

s s s s s s s

Attention Parent/Teacher: Using bright colored pencils, your child may draw pictures of today's items beginning with the sound of **s**. Emphasizing the sound of the letter, instruct your child to trace and write the letter. As your child writes, read the following Zaner-Bloser Stroke Descriptions: Touch below the midline curve back (left); curve forward (right), ending above the baseline.

Today is Friday.

I touch things that begin with the sound of s.

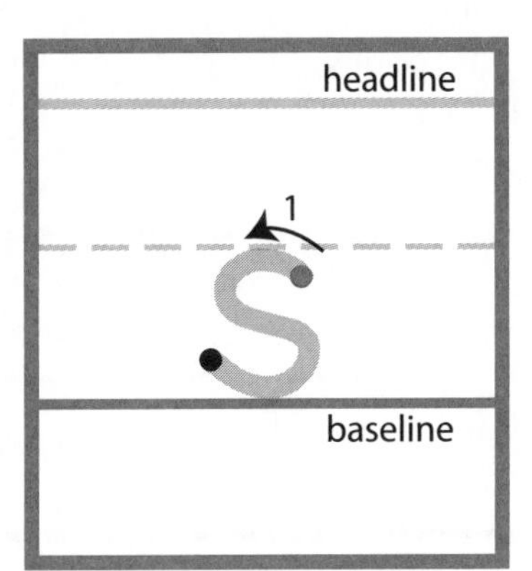

s s s s s s s

Attention Parent/Teacher: Using bright colored pencils, your child may draw pictures of today's items beginning with the sound of **s**. Emphasizing the sound of the letter, instruct your child to trace and write the letter. As your child writes, read the following Zaner-Bloser Stroke Descriptions: Touch below the midline curve back (left); curve forward (right), ending above the baseline.

We've decked Our Lady's altar
With flowers fresh and fair,
And crowned her with a diadem
Of the choicest and most rare!

Touch the blue dot on the headline; pull down straight to the dot on the baseline. Pause; push up; circle forward clockwise all the way around. Lift.

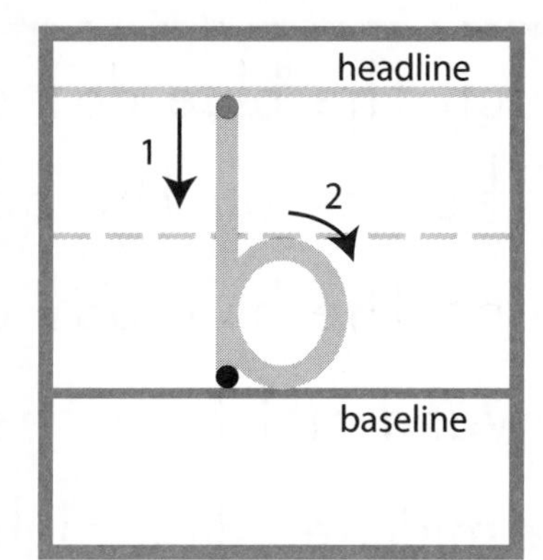

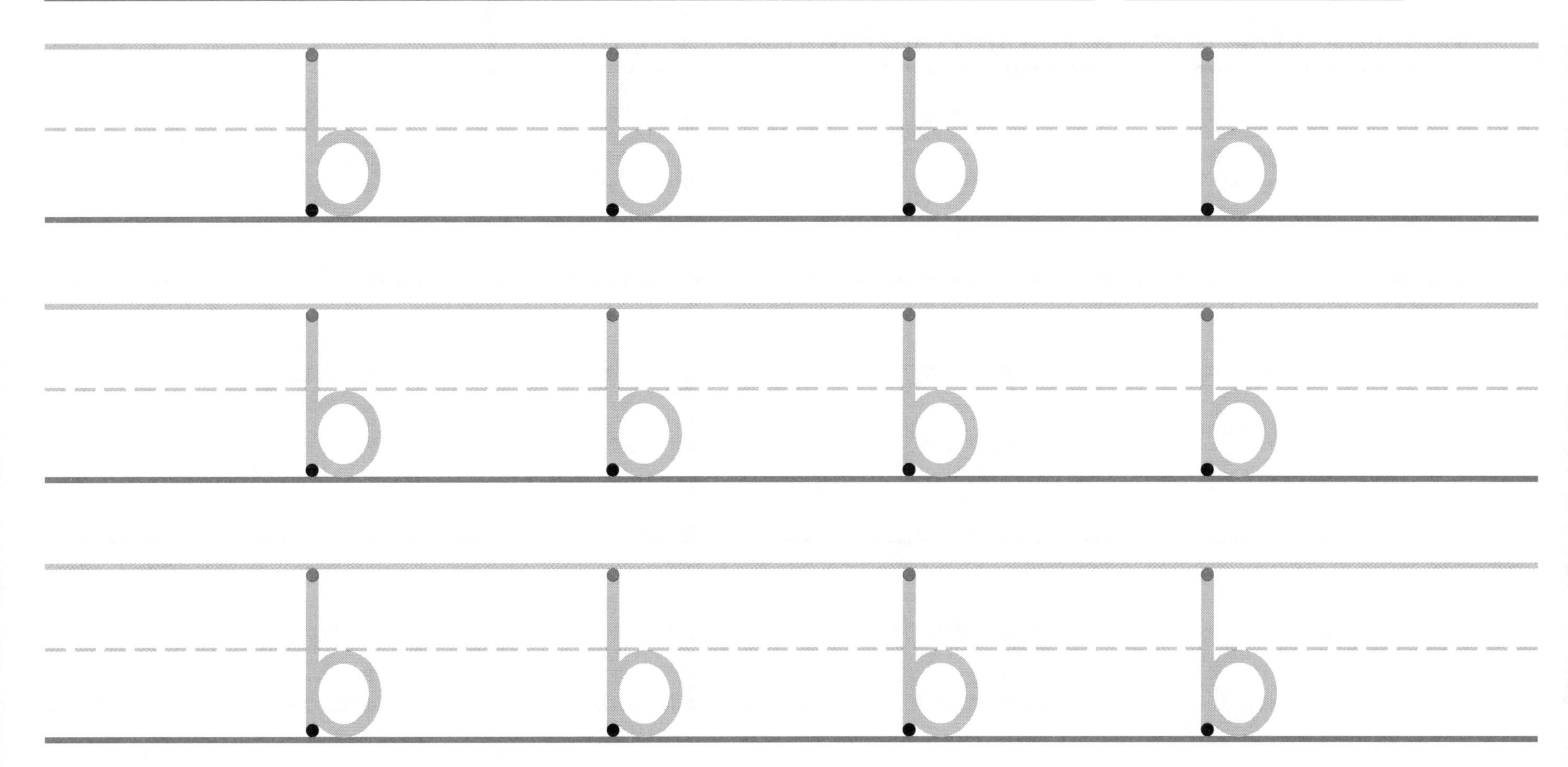

1. Touch the blue dot on the headline; pull down straight to the dot on the baseline. Lift.
2. Touch the blue dot on the headline; slide right; curve forward right to the midline; slide left to the dot on the midline; slide right; curve forward right to the baseline; slide left to the dot on the baseline. Lift.

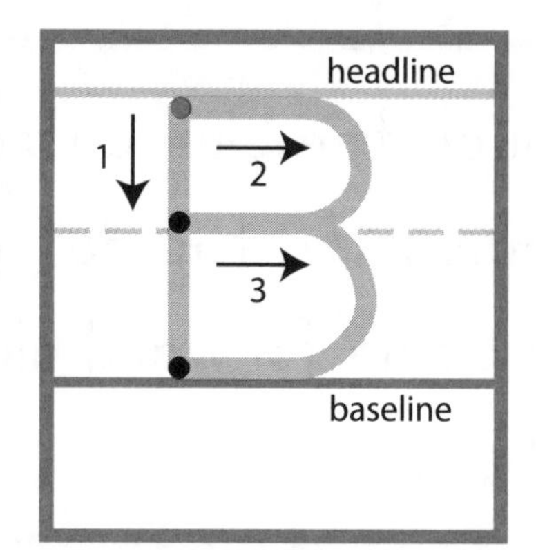

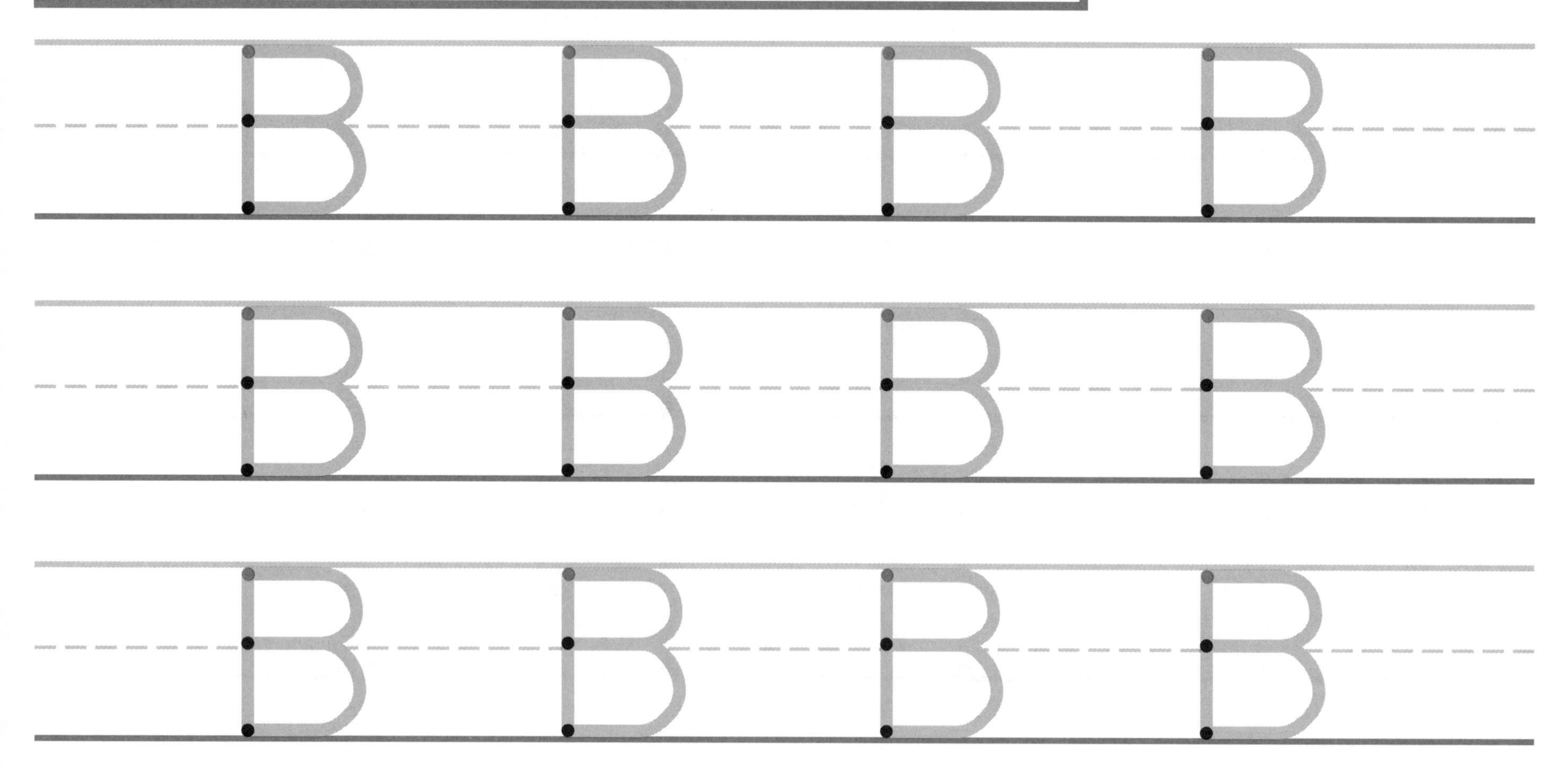

Today is Monday.
I see things that begin with the sound of b.

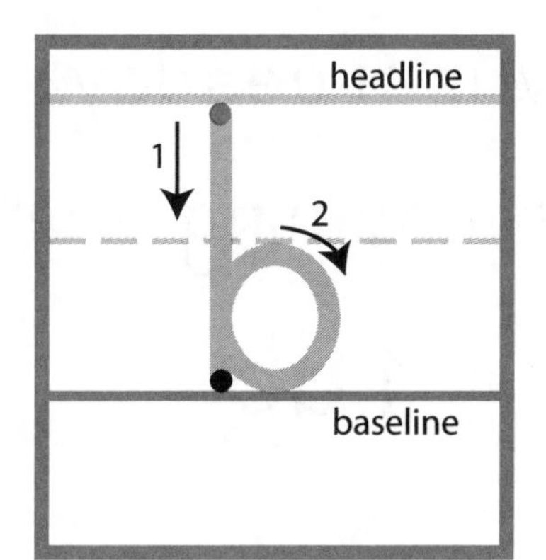

b b b b b b b

Attention Parent/Teacher: Using bright colored pencils, your child may draw pictures of today's items beginning with the sound of **b**. Emphasizing the sound of the letter, instruct your child to trace and write the letter. As your child writes, read the following Zaner-Bloser Stroke Descriptions: Touch the headline; pull down straight to the baseline. Push up; circle forward (right) all the way around.

Today is Tuesday.

I hear rhyming words that end with the sound of b.

tab	dab	lab
mob	sob	rob
bib	fib	rib

b b b b b b b

Attention Parent/Teacher: Read the rhyming words to your child. Emphasizing the sound of the letter, instruct your child to trace and write the letter. As your child writes, read the following Zaner-Bloser Stroke Descriptions: Touch the headline; pull down straight to the baseline. Push up; circle forward (right) all the way around.

Today is Wednesday.

I taste things that begin with the sound of b.

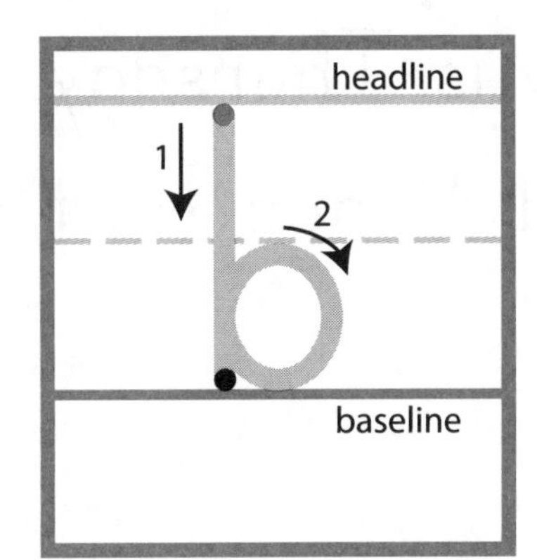

b b b b b b b

Attention Parent/Teacher: Using bright colored pencils, your child may draw pictures of today's items beginning with the sound of **b**. Emphasizing the sound of the letter, instruct your child to trace and write the letter. As your child writes, read the following Zaner-Bloser Stroke Descriptions: Touch the headline; pull down straight to the baseline. Push up; circle forward (right) all the way around.

Today is Thursday.

I smell things that begin with the sound of b.

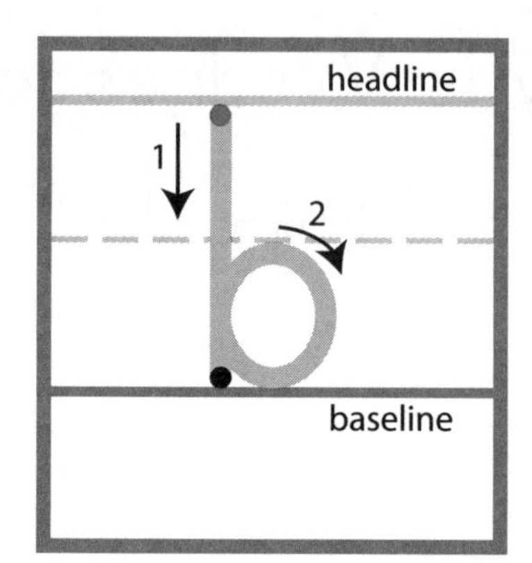

b b b b b b b

Attention Parent/Teacher: Using bright colored pencils, your child may draw pictures of today's items beginning with the sound of **b**. Emphasizing the sound of the letter, instruct your child to trace and write the letter. As your child writes, read the following Zaner-Bloser Stroke Descriptions: Touch the headline; pull down straight to the baseline. Push up; circle forward (right) all the way around.

Today is Friday.

I touch things that begin with the sound of b.

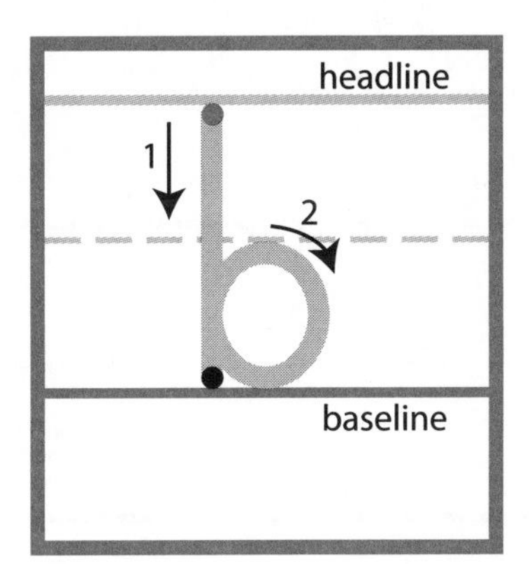

b b b b b b b

Attention Parent/Teacher: Using bright colored pencils, your child may draw pictures of today's items beginning with the sound of **b**. Emphasizing the sound of the letter, instruct your child to trace and write the letter. As your child writes, read the following Zaner-Bloser Stroke Descriptions: Touch the headline; pull down straight to the baseline. Push up; circle forward (right) all the way around.

So at her shrine I long to kneel,
And invoke her as I pray,
Oh, Mary, Queen of Heaven!
Oh, Mary, Queen of May!

Touch the blue dot on the midline; pull down straight through the baseline to the dot on the next guideline. Pause; push up; curve forward clockwise all the way around to the dot above the baseline. Lift.

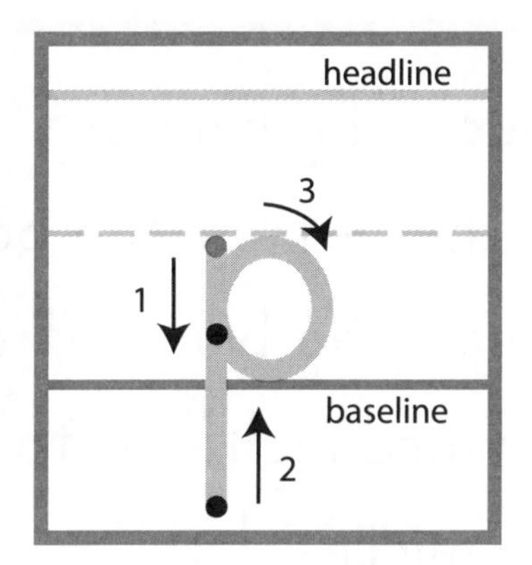

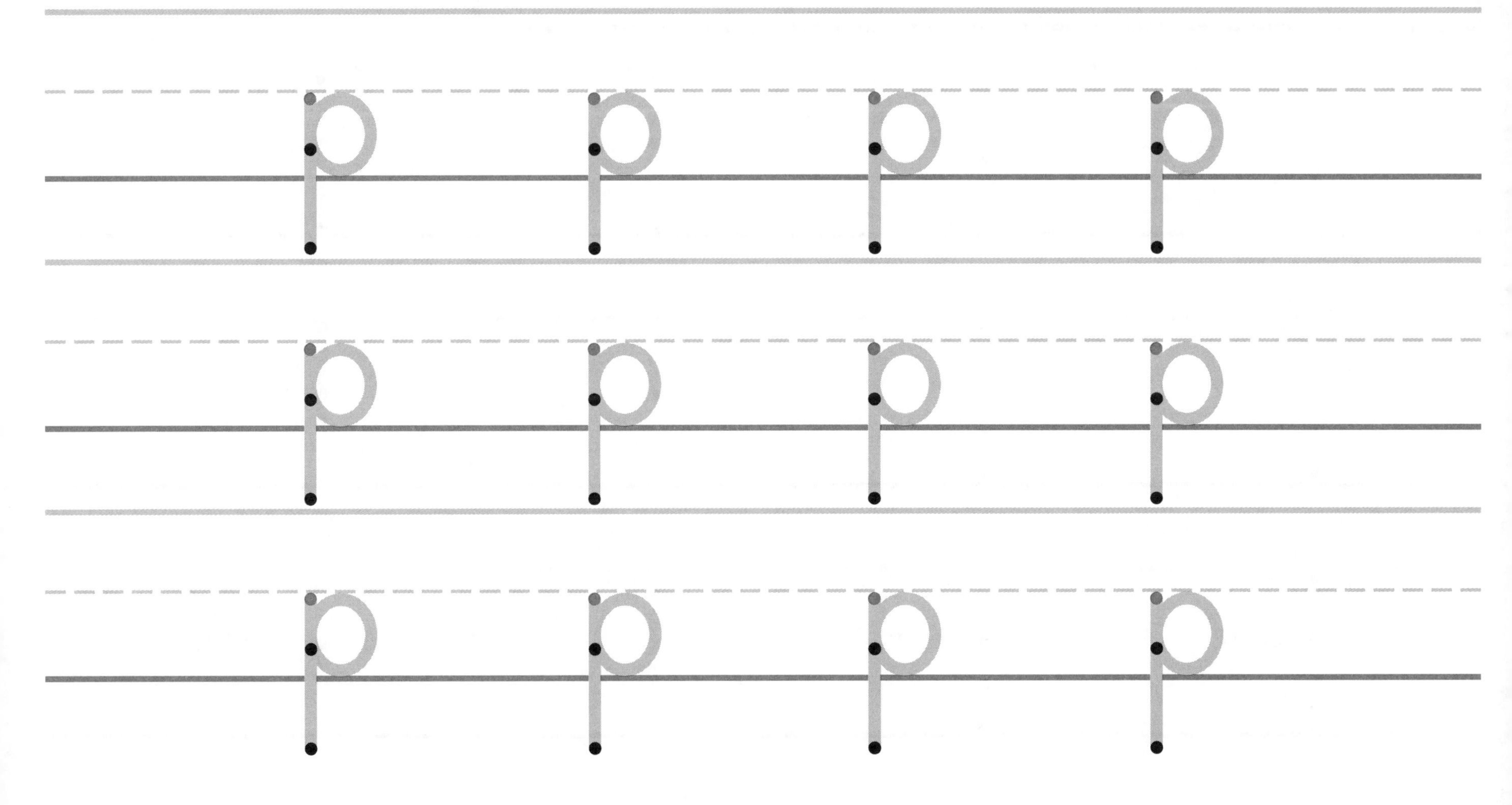

1. Touch the blue dot on the headline; pull down straight to the dot on the baseline. Lift.
2. Touch the blue dot on the headline; slide right; curve forward right to the midline; slide left to the dot on the midline. Lift.

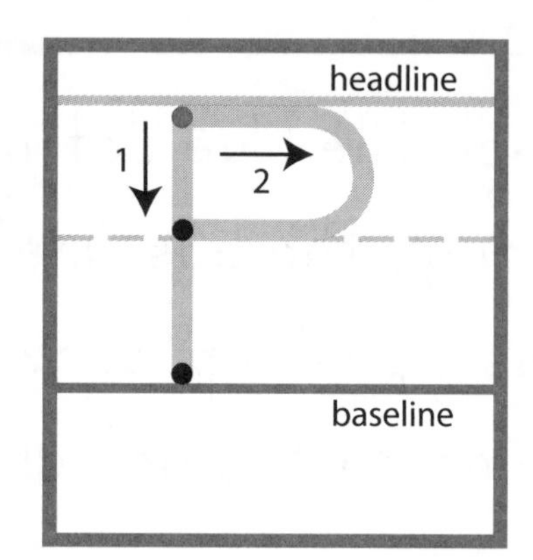

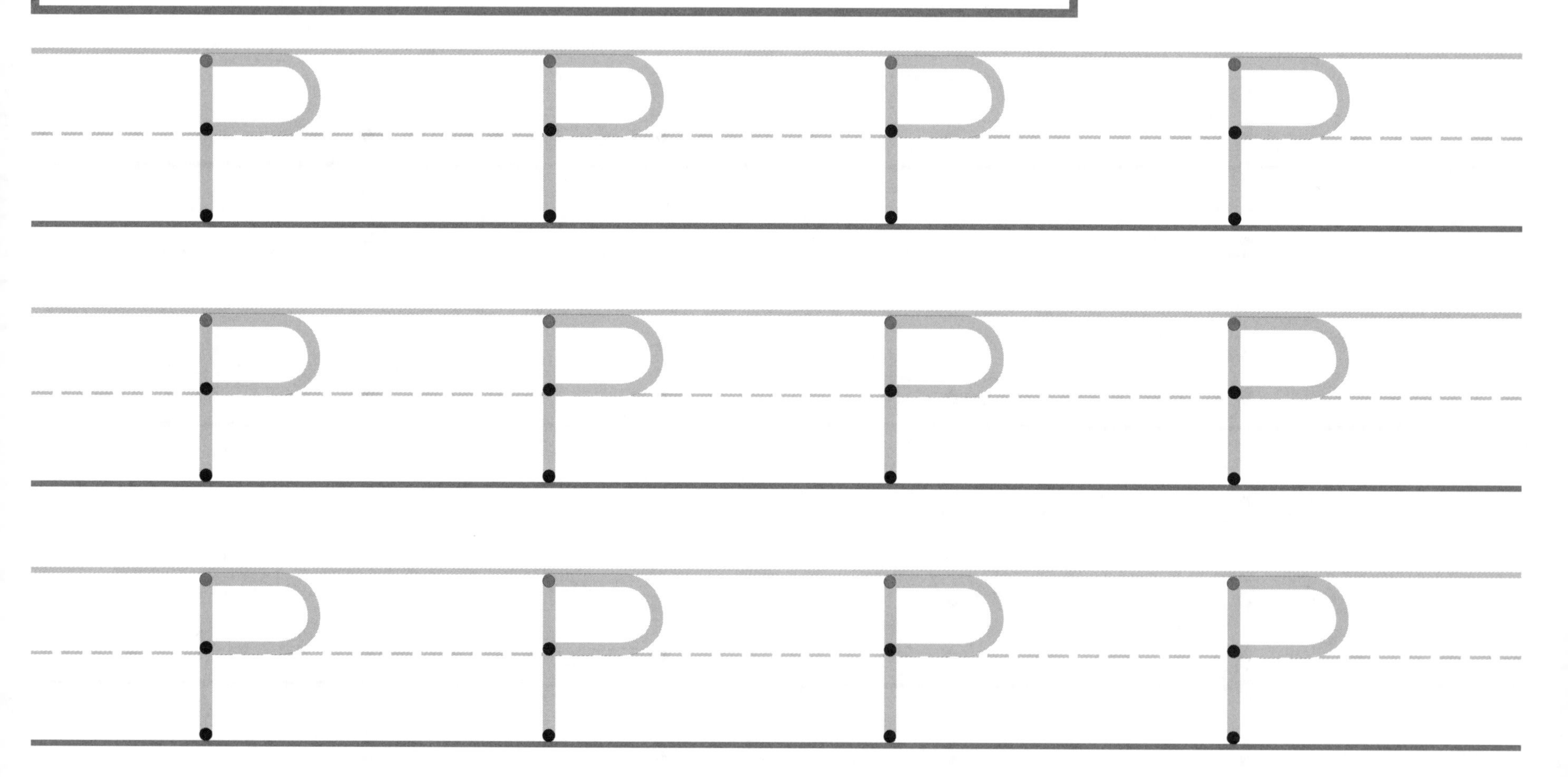

Today is Monday.

I see things that begin with the sound of p.

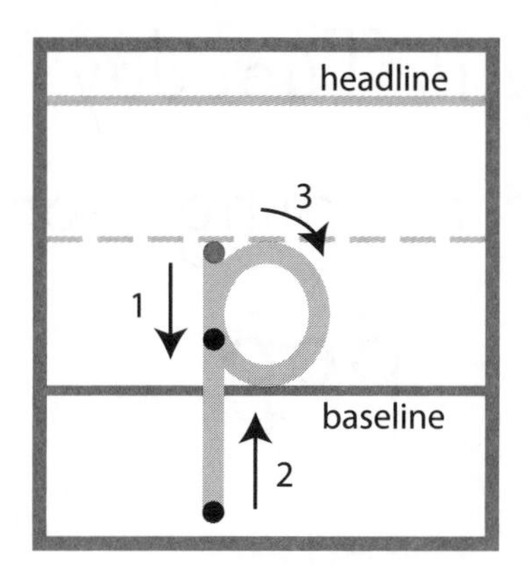

p p p p p p p

Attention Parent/Teacher: Using bright colored pencils, your child may draw pictures of today's items beginning with the sound of **p**. Emphasizing the sound of the letter, instruct your child to trace and write the letter. As your child writes, read the following Zaner-Bloser Stroke Descriptions: Touch the midline; pull down straight through the baseline to the next guideline. Push up; circle forward (right) all the way around.

Today is Tuesday.

I hear rhyming words that end with the sound of p.

pop	hop	cop
dip	hip	sip
cap	lap	map

p p p p p p p

Attention Parent/Teacher: Read the rhyming words to your child. Emphasizing the sound of the letter, instruct your child to trace and write the letter. As your child writes, read the following Zaner-Bloser Stroke Descriptions: Touch the midline; pull down straight through the baseline to the next guideline. Push up; circle forward (right) all the way around.

Today is Wednesday.

I taste things that begin with the sound of p.

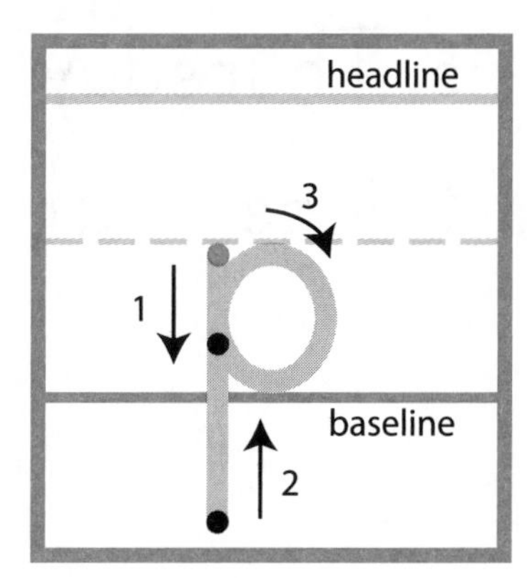

p p p p p p p

Attention Parent/Teacher: Using bright colored pencils, your child may draw pictures of today's items beginning with the sound of **p**. Emphasizing the sound of the letter, instruct your child to trace and write the letter. As your child writes, read the following Zaner-Bloser Stroke Descriptions: Touch the midline; pull down straight through the baseline to the next guideline. Push up; circle forward (right) all the way around.

Today is Thursday.

I smell things that begin with the sound of p.

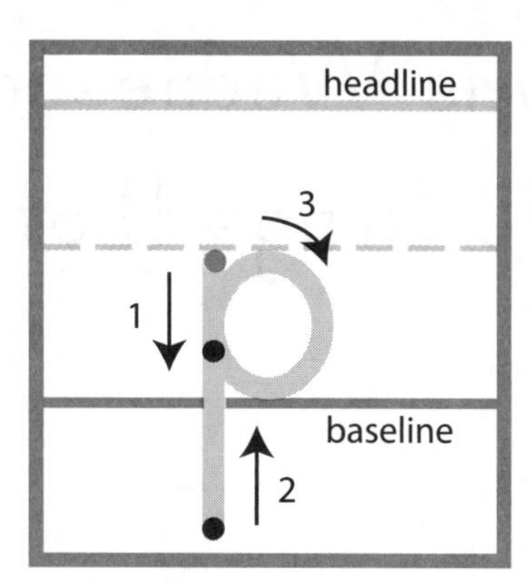

p p p p p p p

Attention Parent/Teacher: Using bright colored pencils, your child may draw pictures of today's items beginning with the sound of **p**. Emphasizing the sound of the letter, instruct your child to trace and write the letter. As your child writes, read the following Zaner-Bloser Stroke Descriptions: Touch the midline; pull down straight through the baseline to the next guideline. Push up; circle forward (right) all the way around.

Today is Friday.

I touch things that begin with the sound of p.

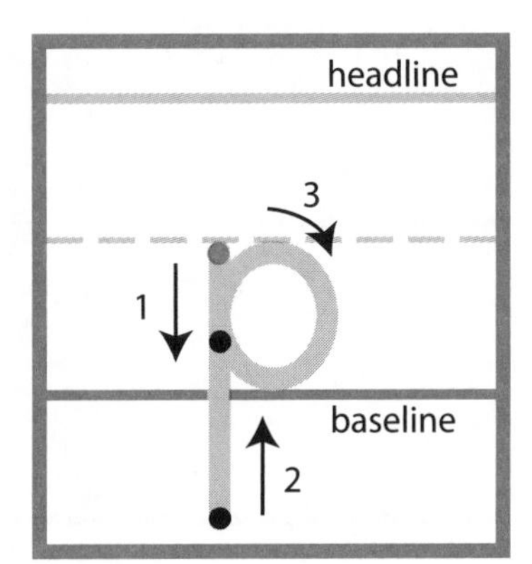

p p p p p p p

Attention Parent/Teacher: Using bright colored pencils, your child may draw pictures of today's items beginning with the sound of **p**. Emphasizing the sound of the letter, instruct your child to trace and write the letter. As your child writes, read the following Zaner-Bloser Stroke Descriptions: Touch the midline; pull down straight through the baseline to the next guideline. Push up; circle forward (right) all the way around.

Hail, Mother of the Savior,
From thy throne in Heaven above,
Look down on me with pity,
And hide me in thy love!

Touch the blue dot on the headline; pull down straight to the dot on the baseline. Pause; push up; curve forward right; pull down straight to the dot on the baseline. Lift.

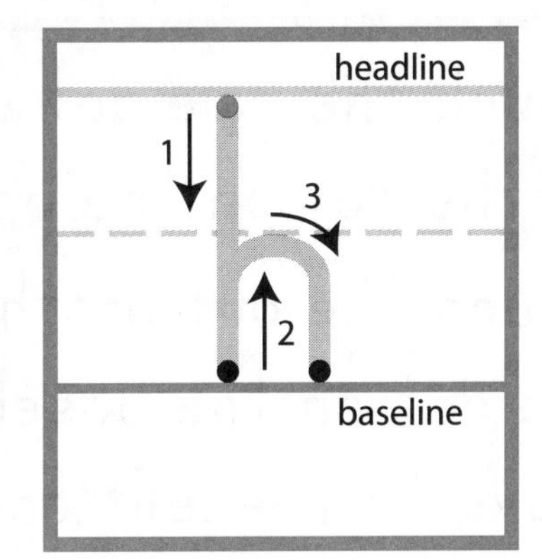

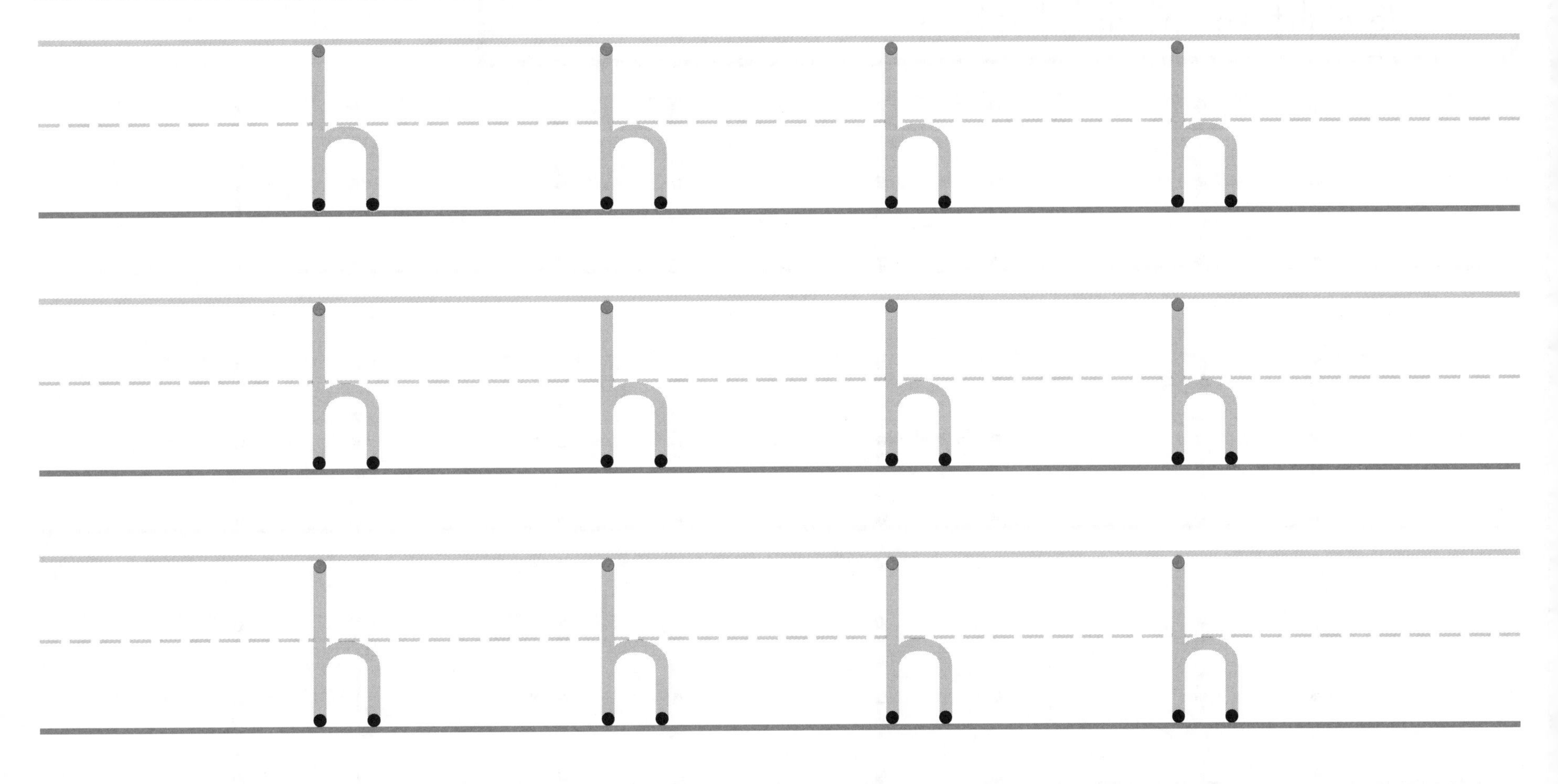

1. Touch the blue dot on the headline; pull down straight to the dot on the baseline. Lift.
2. Touch the dot on the headline; pull down straight to the dot on the baseline. Lift.
3. Move to the left and touch the dot on the midline; slide right to the dot. Lift.

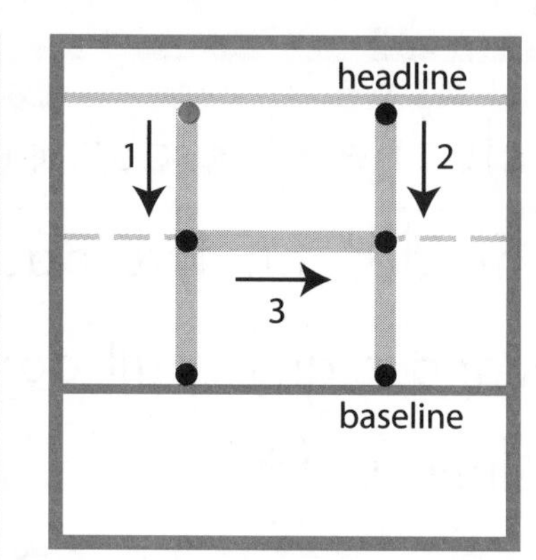

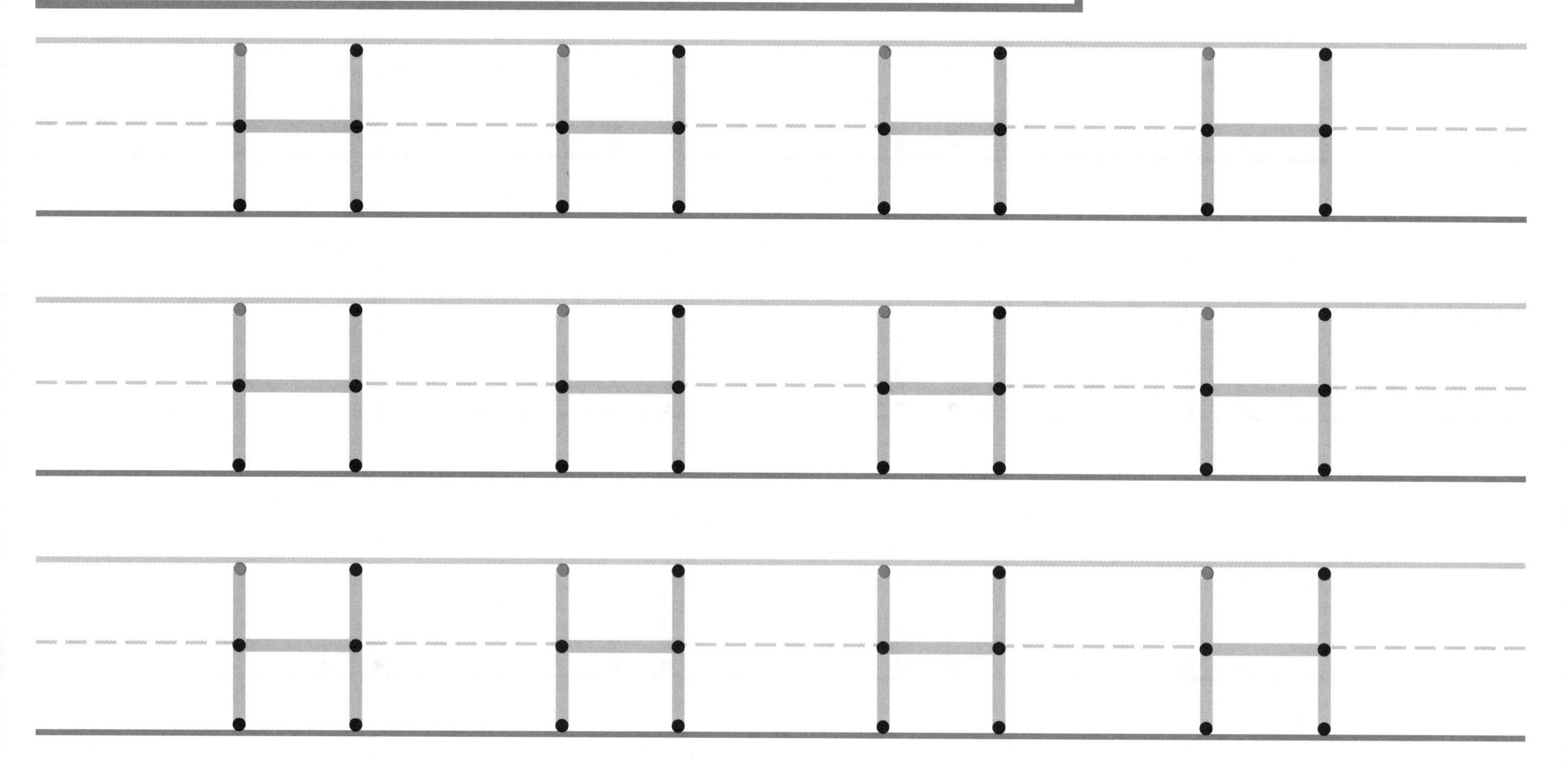

Today is Monday.

I see things that begin with the sound of h.

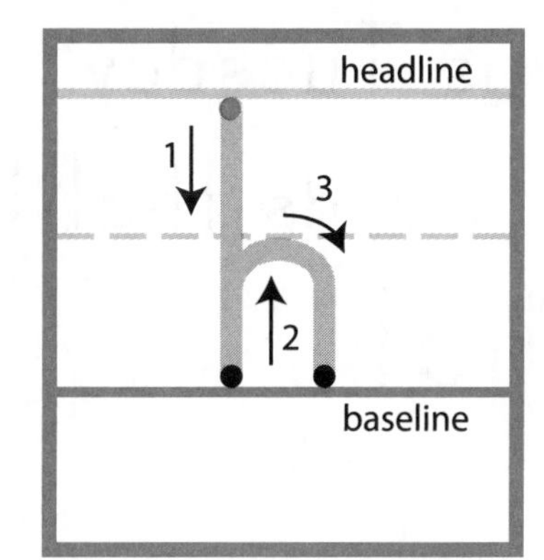

h h h h h h h

Attention Parent/Teacher: Using bright colored pencils, your child may draw pictures of today's items beginning with the sound of **h**. Emphasizing the sound of the letter, instruct your child to trace and write the letter. As your child writes, read the following Zaner-Bloser Stroke Descriptions: Touch the headline; pull down straight to the baseline. Push up; curve forward (right); pull down straight to the baseline.

Today is Tuesday.

I hear words that begin with the sound of h.

hat hut hop him

hit had hip hill

hot hid ham hen

h h h h h h h

Attention Parent/Teacher: Read the words to your child. Emphasizing the sound of the letter, instruct your child to trace and write the letter. As your child writes, read the following Zaner-Bloser Stroke Descriptions: Touch the headline; pull down straight to the baseline. Push up; curve forward (right); pull down straight to the baseline.

Today is Wednesday.

I taste things that begin with the sound of h.

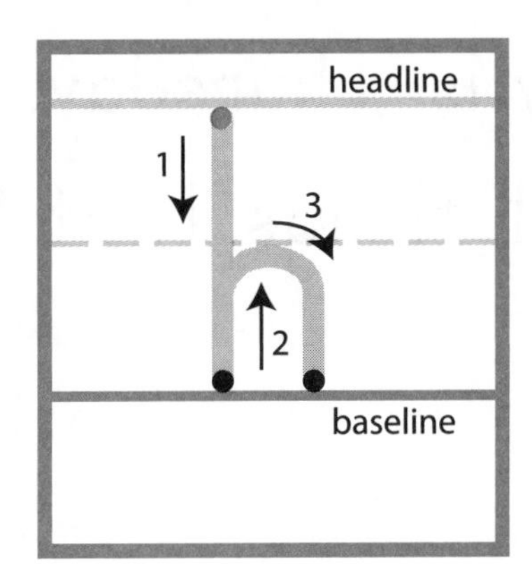

h h h h h h h

Attention Parent/Teacher: Using bright colored pencils, your child may draw pictures of today's items beginning with the sound of **h**. Emphasizing the sound of the letter, instruct your child to trace and write the letter. As your child writes, read the following Zaner-Bloser Stroke Descriptions: Touch the headline; pull down straight to the baseline. Push up; curve forward (right); pull down straight to the baseline.

Today is Thursday.

I smell things that begin with the sound of h.

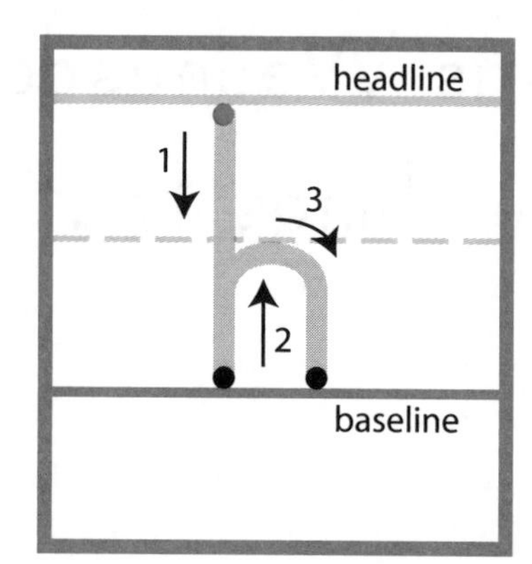

h h h h h h h

Attention Parent/Teacher: Using bright colored pencils, your child may draw pictures of today's items beginning with the sound of **h**. Emphasizing the sound of the letter, instruct your child to trace and write the letter. As your child writes, read the following Zaner-Bloser Stroke Descriptions: Touch the headline; pull down straight to the baseline. Push up; curve forward (right); pull down straight to the baseline.

Today is Friday.

I touch things that begin with the sound of h.

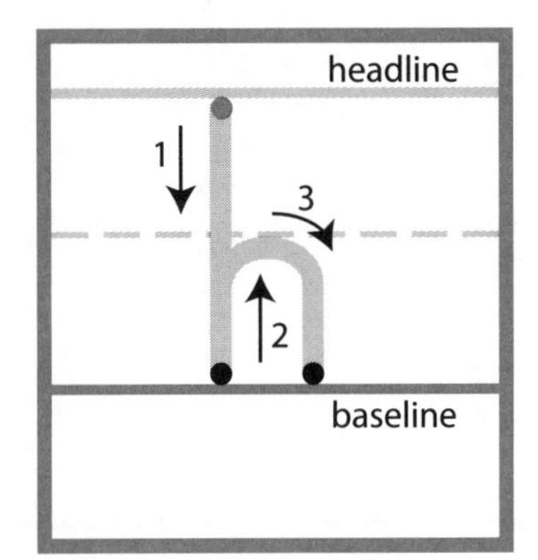

h h h h h h h

Attention Parent/Teacher: Using bright colored pencils, your child may draw pictures of today's items beginning with the sound of **h**. Emphasizing the sound of the letter, instruct your child to trace and write the letter. As your child writes, read the following Zaner-Bloser Stroke Descriptions: Touch the headline; pull down straight to the baseline. Push up; curve forward (right); pull down straight to the baseline.

When life's sands are running out,
I'll clasp my hands and pray
To Mary, Queen of Heaven,
To Mary, Queen of May!

Touch the blue dot on the midline; pull down straight to the dot on the baseline. Pause; push up; curve forward right, touching the midline; pull down straight to the dot on the baseline. Lift.

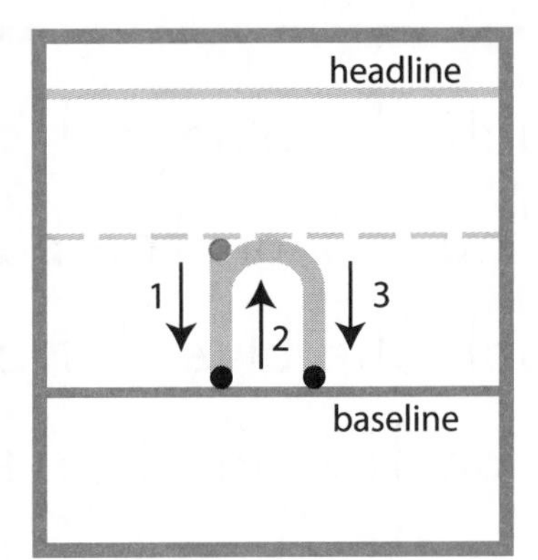

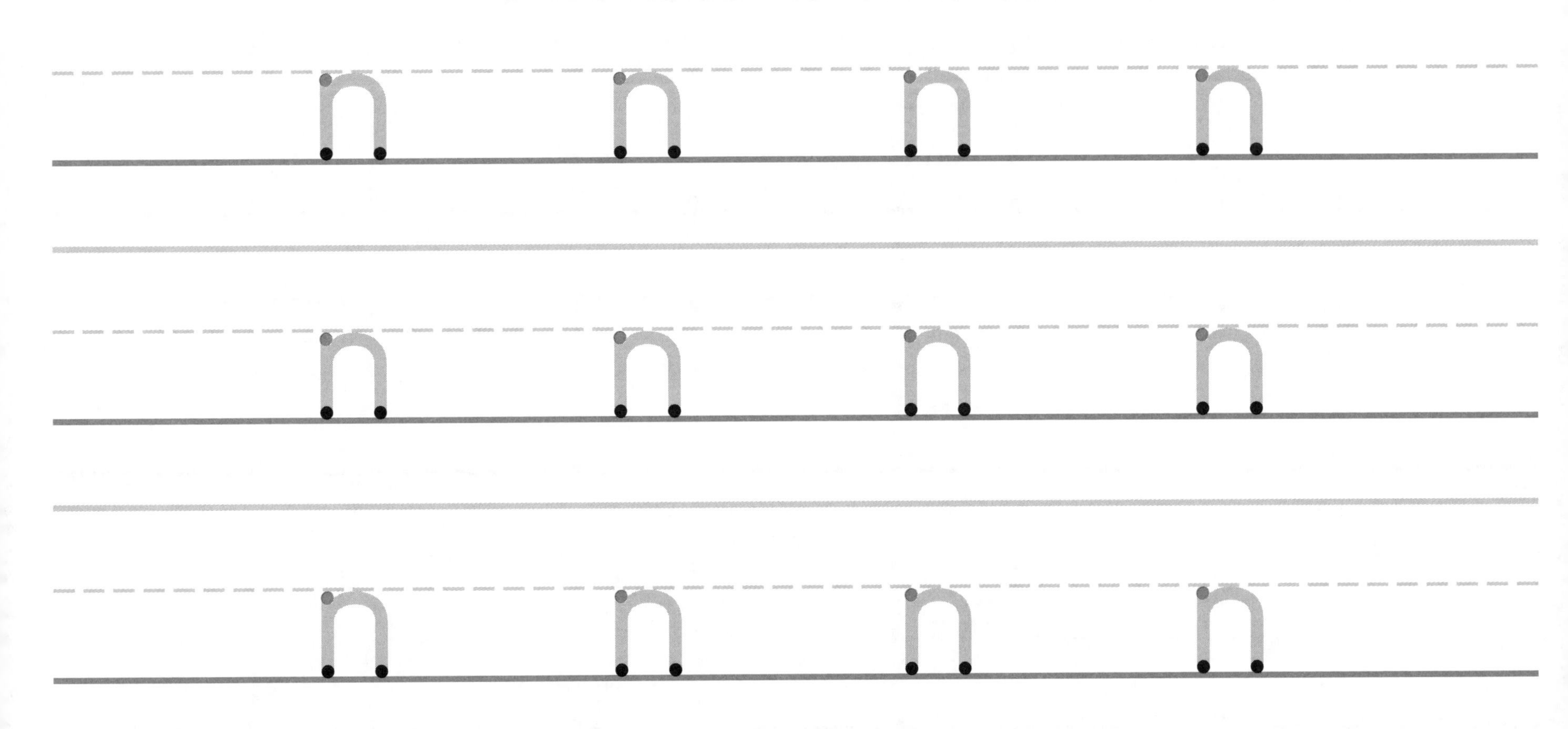

1. Touch the blue dot on the headline; pull down straight to the dot on the baseline. Lift.
2. Touch the blue dot on the headline; slant right to the dot on the baseline. Pause; push up straight to the dot on the headline. Lift.

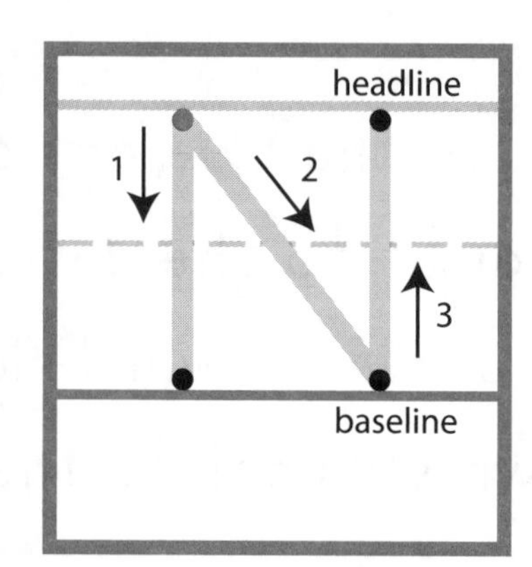

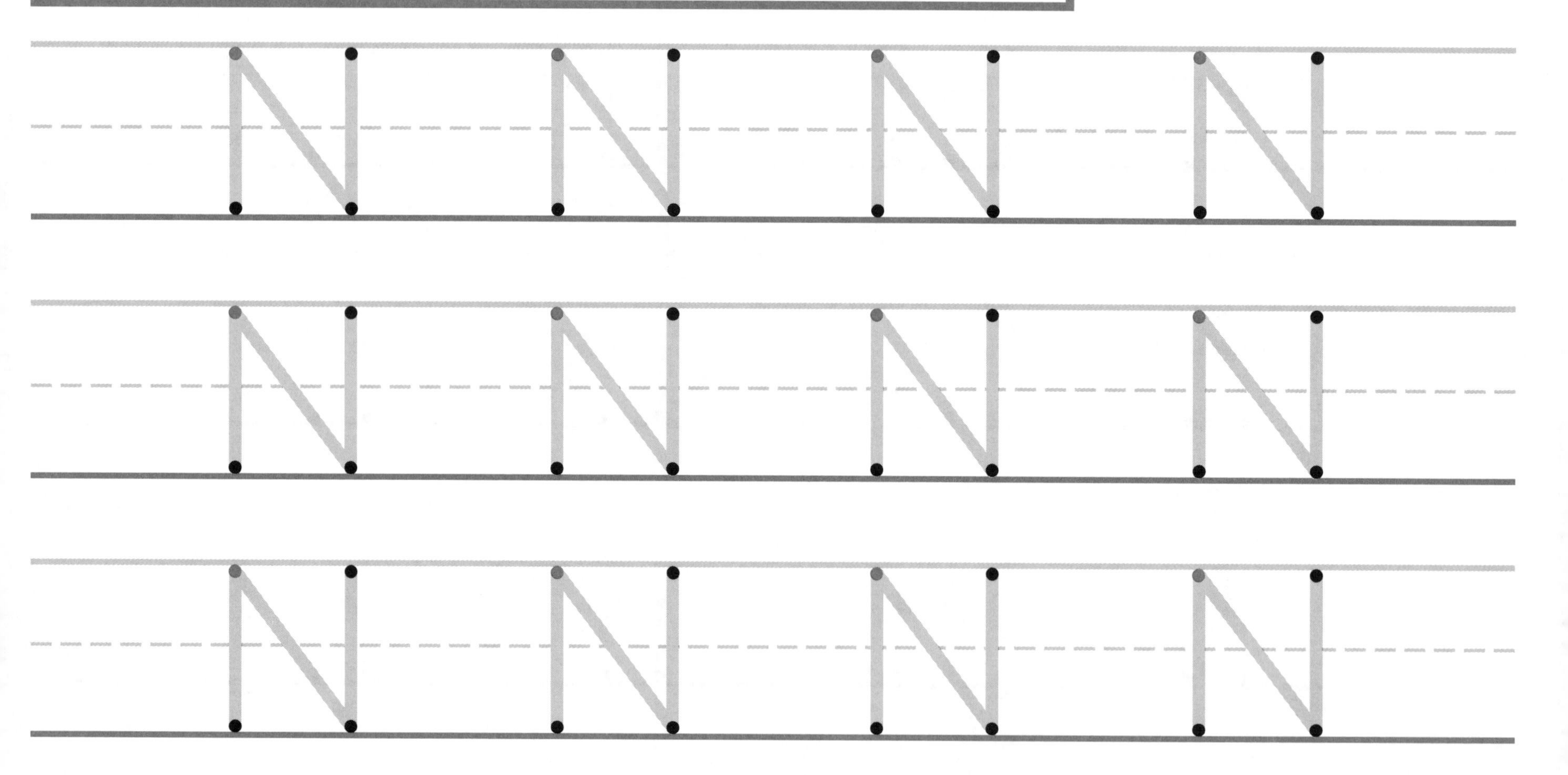

Today is Monday.

I see things that begin with the sound of n.

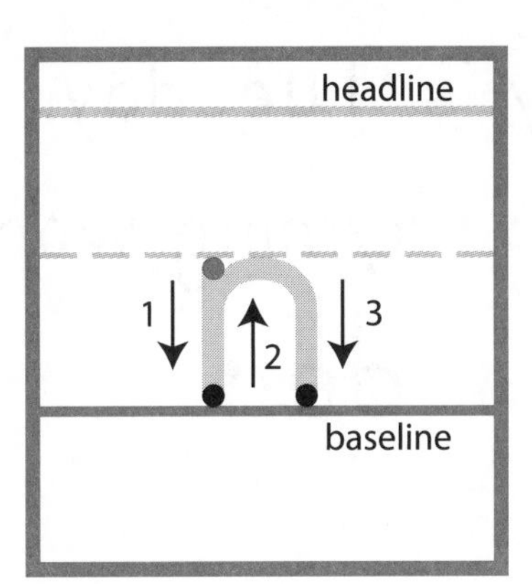

n n n n n n n

Attention Parent/Teacher: Using bright colored pencils, your child may draw pictures of today's items beginning with the sound of **n**. Emphasizing the sound of the letter, instruct your child to trace and write the letter. As your child writes, read the following Zaner-Bloser Stroke Descriptions: Touch the midline; pull down straight to the baseline. Push up; curve forward (right); pull down straight to the baseline.

Today is Tuesday.

I hear rhyming words that end with the sound of n.

den	hen	pen
bin	fin	pin
bun	fun	sun

n n n n n n n

Attention Parent/Teacher: Read the rhyming words to your child. Emphasizing the sound of the letter, instruct your child to trace and write the letter. As your child writes, read the following Zaner-Bloser Stroke Descriptions: Touch the midline; pull down straight to the baseline. Push up; curve forward (right); pull down straight to the baseline.

Today is Wednesday.
I taste things that begin with the sound of n.

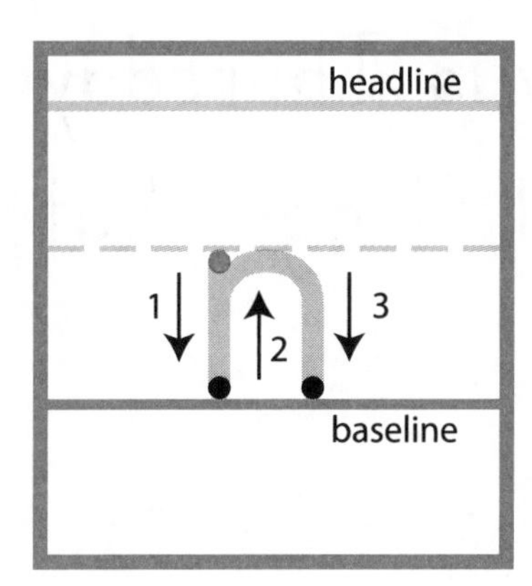

n n n n n n n

Attention Parent/Teacher: Using bright colored pencils, your child may draw pictures of today's items beginning with the sound of **n**. Emphasizing the sound of the letter, instruct your child to trace and write the letter. As your child writes, read the following Zaner-Bloser Stroke Descriptions: Touch the midline; pull down straight to the baseline. Push up; curve forward (right); pull down straight to the baseline.

Today is Thursday.

I smell things that begin with the sound of n.

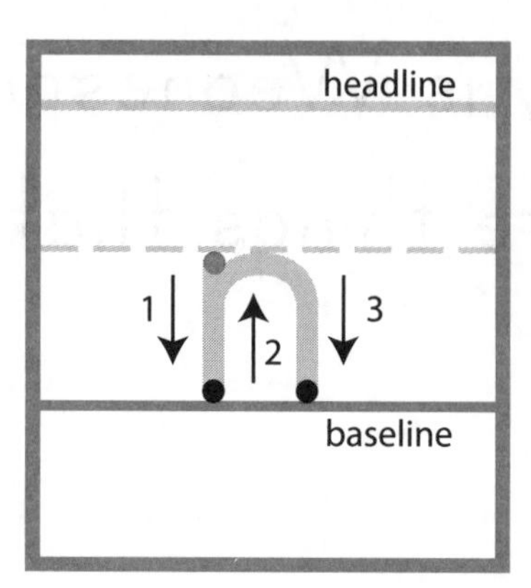

n n n n n n n

Attention Parent/Teacher: Using bright colored pencils, your child may draw pictures of today's items beginning with the sound of **n**. Emphasizing the sound of the letter, instruct your child to trace and write the letter. As your child writes, read the following Zaner-Bloser Stroke Descriptions: Touch the midline; pull down straight to the baseline. Push up; curve forward (right); pull down straight to the baseline.

Today is Friday.

I touch things that begin with the sound of n.

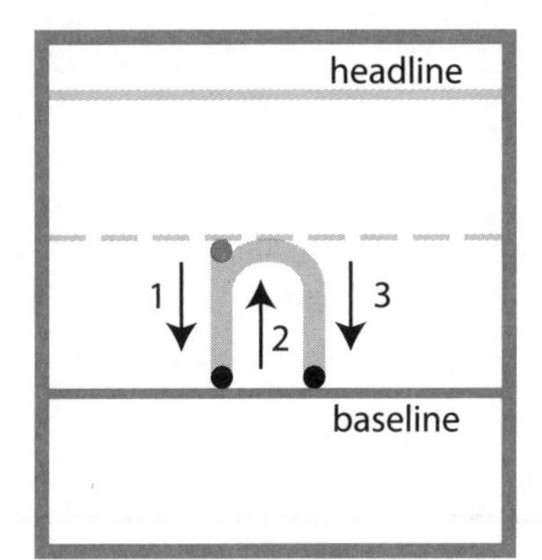

n n n n n n n

Attention Parent/Teacher: Using bright colored pencils, your child may draw pictures of today's items beginning with the sound of **n**. Emphasizing the sound of the letter, instruct your child to trace and write the letter. As your child writes, read the following Zaner-Bloser Stroke Descriptions: Touch the midline; pull down straight to the baseline. Push up; curve forward (right); pull down straight to the baseline.

Daily, daily, sing to Mary,
Sing, my soul, her praises due.
All her feasts, her actions worship
With the heart's devotion true.

Touch the blue dot on the midline; pull down straight to the dot on the baseline. Pause; push up; curve forward right; pull down straight to the dot on the baseline. Pause; push up; curve forward right; pull down straight to the dot on the baseline. Lift.

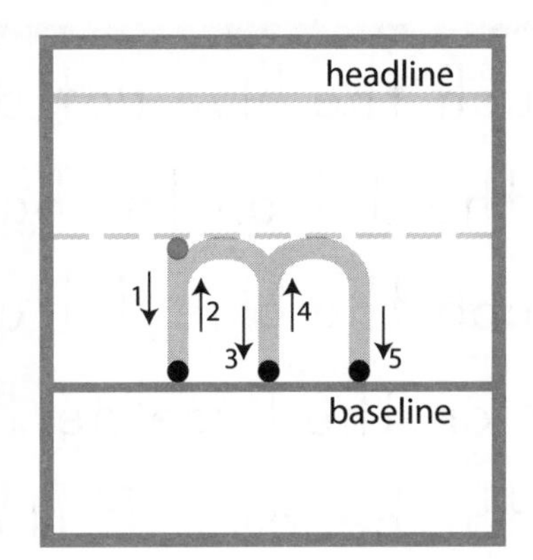

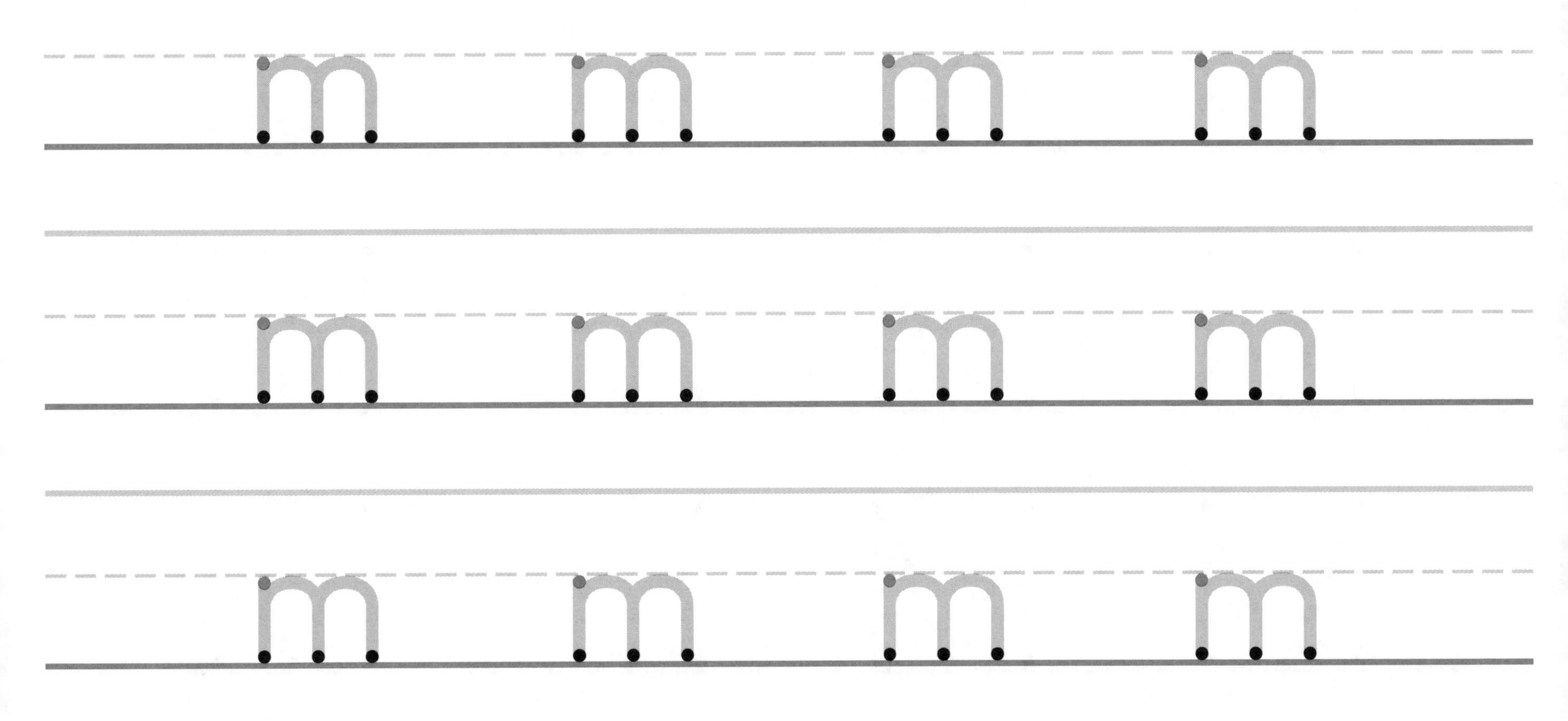

1. Touch the blue dot on the headline; pull down straight to the dot on the baseline. Lift.
2. Touch the blue dot on the headline; slant right to the dot on the baseline. Pause; slant up right to the dot on the headline. Pull down straight to the dot on the baseline. Lift.

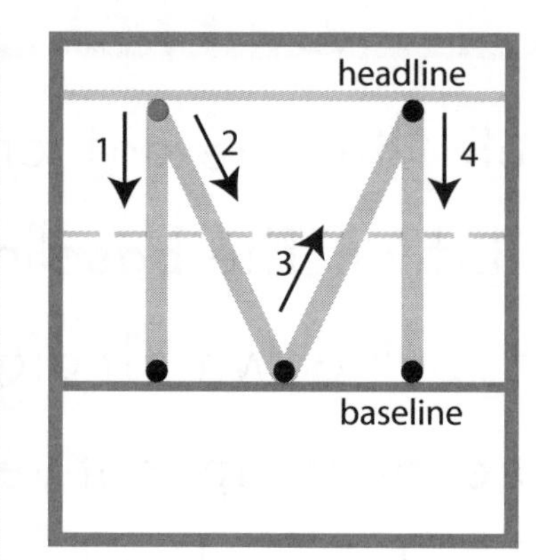

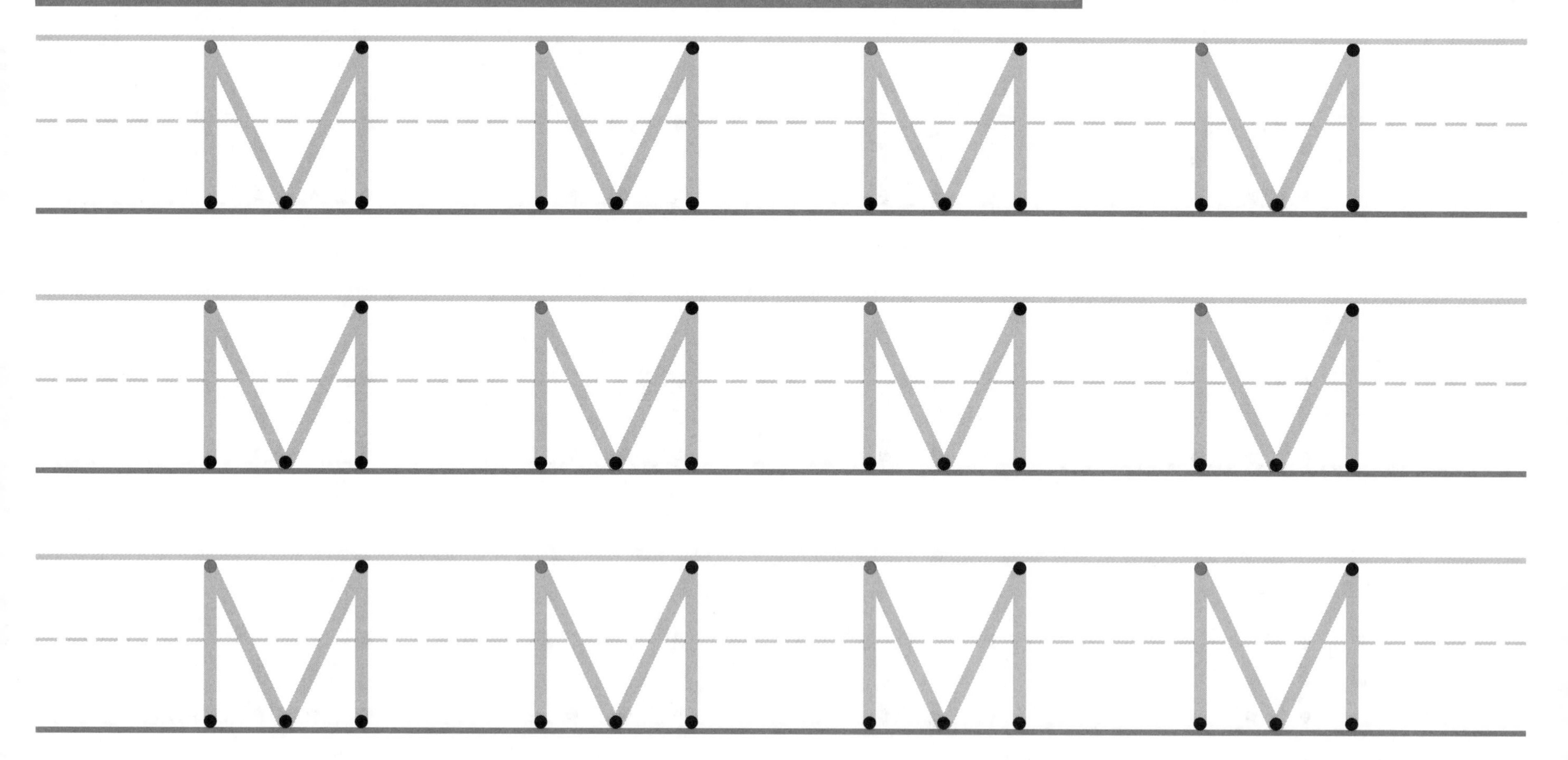

Today is Monday.

I see things that begin with the sound of m.

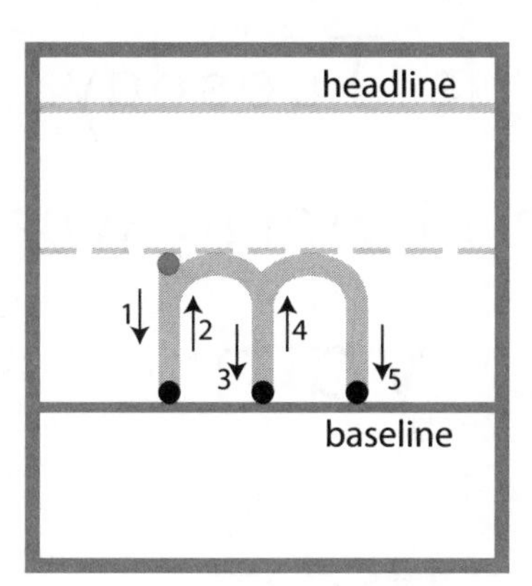

m m m m m m

Attention Parent/Teacher: Using bright colored pencils, your child may draw pictures of today's items beginning with the sound of **m**. Emphasizing the sound of the letter, instruct your child to trace and write the letter. As your child writes, read the following Zaner-Bloser Stroke Descriptions: Touch the midline; pull down straight to the baseline. Push up; curve forward (right); pull down straight to the baseline. Push up; curve forward (right); pull down straight to the baseline.

Today is Tuesday.

I hear rhyming words that end with the sound of m.

yam	ham	jam
mom	tom	prom
bum	hum	gum

m m m m m m

Attention Parent/Teacher: Read the rhyming words to your child. Emphasizing the sound of the letter, instruct your child to trace and write the letter. As your child writes, read the following Zaner-Bloser Stroke Descriptions: Touch the midline; pull down straight to the baseline. Push up; curve forward (right); pull down straight to the baseline. Push up; curve forward (right); pull down straight to the baseline.

Today is Wednesday.

I taste things that begin with the sound of m.

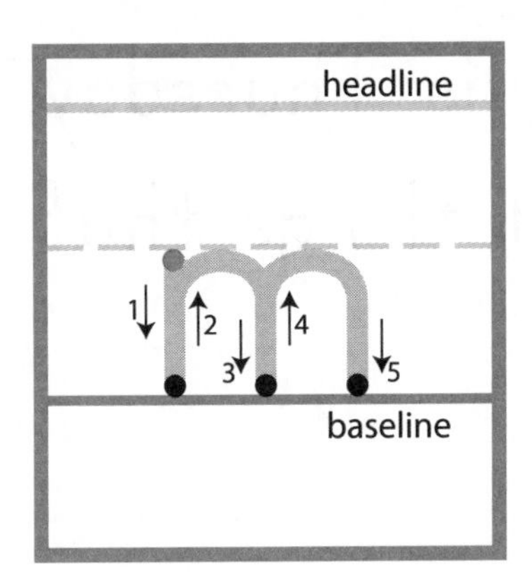

m m m m m m

Attention Parent/Teacher: Using bright colored pencils, your child may draw pictures of today's items beginning with the sound of **m**. Emphasizing the sound of the letter, instruct your child to trace and write the letter. As your child writes, read the following Zaner-Bloser Stroke Descriptions: Touch the midline; pull down straight to the baseline. Push up; curve forward (right); pull down straight to the baseline. Push up; curve forward (right); pull down straight to the baseline.

Today is Thursday.

I smell things that begin with the sound of m.

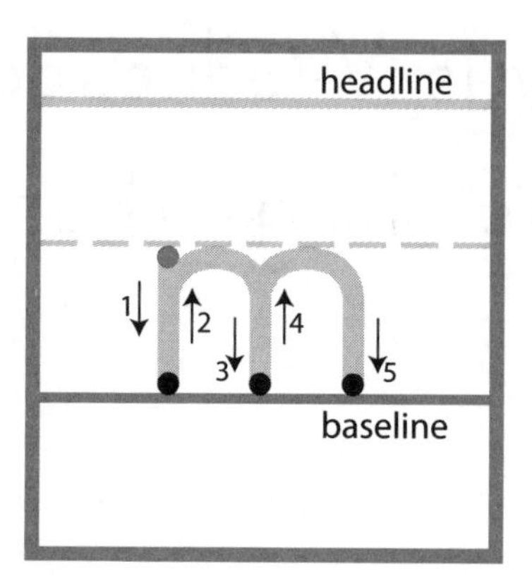

m m m m m m

Attention Parent/Teacher: Using bright colored pencils, your child may draw pictures of today's items beginning with the sound of **m**. Emphasizing the sound of the letter, instruct your child to trace and write the letter. As your child writes, read the following Zaner-Bloser Stroke Descriptions: Touch the midline; pull down straight to the baseline. Push up; curve forward (right); pull down straight to the baseline. Push up; curve forward (right); pull down straight to the baseline.

Today is Friday.

I touch things that begin with the sound of m.

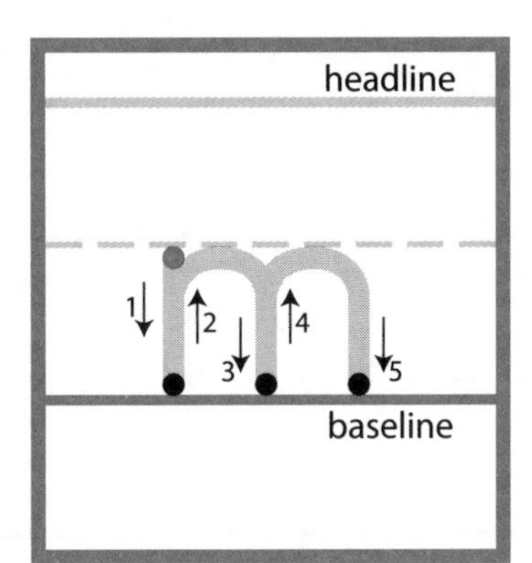

m m m m m m

Attention Parent/Teacher: Using bright colored pencils, your child may draw pictures of today's items beginning with the sound of **m**. Emphasizing the sound of the letter, instruct your child to trace and write the letter. As your child writes, read the following Zaner-Bloser Stroke Descriptions: Touch the midline; pull down straight to the baseline. Push up; curve forward (right); pull down straight to the baseline. Push up; curve forward (right); pull down straight to the baseline.

Lost in wondering contemplation,
Be her majesty confessed;
Call her Mother, call her Virgin,
Happy Mother, Virgin blest!

Touch the blue dot on the midline; pull down straight to the dot on the baseline. Pause; push up; curve forward right to the dot just under the midline. Lift.

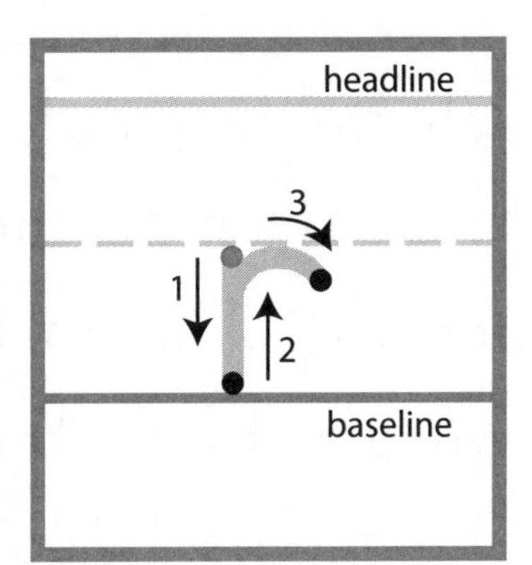

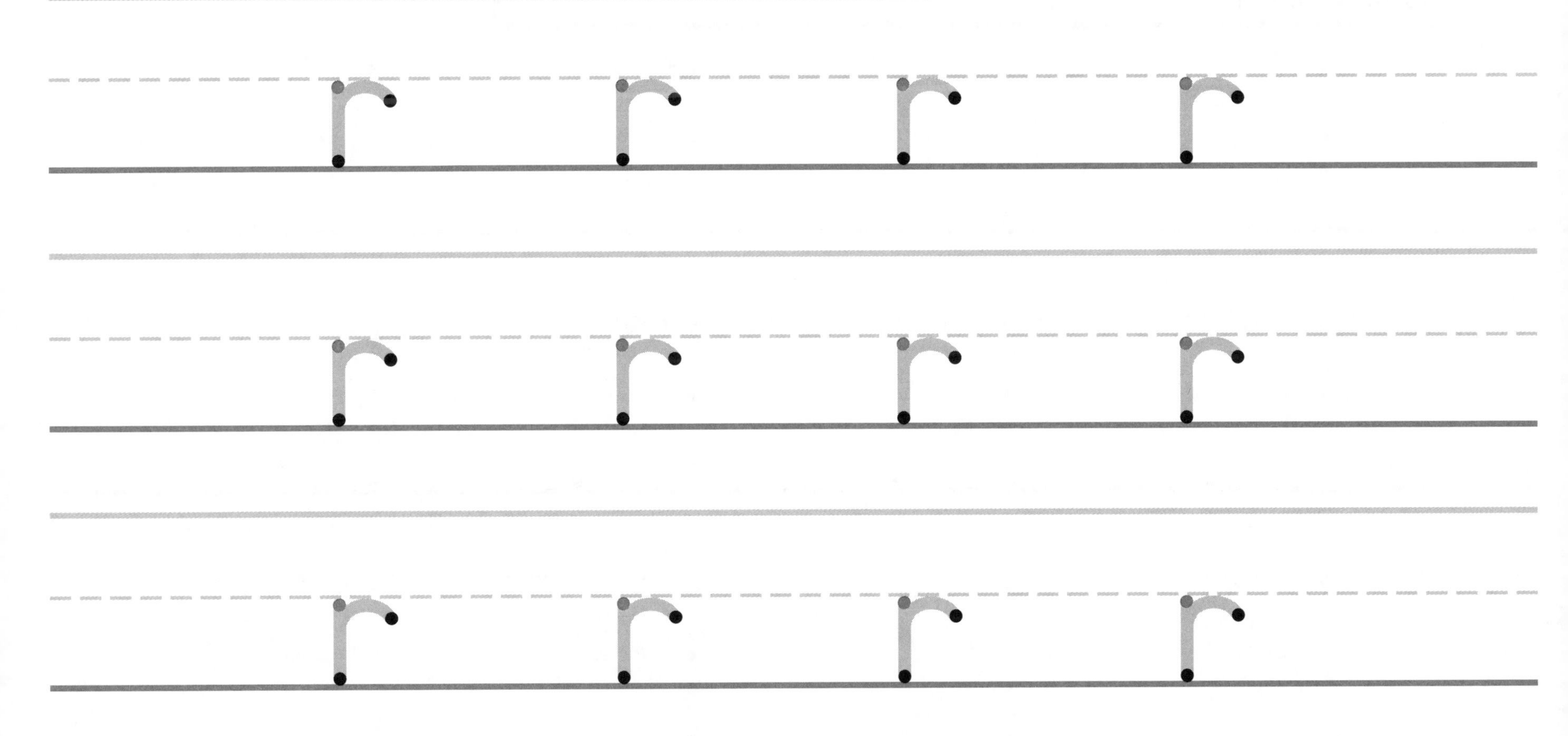

1. Touch the blue dot on the headline; pull down straight to the dot on the baseline. Lift.
2. Touch the blue dot on the headline; slide right; curve forward right to the midline; slide left to the dot on the midline. Pause; slant right to the dot on the baseline. Lift.

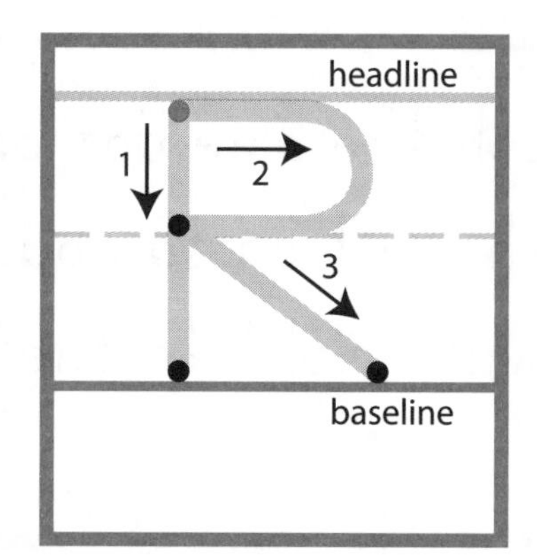

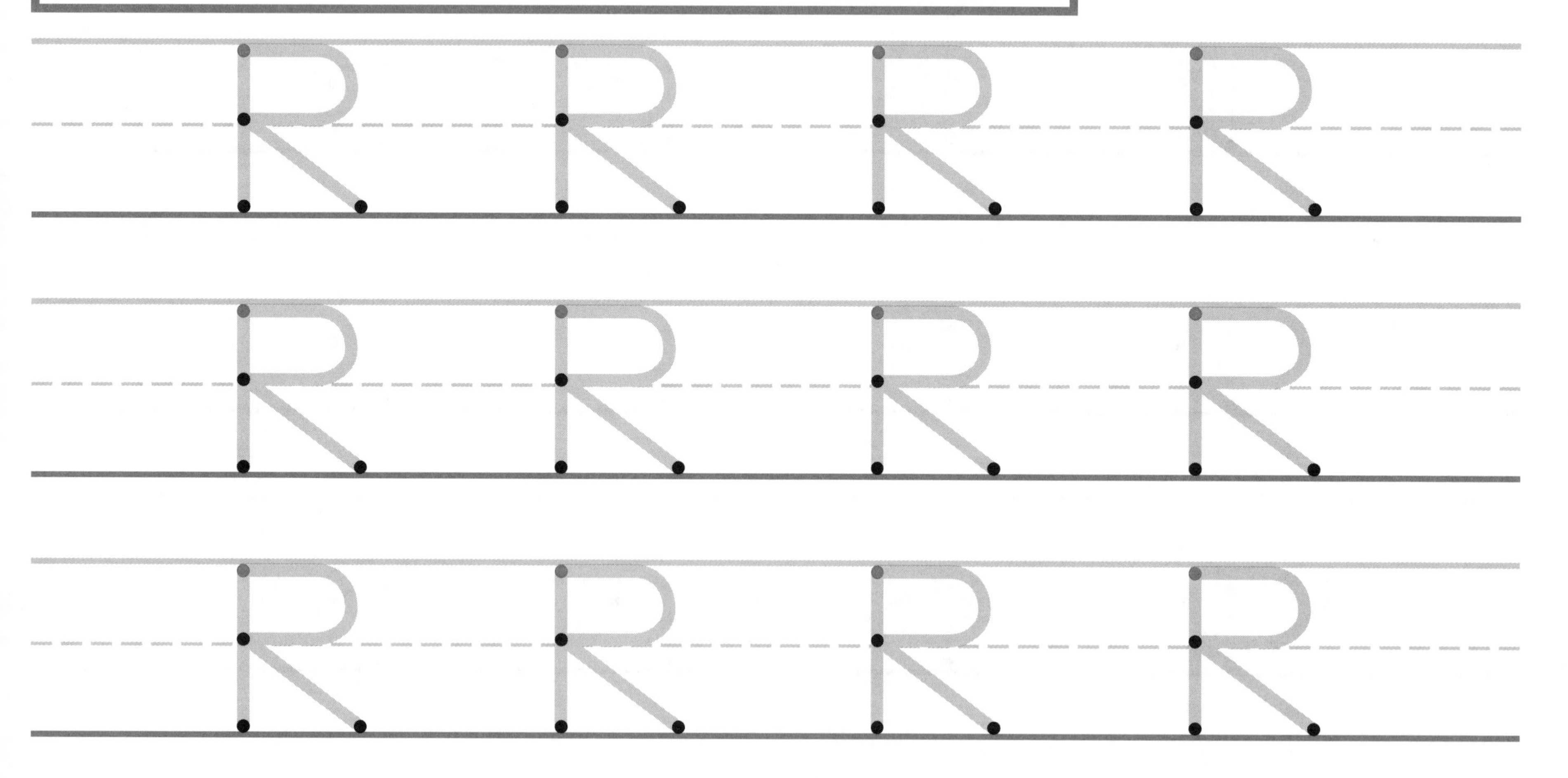

Today is Monday.

I see things that begin with the sound of r.

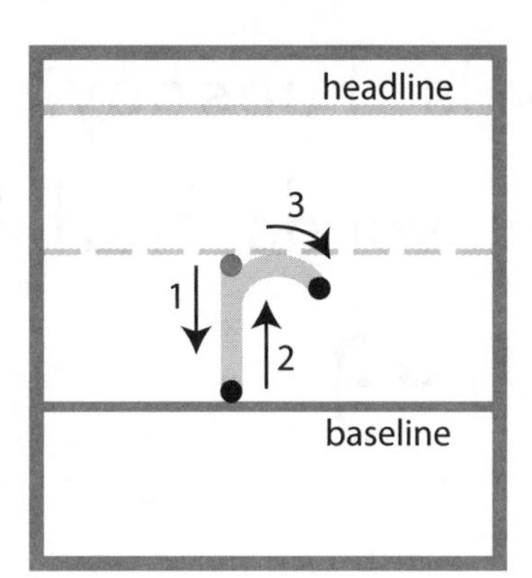

r r r r r r r

Attention Parent/Teacher: Using bright colored pencils, your child may draw pictures of today's items beginning with the sound of **r**. Emphasizing the sound of the letter, instruct your child to trace and write the letter. As your child writes, read the following Zaner-Bloser Stroke Descriptions: Touch the midline; pull down straight to the baseline. Push up; curve forward (right).

Today is Tuesday.

I hear words that begin with the sound of r.

rag	red	rim	rock
ran	rib	rip	rug
rat	rid	rob	run

r r r r r r r

Attention Parent/Teacher: Read the words to your child. Emphasizing the sound of the letter, instruct your child to trace and write the letter. As your child writes, read the following Zaner-Bloser Stroke Descriptions: Touch the midline; pull down straight to the baseline. Push up; curve forward (right).

Today is Wednesday.

I taste things that begin with the sound of r.

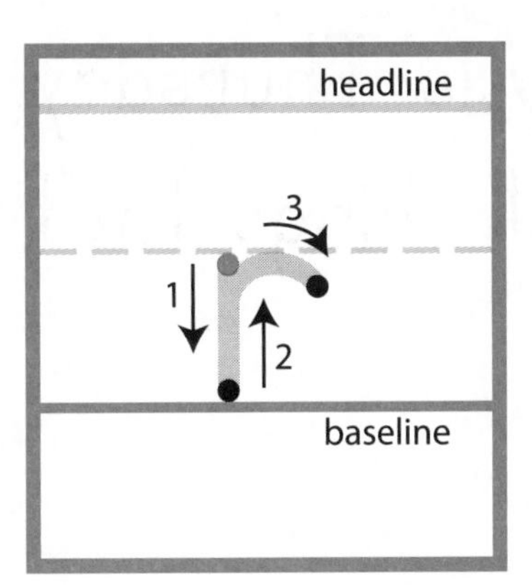

r r r r r r r

Attention Parent/Teacher: Using bright colored pencils, your child may draw pictures of today's items beginning with the sound of **r**. Emphasizing the sound of the letter, instruct your child to trace and write the letter. As your child writes, read the following Zaner-Bloser Stroke Descriptions: Touch the midline; pull down straight to the baseline. Push up; curve forward (right).

Today is Thursday.

I smell things that begin with the sound of r.

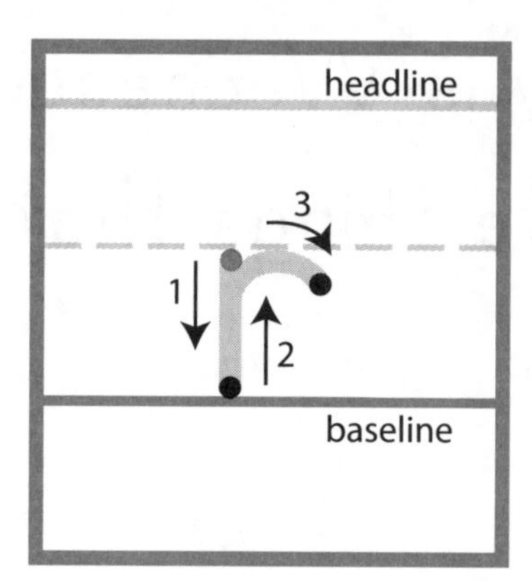

r r r r r r r

Attention Parent/Teacher: Using bright colored pencils, your child may draw pictures of today's items beginning with the sound of **r**. Emphasizing the sound of the letter, instruct your child to trace and write the letter. As your child writes, read the following Zaner-Bloser Stroke Descriptions: Touch the midline; pull down straight to the baseline. Push up; curve forward (right).

Today is Friday.

I touch things that begin with the sound of r.

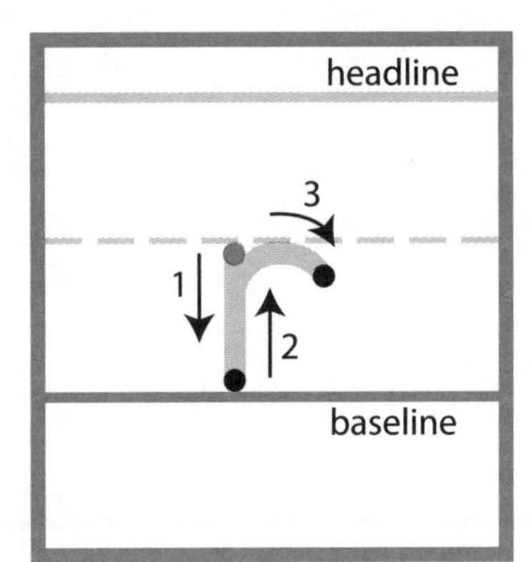

r r r r r r r

Attention Parent/Teacher: Using bright colored pencils, your child may draw pictures of today's items beginning with the sound of **r**. Emphasizing the sound of the letter, instruct your child to trace and write the letter. As your child writes, read the following Zaner-Bloser Stroke Descriptions: Touch the midline; pull down straight to the baseline. Push up; curve forward (right).

She is mighty to deliver;
Call her, trust her lovingly.
When the tempest rages round thee,
She will calm the troubled sea.

1. Touch the blue dot on the headline; pull down straight to the dot on the baseline. Lift.
2. Touch the dot on the midline; slide right to the dot. Lift.

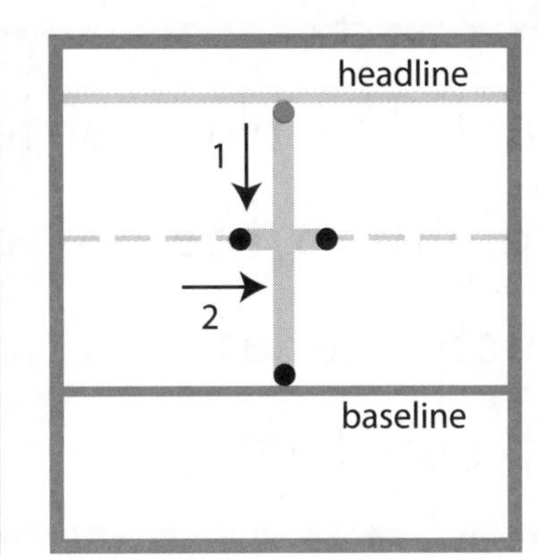

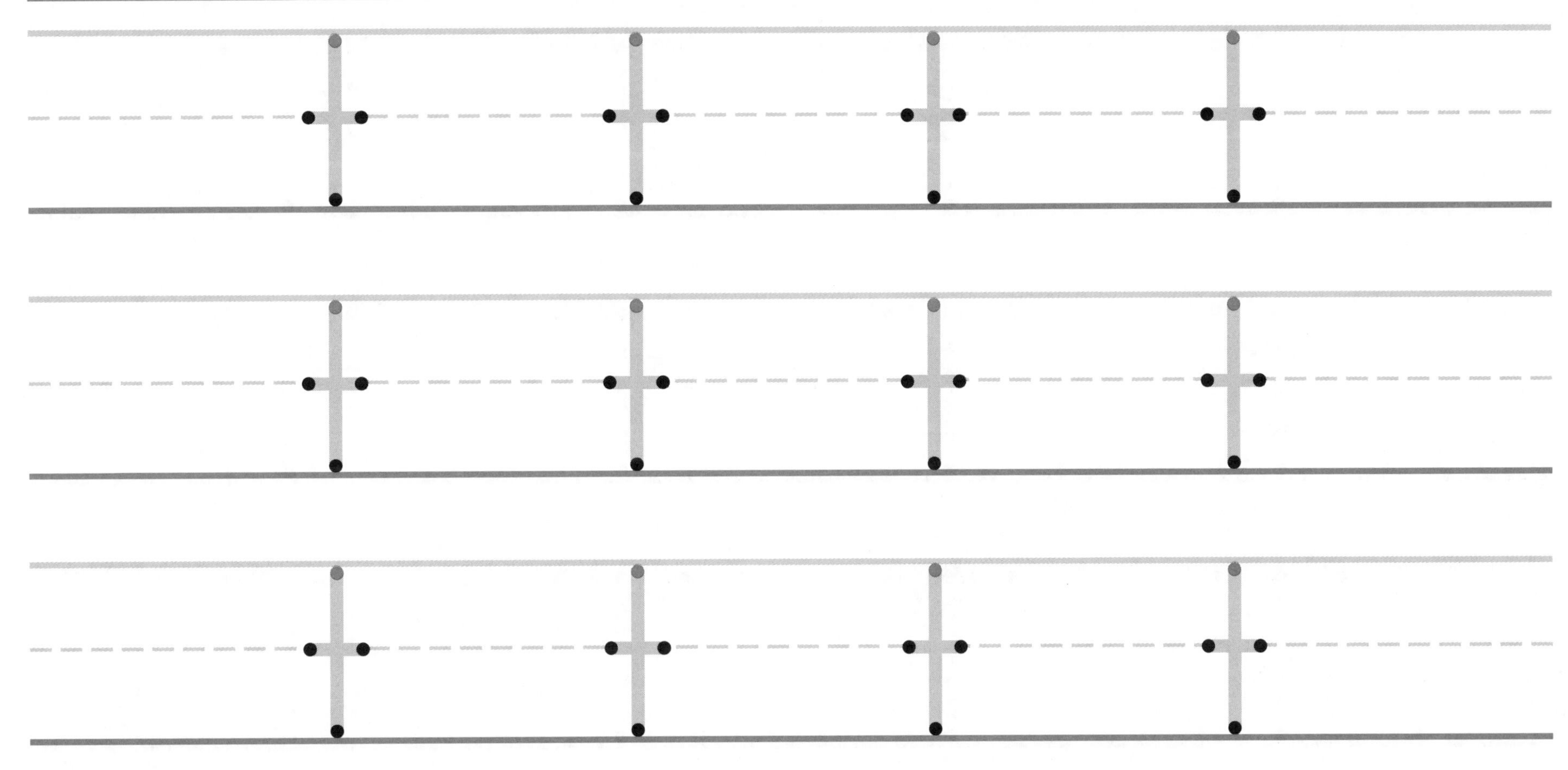

1. Touch the blue center dot on the headline; pull down straight to the dot on the baseline. Lift.
2. Touch the left dot on the headline; slide right to the last dot. Lift.

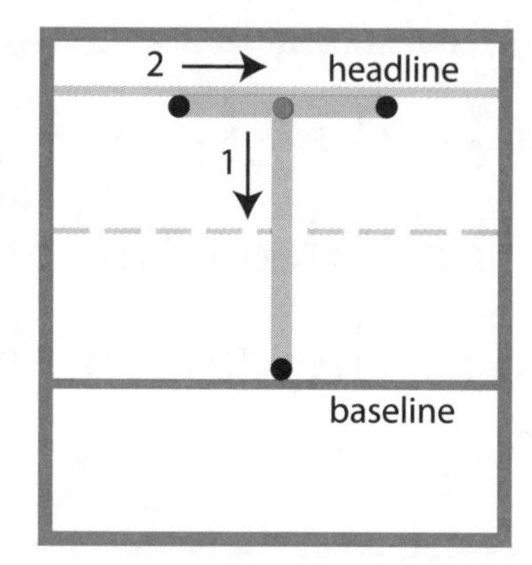

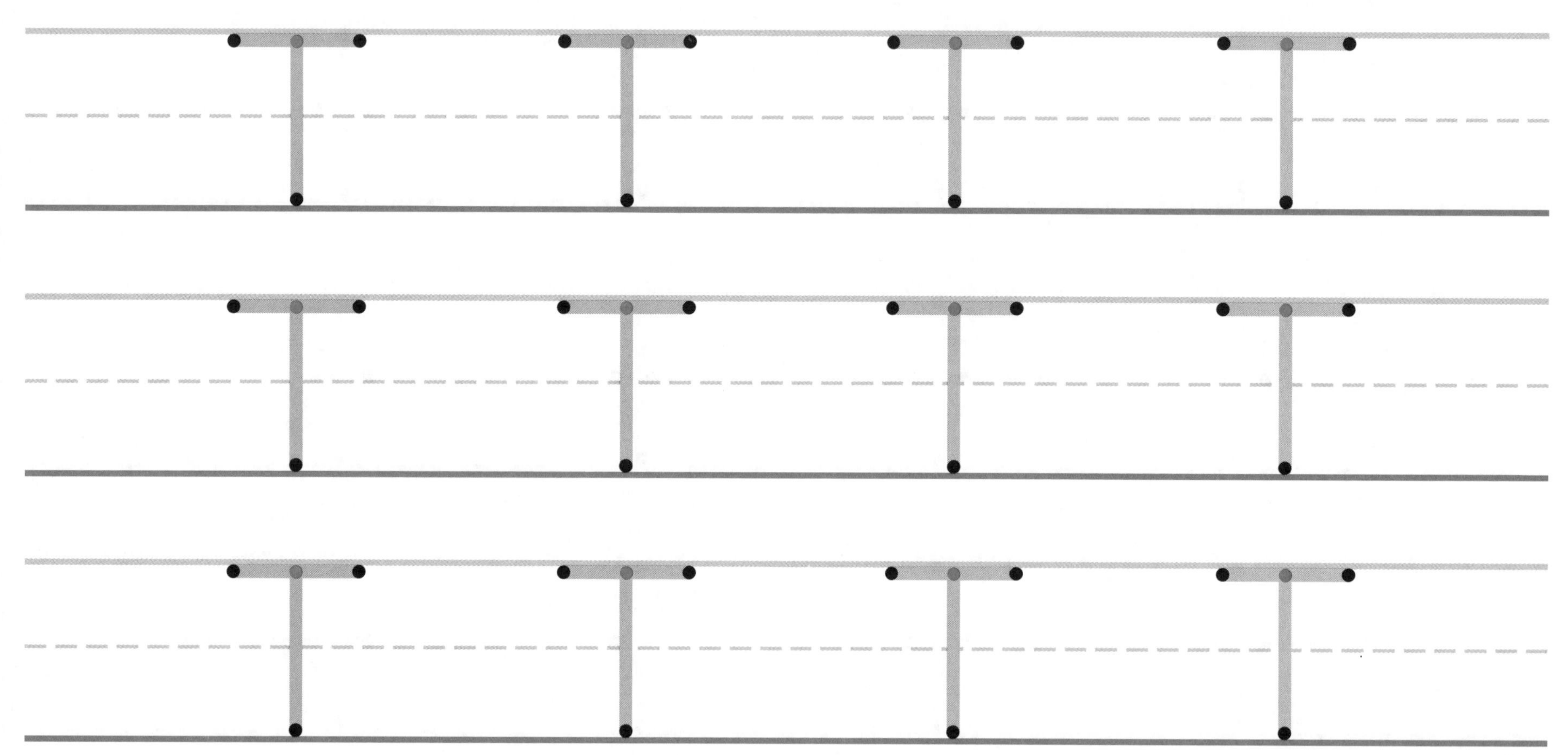

Today is Monday.

I see things that begin with the sound of t.

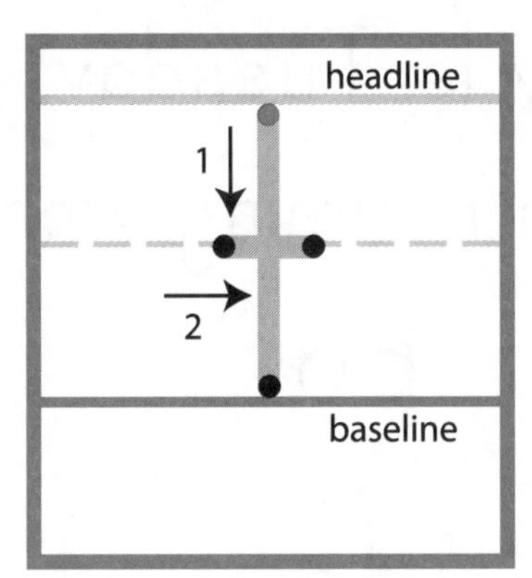

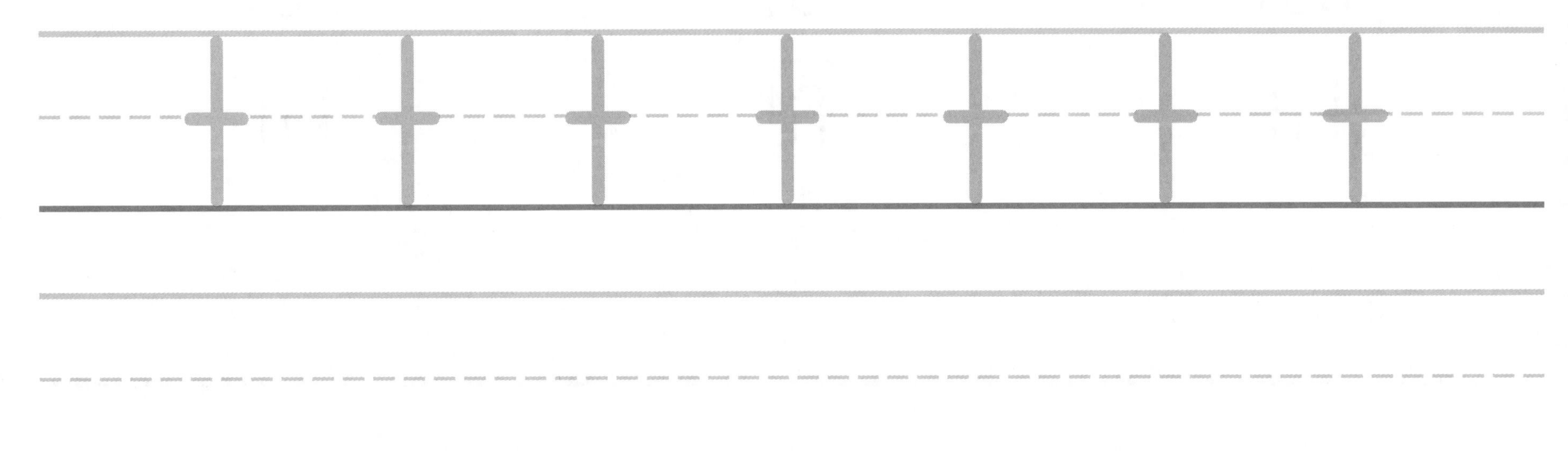

Attention Parent/Teacher: Using bright colored pencils, your child may draw pictures of today's items beginning with the sound of **t**. Emphasizing the sound of the letter, instruct your child to trace and write the letter. As your child writes, read the following Zaner-Bloser Stroke Descriptions: Touch the headline; pull down straight to the baseline. Lift. Touch the midline; slide right.

Today is Tuesday.

I hear rhyming words that end with the sound of t.

bat	hat	pat
dot	lot	not
bit	fit	kit

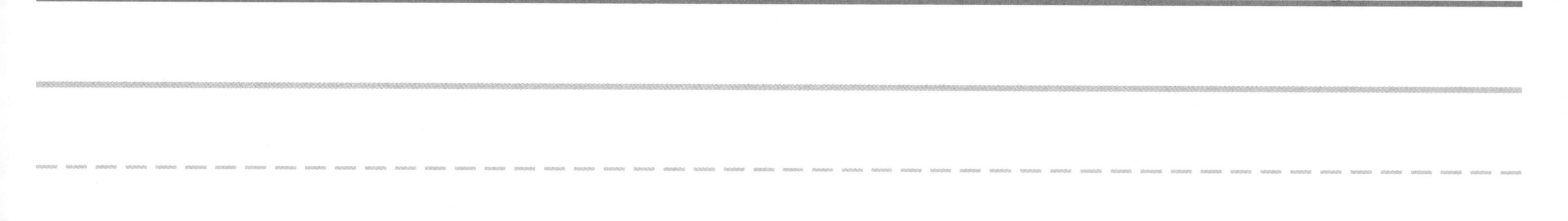

Attention Parent/Teacher: Read the rhyming words to your child. Emphasizing the sound of the letter, instruct your child to trace and write the letter. As your child writes, read the following Zaner-Bloser Stroke Descriptions: Touch the headline; pull down straight to the baseline. Lift. Touch the midline; slide right.

Today is Wednesday.
I taste things that begin with the sound of t.

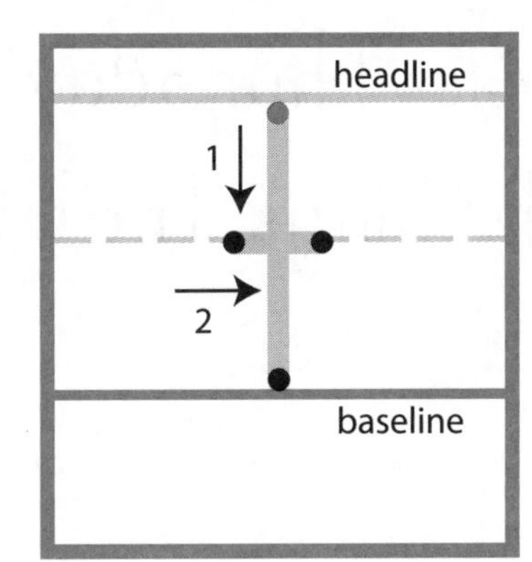

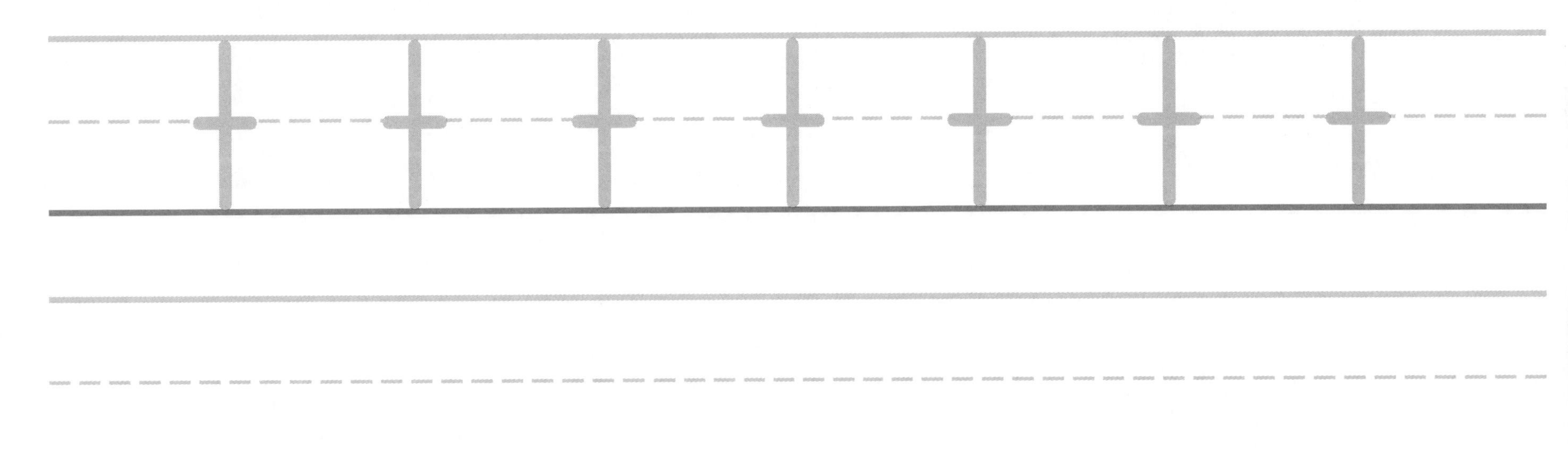

Attention Parent/Teacher: Using bright colored pencils, your child may draw pictures of today's items beginning with the sound of **t**. Emphasizing the sound of the letter, instruct your child to trace and write the letter. As your child writes, read the following Zaner-Bloser Stroke Descriptions: Touch the headline; pull down straight to the baseline. Lift. Touch the midline; slide right.

Today is Thursday.

I smell things that begin with the sound of t.

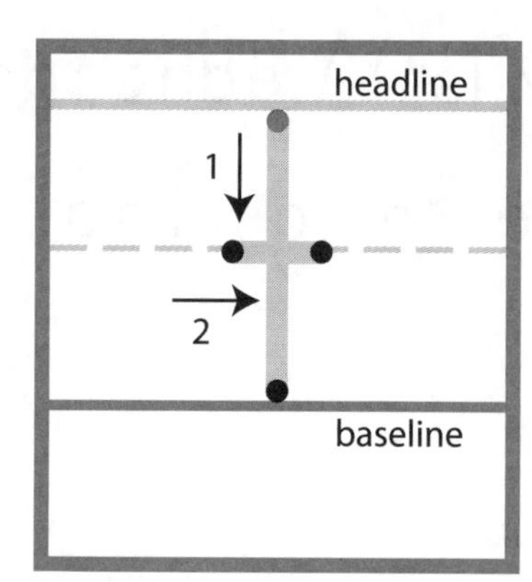

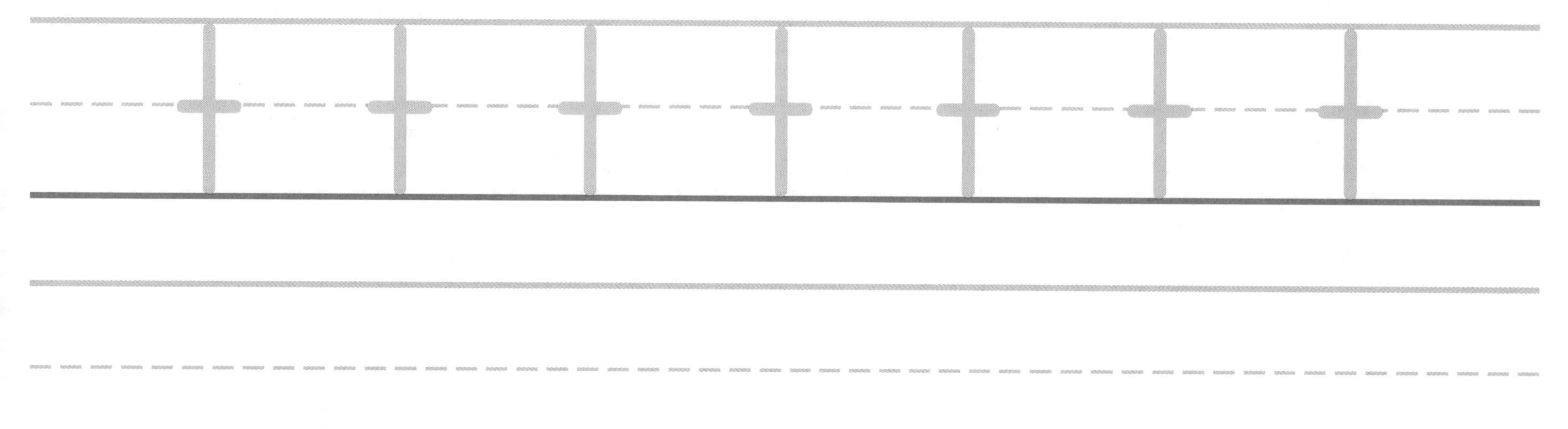

Attention Parent/Teacher: Using bright colored pencils, your child may draw pictures of today's items beginning with the sound of **t**. Emphasizing the sound of the letter, instruct your child to trace and write the letter. As your child writes, read the following Zaner-Bloser Stroke Descriptions: Touch the headline; pull down straight to the baseline. Lift. Touch the midline; slide right.

Today is Friday.

I touch things that begin with the sound of t.

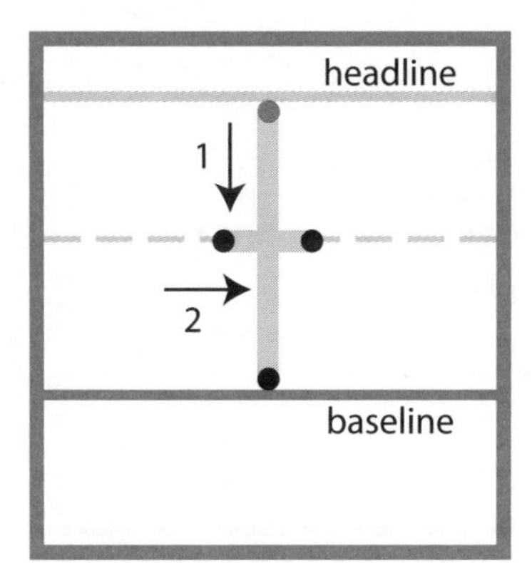

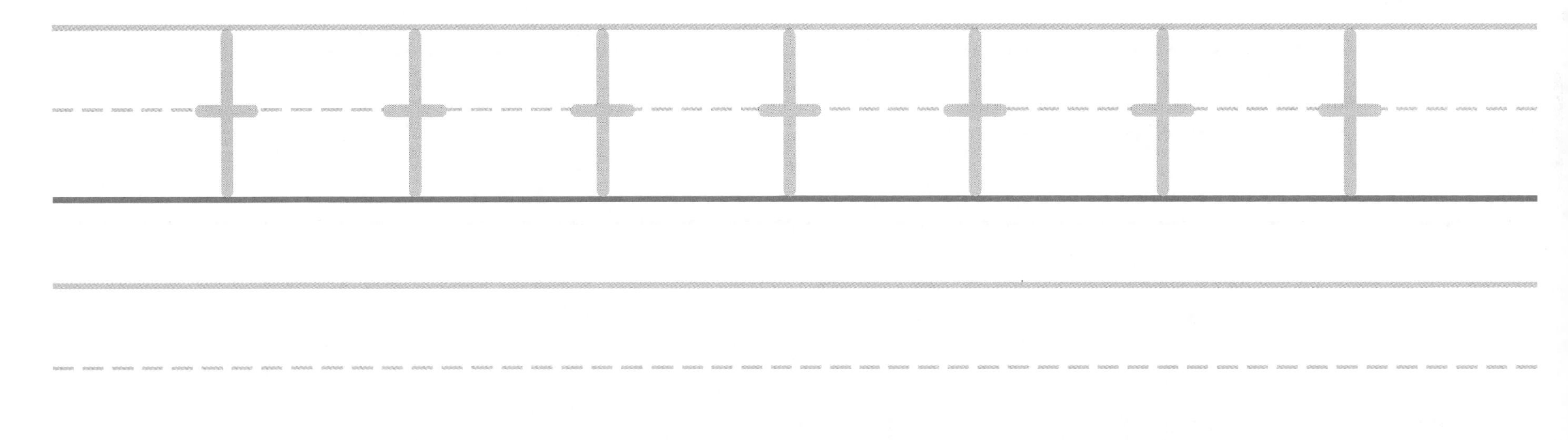

Attention Parent/Teacher: Using bright colored pencils, your child may draw pictures of today's items beginning with the sound of **t**. Emphasizing the sound of the letter, instruct your child to trace and write the letter. As your child writes, read the following Zaner-Bloser Stroke Descriptions: Touch the headline; pull down straight to the baseline. Lift. Touch the midline; slide right.

Gifts of Heaven she has given,
Noble Lady to our race;
She, the Queen, who decks her subjects
With the light of God's own grace.

Touch the blue dot halfway between the midline and baseline; slide right to the dot; circle back counterclockwise, touching the midline, and the baseline, and ending on the dot above the baseline. Lift.

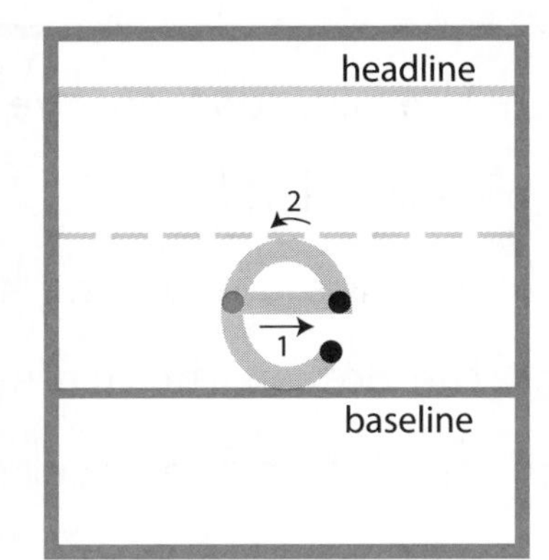

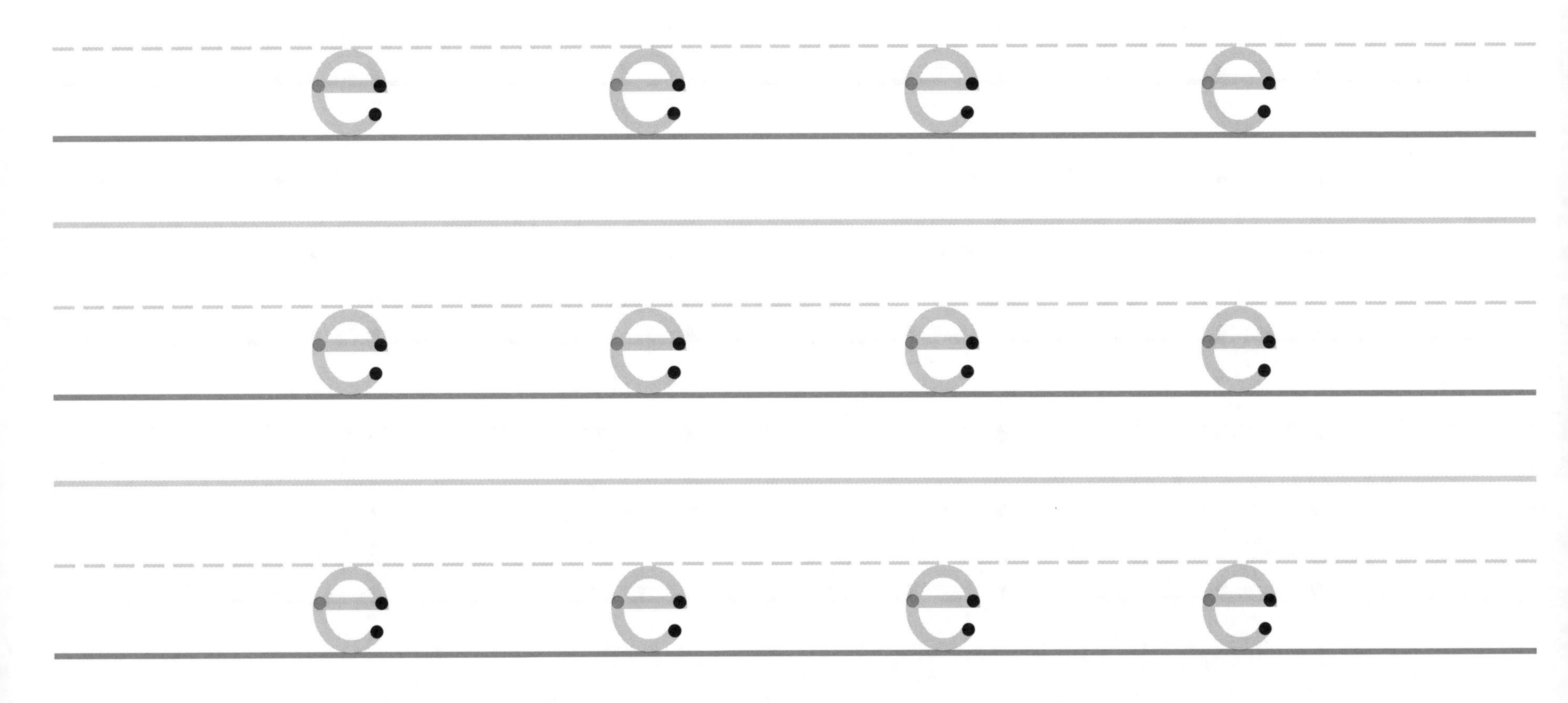

1. Touch the blue dot on the headline; pull down straight to the dot on the baseline. Lift.
2. Touch the blue dot on the headline; slide right to the dot. Lift.
3. Touch the dot on the midline; slide right to the dot. Lift.
4. Touch the dot on the baseline; slide right to the dot. Lift.

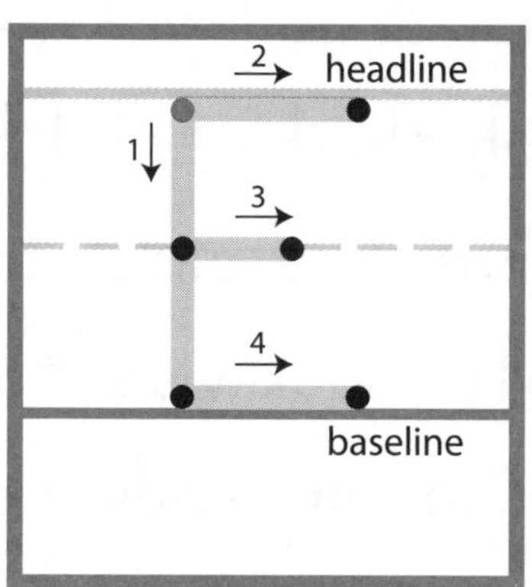

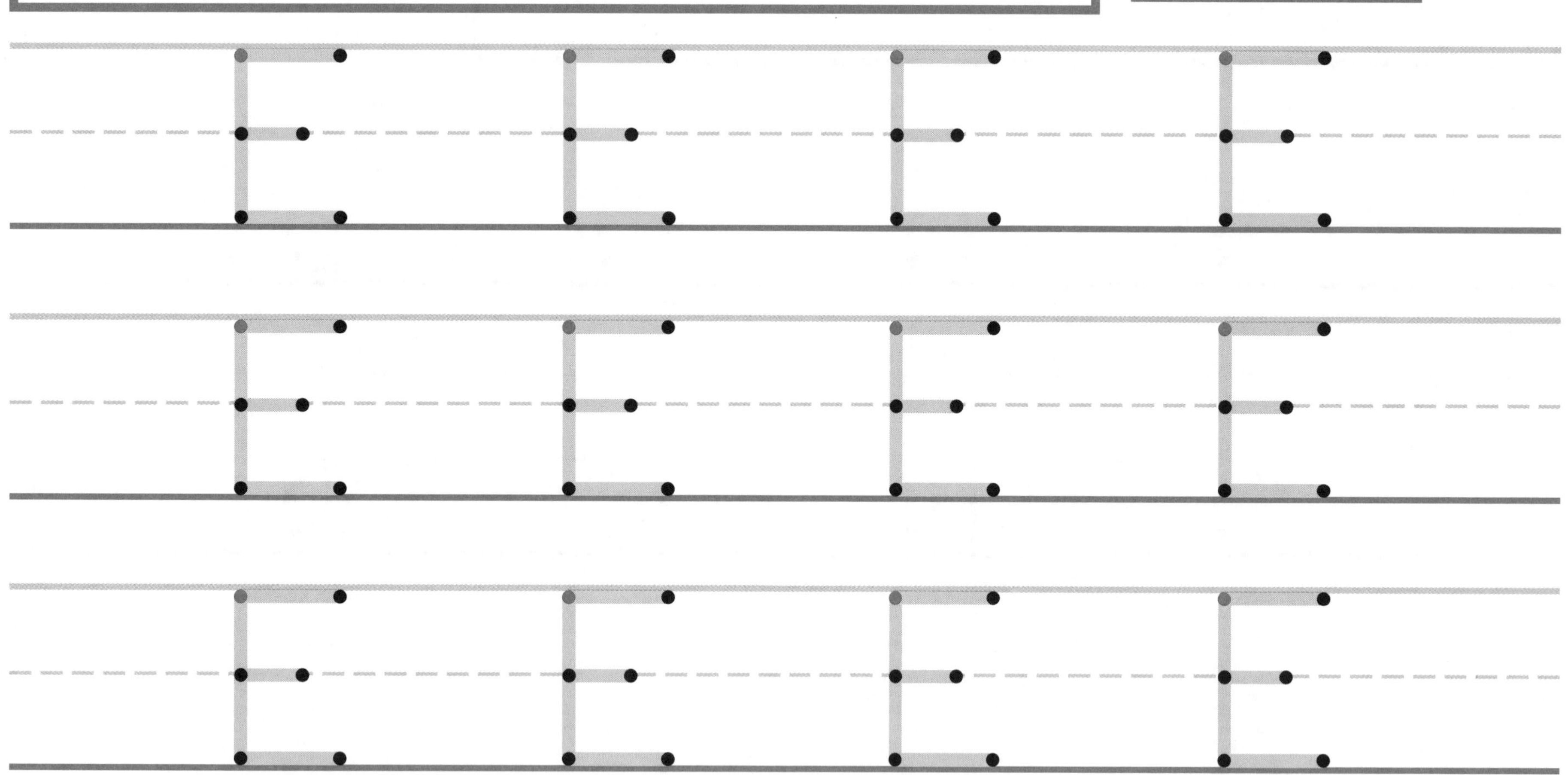

Today is Monday.

I see things that begin with the sound of e.

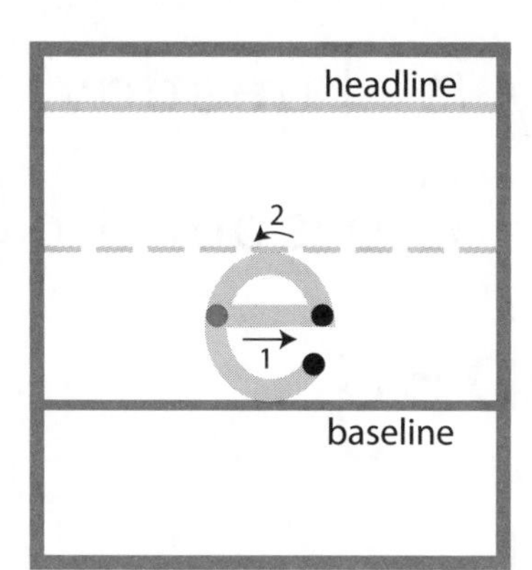

e e e e e e e

Attention Parent/Teacher: Using bright colored pencils, your child may draw pictures of today's items beginning with the sound of **e**. Emphasizing the sound of the letter, instruct your child to trace and write the letter. As your child writes, read the following Zaner-Bloser Stroke Descriptions: Touch halfway between the midline and baseline; slide right; circle back (left), ending above the baseline.

Today is Tuesday.

I hear the sound of e in the middle of words.

beg	peg	red	hen
keg	bed	wed	pen
leg	fed	den	men

e e e e e e e

Attention Parent/Teacher: Read the words to your child. Emphasizing the sound of the letter, instruct your child to trace and write the letter. As your child writes, read the following Zaner-Bloser Stroke Descriptions: Touch halfway between the midline and baseline; slide right; circle back (left), ending above the baseline.

Today is Wednesday.

I taste things that begin with the sound of e.

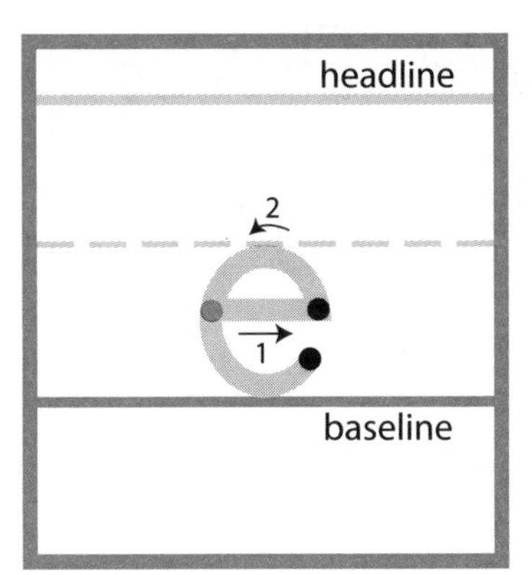

e e e e e e e

Attention Parent/Teacher: Using bright colored pencils, your child may draw pictures of today's items beginning with the sound of **e**. Emphasizing the sound of the letter, instruct your child to trace and write the letter. As your child writes, read the following Zaner-Bloser Stroke Descriptions: Touch halfway between the midline and baseline; slide right; circle back (left), ending above the baseline.

Today is Thursday.

I smell things that begin with the sound of e.

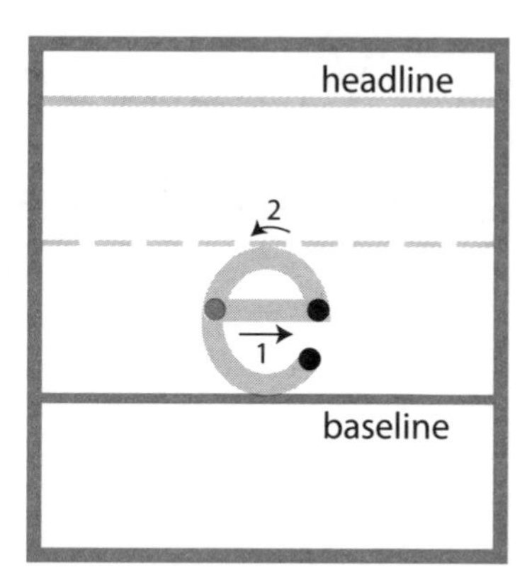

e e e e e e e

Attention Parent/Teacher: Using bright colored pencils, your child may draw pictures of today's items beginning with the sound of **e**. Emphasizing the sound of the letter, instruct your child to trace and write the letter. As your child writes, read the following Zaner-Bloser Stroke Descriptions: Touch halfway between the midline and baseline; slide right; circle back (left), ending above the baseline.

Today is Friday.
I touch things that begin with the sound of e.

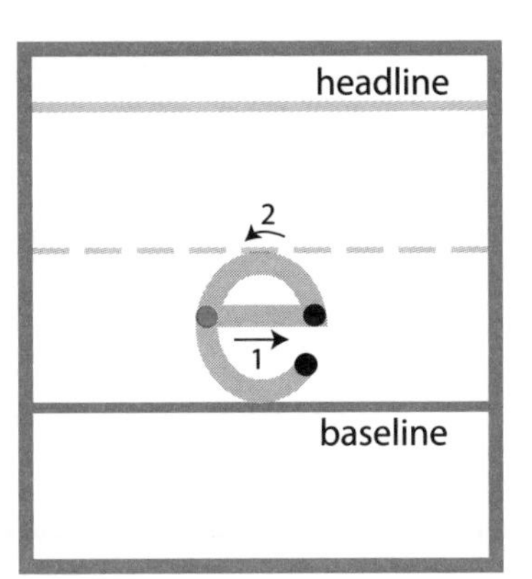

e e e e e e e

Attention Parent/Teacher: Using bright colored pencils, your child may draw pictures of today's items beginning with the sound of **e**. Emphasizing the sound of the letter, instruct your child to trace and write the letter. As your child writes, read the following Zaner-Bloser Stroke Descriptions: Touch halfway between the midline and baseline; slide right; circle back (left), ending above the baseline.

Sing my tongue, the Virgin's trophies,
Who for us our Maker bore;
For the curse of old inflicted,
Peace and blessing to restore.

1. Touch the blue dot below the headline; curve back left; pull down straight to the dot on the baseline. Lift.
2. Touch the dot on the midline; slide right to the dot. Lift.

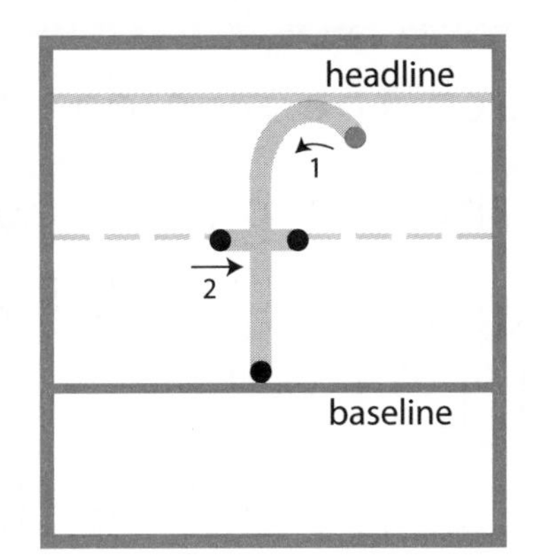

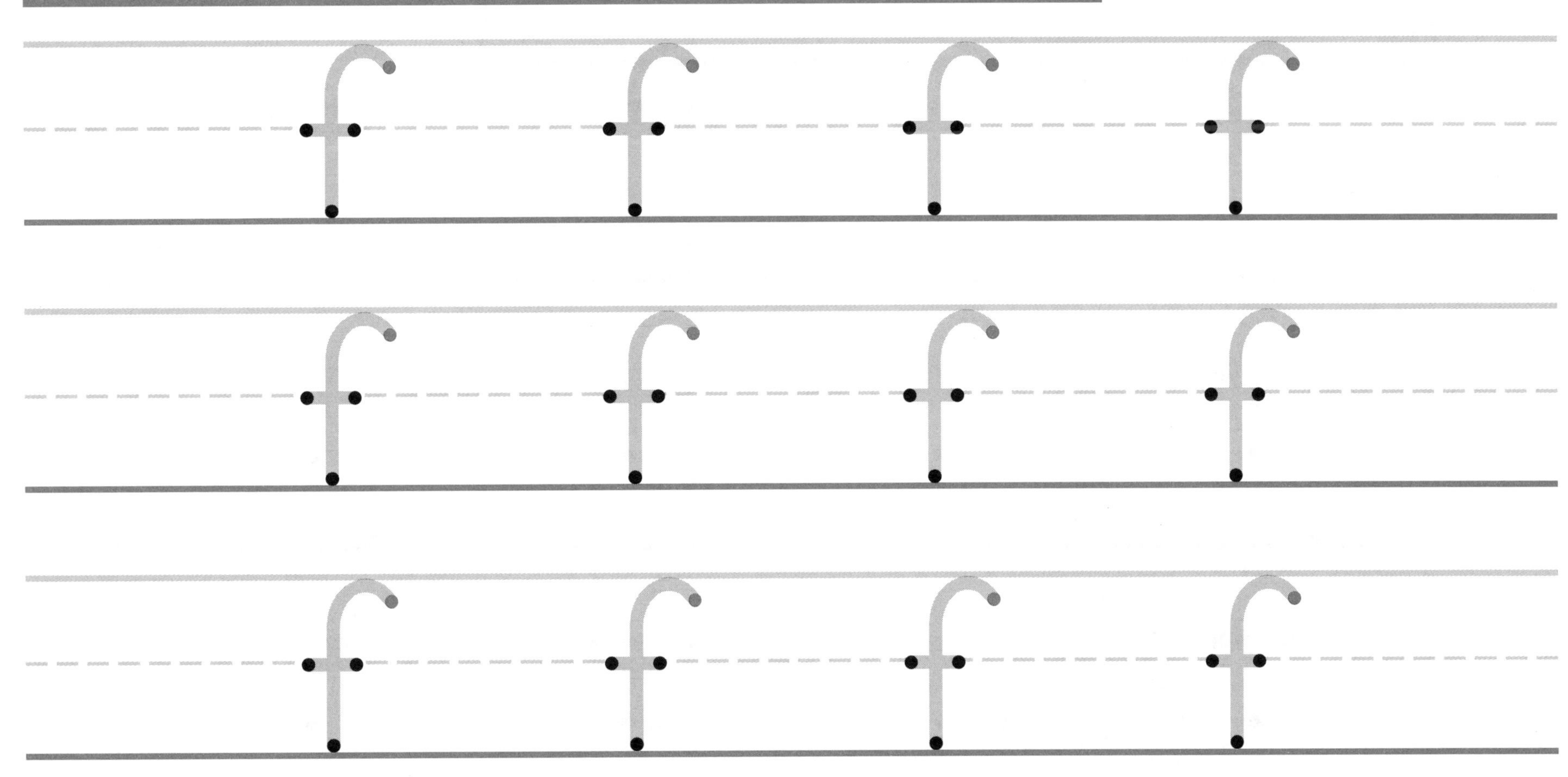

1. Touch the blue dot on the headline; pull down straight to the dot on the baseline. Lift.
2. Touch the blue dot on the headline; slide right to the dot. Lift.
3. Touch the dot on the midline; slide right to the dot. Lift.

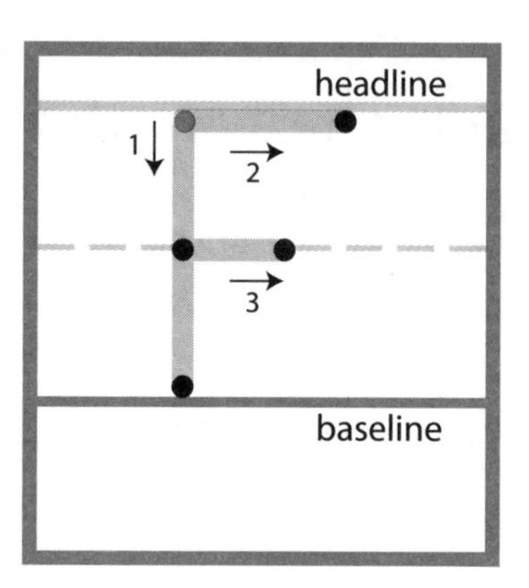

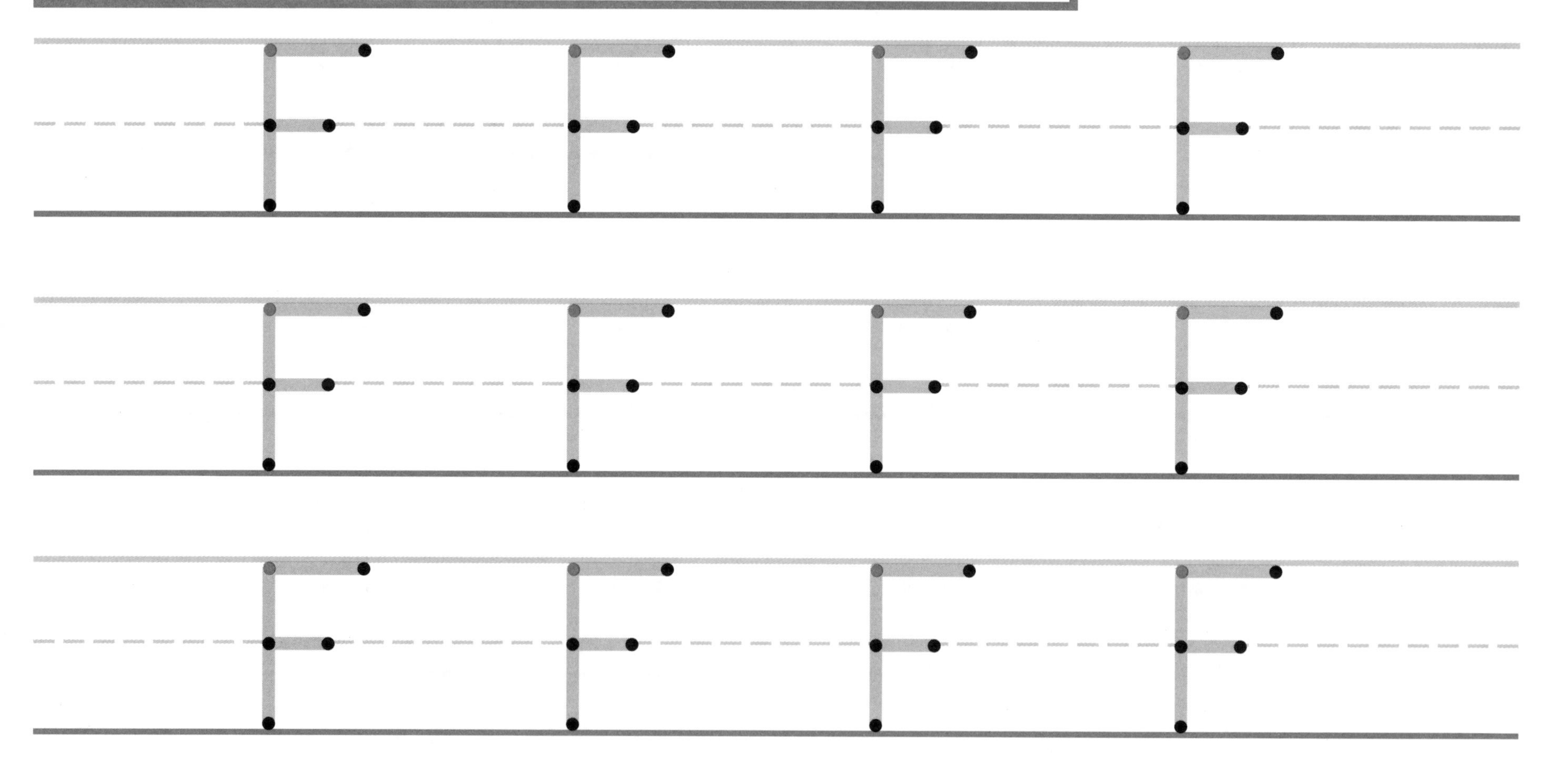

Today is Monday.

I see things that begin with the sound of f.

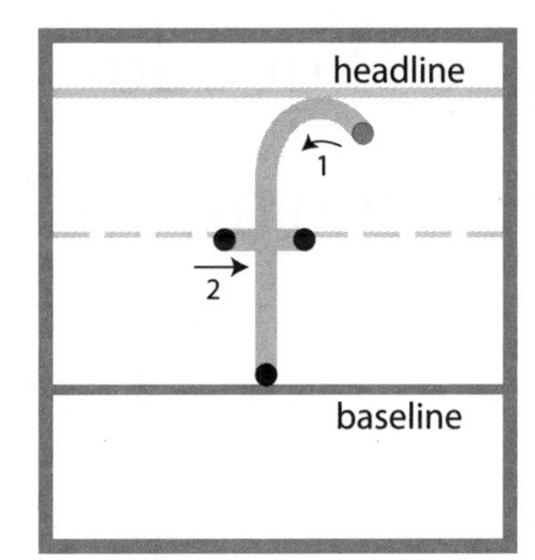

f f f f f f f

Attention Parent/Teacher: Using bright colored pencils, your child may draw pictures of today's items beginning with the sound of **f**. Emphasizing the sound of the letter, instruct your child to trace and write the letter. As your child writes, read the following Zaner-Bloser Stroke Descriptions: Touch below the headline; curve back (left); pull down straight to the baseline. Lift. Touch the midline; slide right.

Today is Tuesday.

I hear rhyming words that end with the sound of f.

if

stiff

sniff

puff

huff

stuff

f f f f f f f

Attention Parent/Teacher: Read the rhyming words to your child. Emphasizing the sound of the letter, instruct your child to trace and write the letter. As your child writes, read the following Zaner-Bloser Stroke Descriptions: Touch below the headline; curve back (left); pull down straight to the baseline. Lift. Touch the midline; slide right.

Today is Wednesday.
I taste things that begin with the sound of f.

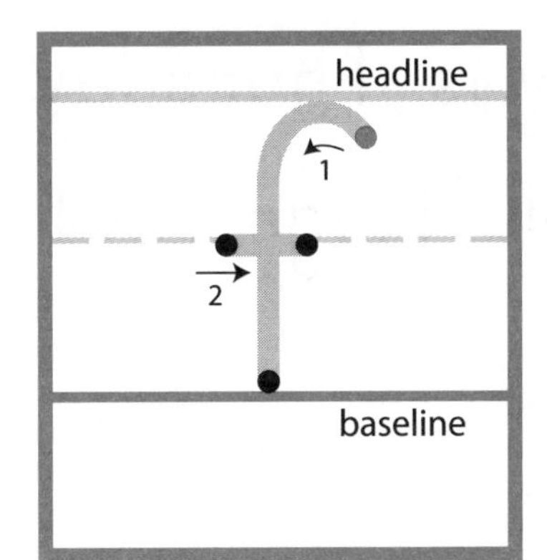

f f f f f f f

Attention Parent/Teacher: Using bright colored pencils, your child may draw pictures of today's items beginning with the sound of **f**. Emphasizing the sound of the letter, instruct your child to trace and write the letter. As your child writes, read the following Zaner-Bloser Stroke Descriptions: Touch below the headline; curve back (left); pull down straight to the baseline. Lift. Touch the midline; slide right.

Today is Thursday.

I smell things that begin with the sound of f.

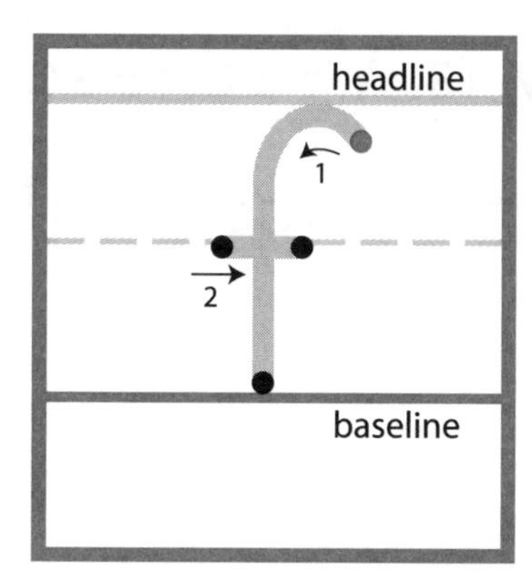

f f f f f f f

Attention Parent/Teacher: Using bright colored pencils, your child may draw pictures of today's items beginning with the sound of **f**. Emphasizing the sound of the letter, instruct your child to trace and write the letter. As your child writes, read the following Zaner-Bloser Stroke Descriptions: Touch below the headline; curve back (left); pull down straight to the baseline. Lift. Touch the midline; slide right.

Today is Friday.

I touch things that begin with the sound of f.

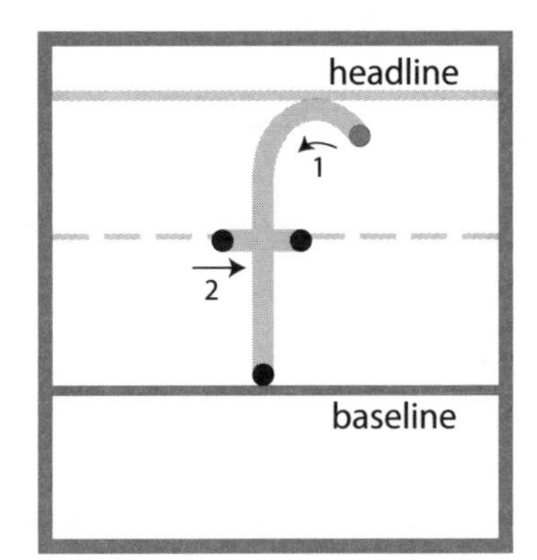

Attention Parent/Teacher: Using bright colored pencils, your child may draw pictures of today's items beginning with the sound of **f**. Emphasizing the sound of the letter, instruct your child to trace and write the letter. As your child writes, read the following Zaner-Bloser Stroke Descriptions: Touch below the headline; curve back (left); pull down straight to the baseline. Lift. Touch the midline; slide right.

Sing in songs of praise unending,
Sing the world's majestic Queen.
Weary not nor faint in telling
All the gifts she gives we've seen.

Touch the blue dot on the midline; slide right to the dot. Pause; slant left to the dot on the baseline. Pause; slide right to the dot. Lift.

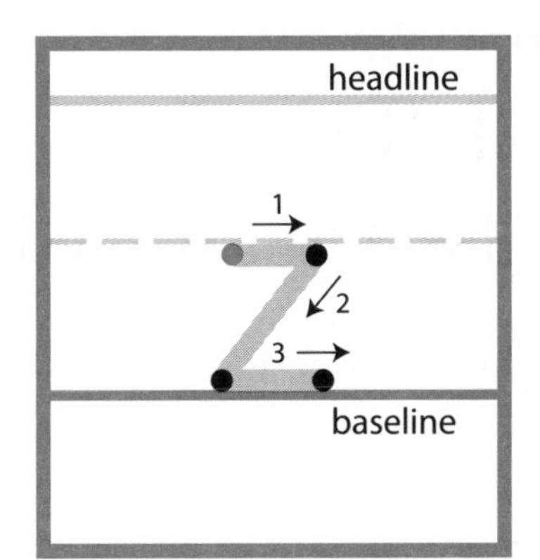

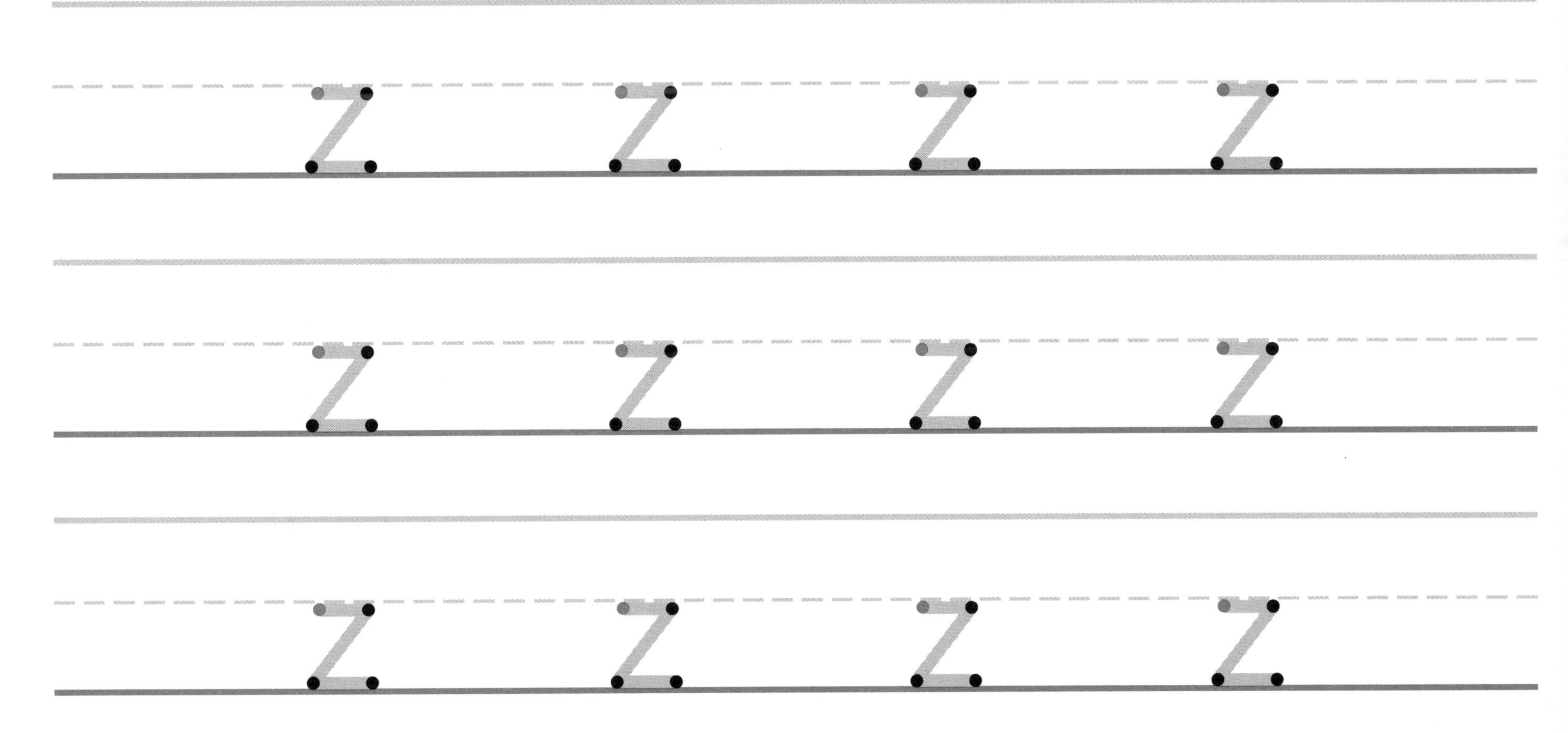

Touch the blue dot on the headline; slide right to the dot. Pause; slant left to the dot on the baseline. Pause; slide right to the dot. Lift.

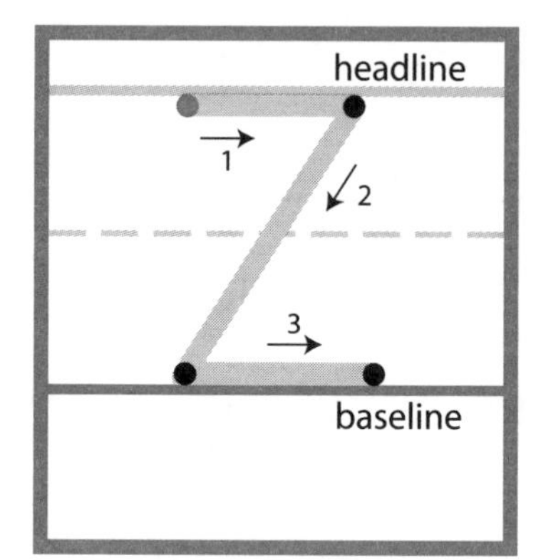

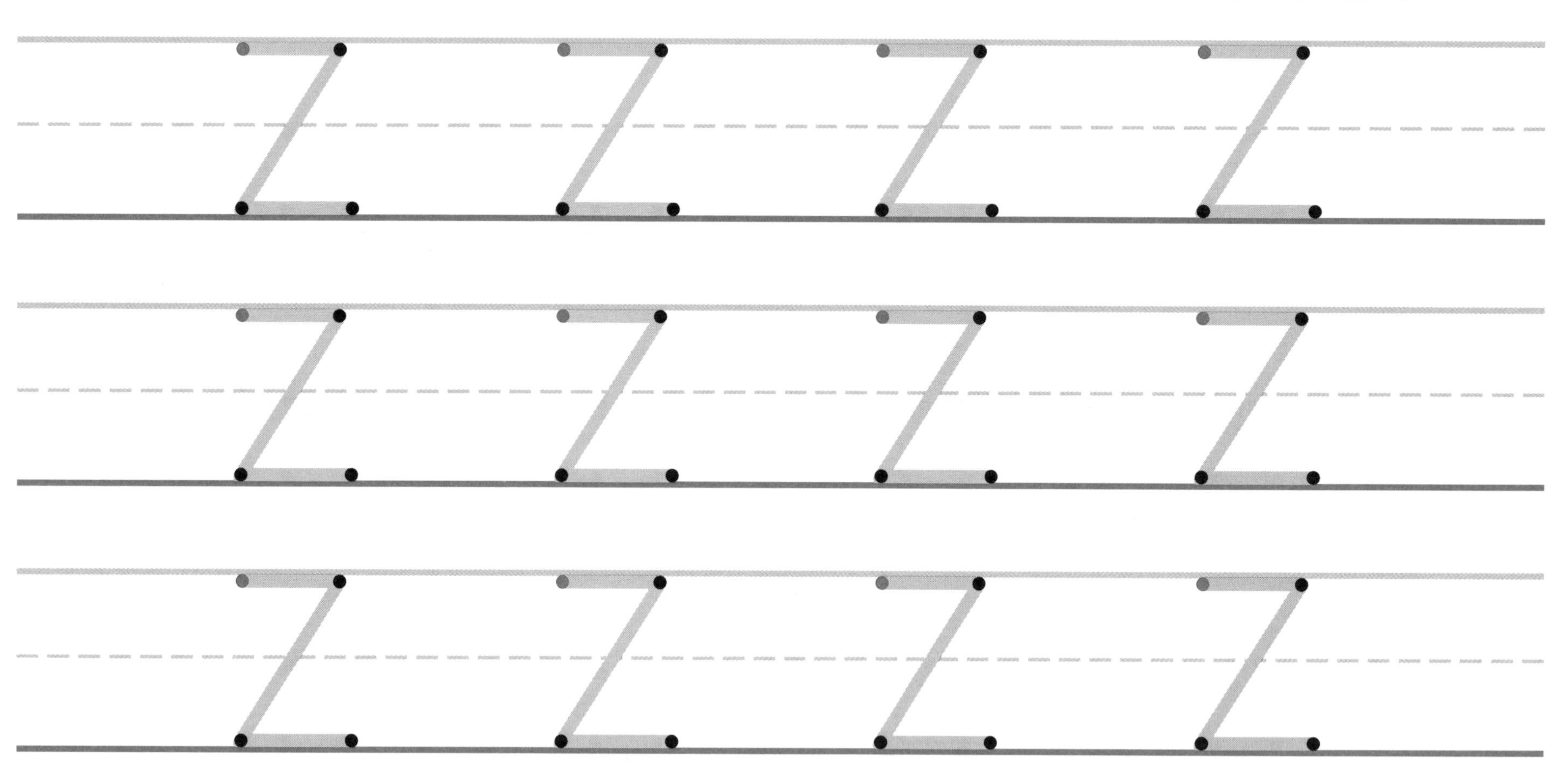

Today is Monday.
I see things that begin with the sound of z.

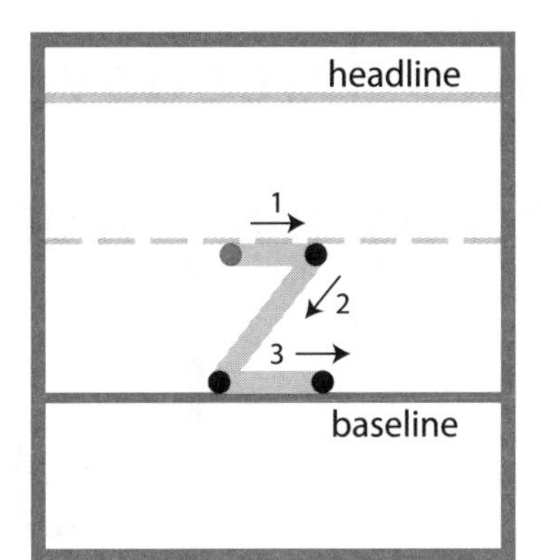

z z z z z z z

Attention Parent/Teacher: Using bright colored pencils, your child may draw pictures of today's items beginning with the sound of **z**. Emphasizing the sound of the letter, instruct your child to trace and write the letter. As your child writes, read the following Zaner-Bloser Stroke Descriptions: Touch the midline; slide right. Slant left to the baseline. Slide right.

Today is Tuesday.

I hear rhyming words that end with the sound of z.

buzz fuzz

z z z z z z z

Attention Parent/Teacher: Read the rhyming words to your child. Emphasizing the sound of the letter, instruct your child to trace and write the letter. As your child writes, read the following Zaner-Bloser Stroke Descriptions: Touch the midline; slant right to the baseline. Lift. Move to the right and touch the midline; slant left to the baseline.

Today is Wednesday.
I taste things that begin with the sound of z.

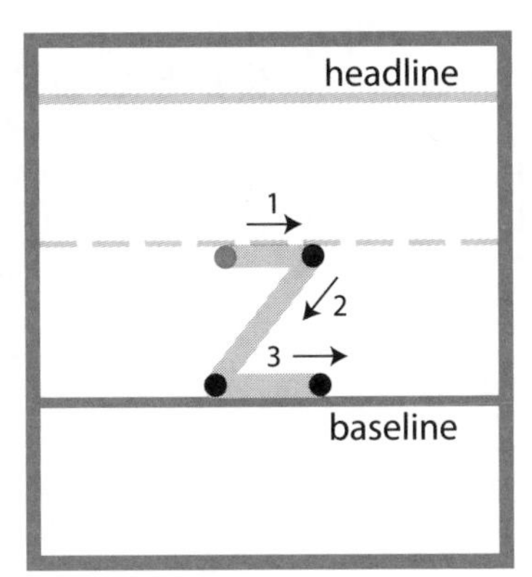

z z z z z z z

Attention Parent/Teacher: Using bright colored pencils, your child may draw pictures of today's items beginning with the sound of **z**. Emphasizing the sound of the letter, instruct your child to trace and write the letter. As your child writes, read the following Zaner-Bloser Stroke Descriptions: Touch the midline; slide right. Slant left to the baseline. Slide right.

Today is Thursday.

I smell things that begin with the sound of z.

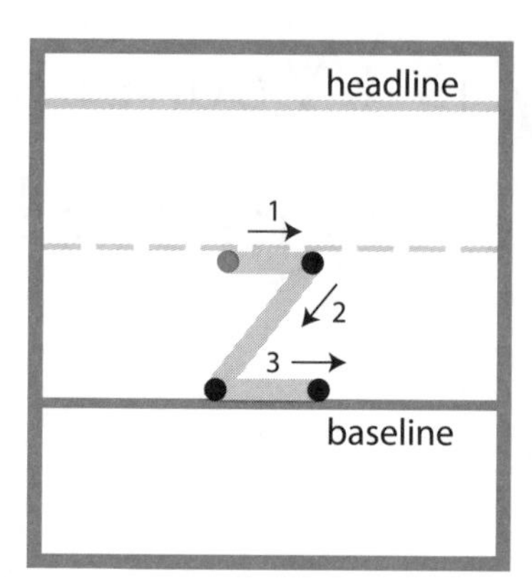

z z z z z z z

Attention Parent/Teacher: Using bright colored pencils, your child may draw pictures of today's items beginning with the sound of **z**. Emphasizing the sound of the letter, instruct your child to trace and write the letter. As your child writes, read the following Zaner-Bloser Stroke Descriptions: Touch the midline; slide right. Slant left to the baseline. Slide right.

Today is Friday.

I touch things that begin with the sound of z.

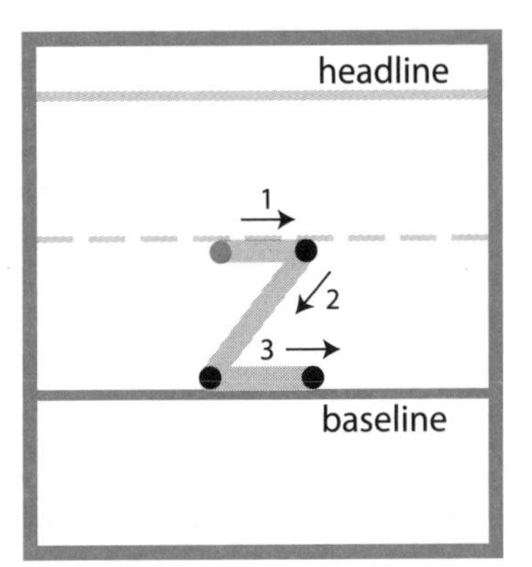

z z z z z z z

Attention Parent/Teacher: Using bright colored pencils, your child may draw pictures of today's items beginning with the sound of **z**. Emphasizing the sound of the letter, instruct your child to trace and write the letter. As your child writes, read the following Zaner-Bloser Stroke Descriptions: Touch the midline; slide right. Slant left to the baseline. Slide right.

All my senses, heart, affections,
Strive to sound her glory forth:
Spread abroad the sweet memorials
Of the Virgin's priceless worth.

1. Touch the blue dot on the headline; pull down straight to the dot on the baseline. Lift.
2. Move to the right and touch the dot on the midline; slant left to the dot. Pause; slant right to the dot on the baseline. Lift.

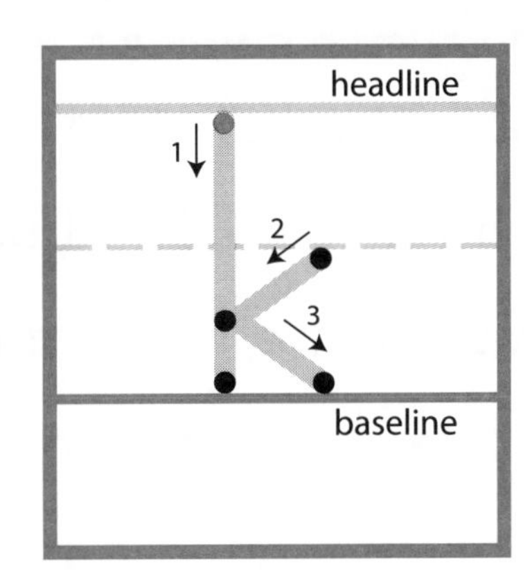

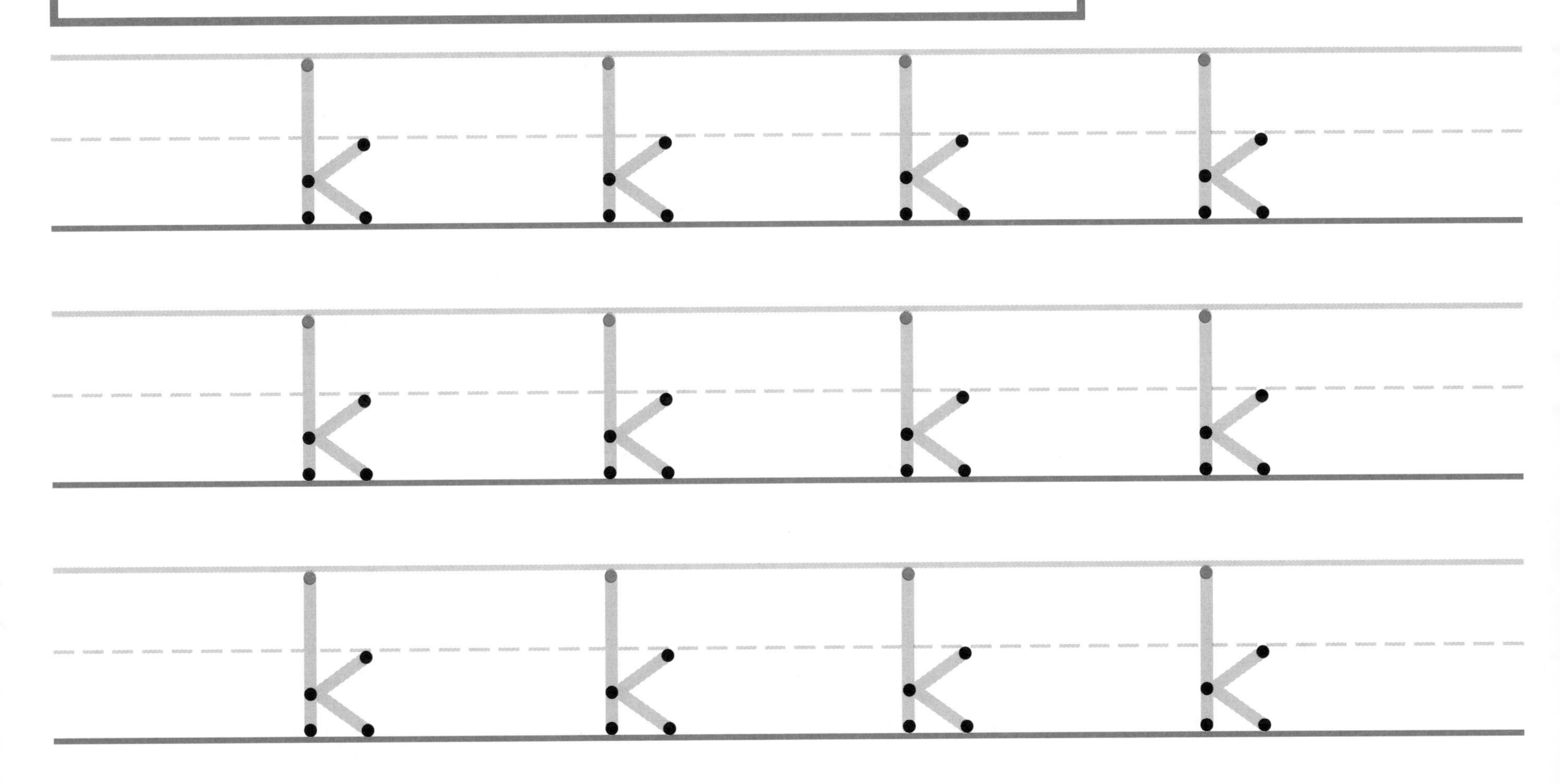

1. Touch the blue dot on the headline; pull down straight to the dot on the baseline. Lift.
2. Move to the right and touch the dot on the headline; slant left to the dot on the midline. Pause; slant right to the dot on the baseline. Lift.

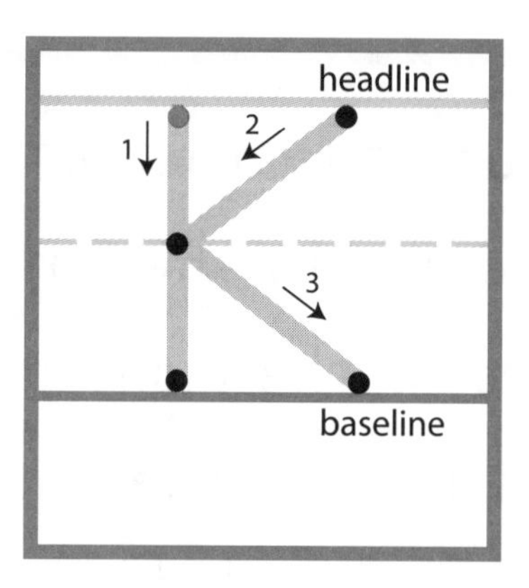

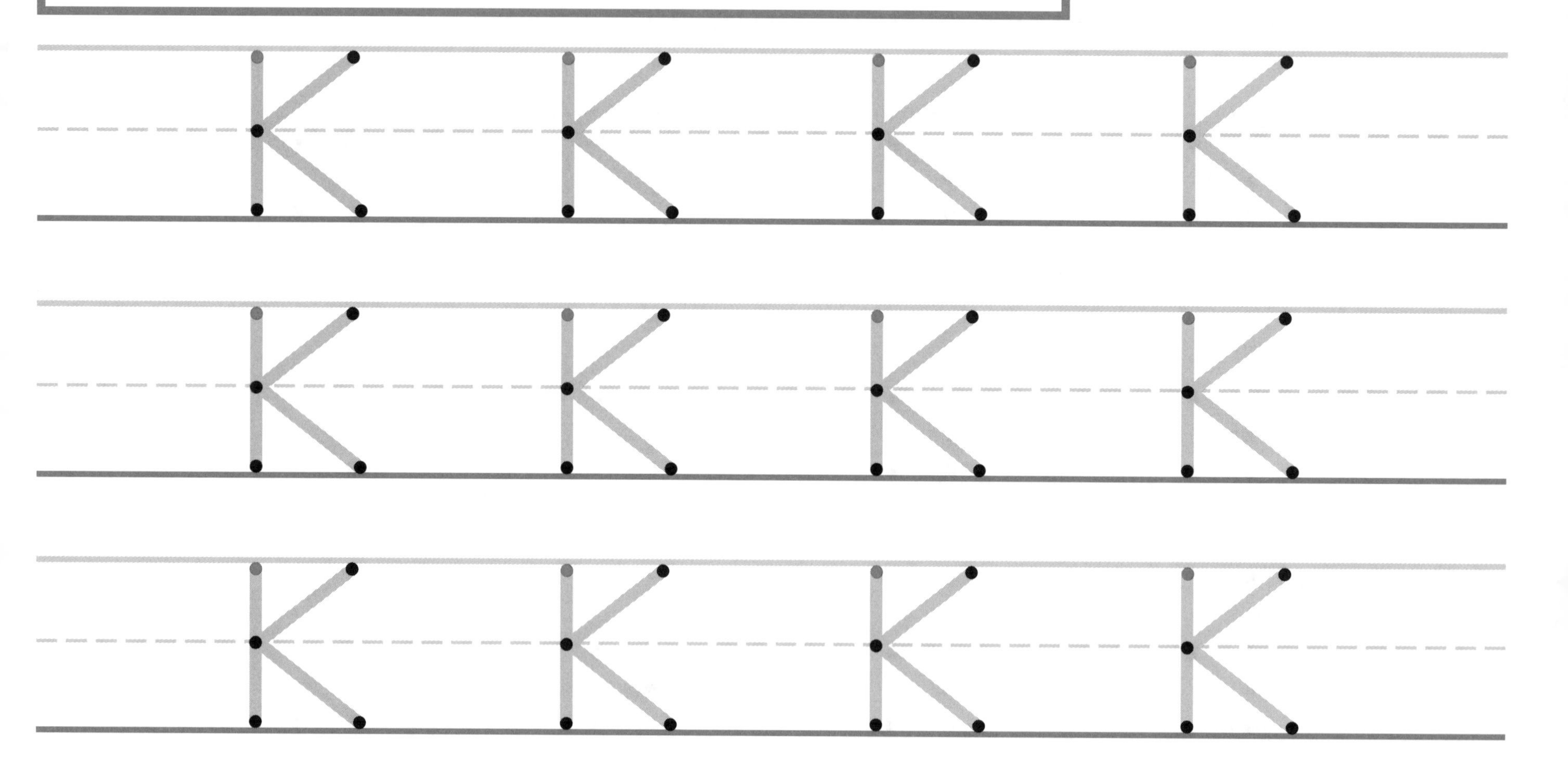

Today is Monday.
I see things that begin with the sound of k.

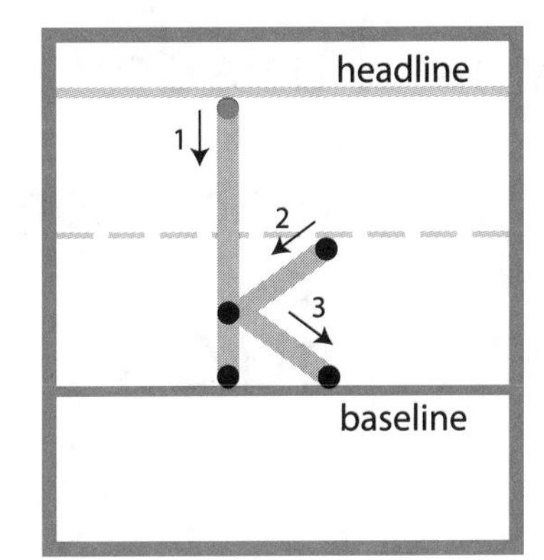

k k k k k k k

Attention Parent/Teacher: Using bright colored pencils, your child may draw pictures of today's items beginning with the sound of **k**. Emphasizing the sound of the letter, instruct your child to trace and write the letter. As your child writes, read the following Zaner-Bloser Stroke Descriptions: Touch the headline; pull down straight to the baseline. Lift. Move to the right and touch the midline; slant left. Slant right to the baseline.

Today is Tuesday.

I hear rhyming words that end with the sound of k.

duck	back	kick
luck	lack	lick
truck	quack	quick

k k k k k k k

Attention Parent/Teacher: Read the rhyming words to your child. Emphasizing the sound of the letter, instruct your child to trace and write the letter. As your child writes, read the following Zaner-Bloser Stroke Descriptions: Touch the headline; pull down straight to the baseline. Lift. Move to the right and touch the midline; slant left. Slant right to the baseline.

Today is Wednesday.
I taste things that begin with the sound of k.

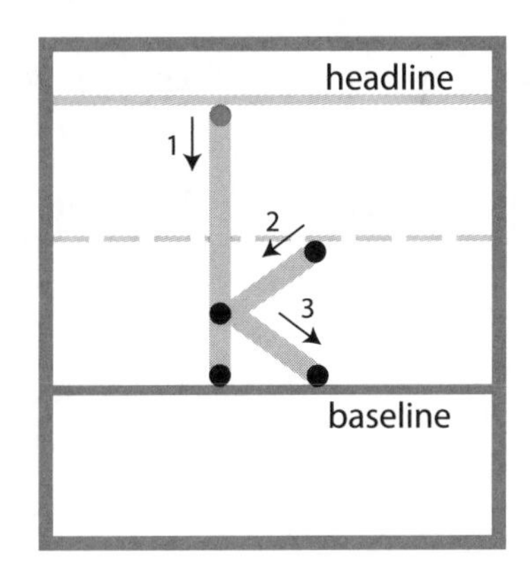

k k k k k k k

Attention Parent/Teacher: Using bright colored pencils, your child may draw pictures of today's items beginning with the sound of **k**. Emphasizing the sound of the letter, instruct your child to trace and write the letter. As your child writes, read the following Zaner-Bloser Stroke Descriptions: Touch the headline; pull down straight to the baseline. Lift. Move to the right and touch the midline; slant left. Slant right to the baseline.

Today is Thursday.

I smell things that begin with the sound of k.

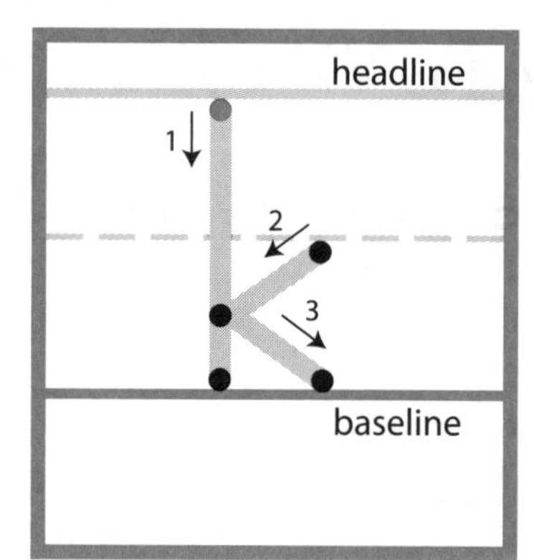

k k k k k k k

Attention Parent/Teacher: Using bright colored pencils, your child may draw pictures of today's items beginning with the sound of **k**. Emphasizing the sound of the letter, instruct your child to trace and write the letter. As your child writes, read the following Zaner-Bloser Stroke Descriptions: Touch the headline; pull down straight to the baseline. Lift. Move to the right and touch the midline; slant left. Slant right to the baseline.

Today is Friday.

I touch things that begin with the sound of k.

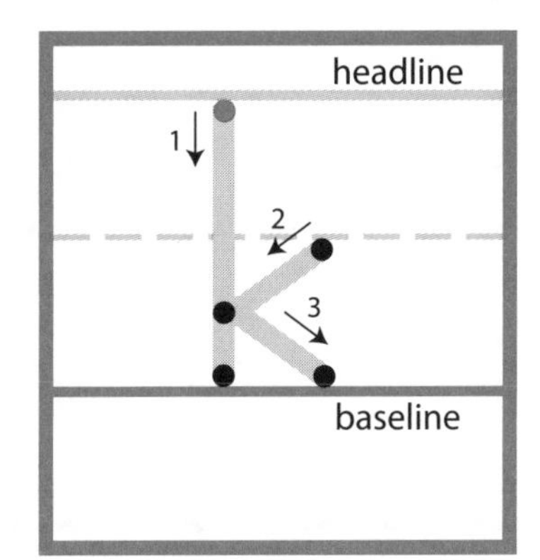

k k k k k k k

Attention Parent/Teacher: Using bright colored pencils, your child may draw pictures of today's items beginning with the sound of **k**. Emphasizing the sound of the letter, instruct your child to trace and write the letter. As your child writes, read the following Zaner-Bloser Stroke Descriptions: Touch the headline; pull down straight to the baseline. Lift. Move to the right and touch the midline; slant left. Slant right to the baseline.

Where the voice of music thrilling,
Where the tongue of eloquence,
That can utter hymns beseeming
All her matchless excellence?

Touch the blue dot on the midline; slant right to the dot on the baseline. Pause; slant up right to the dot on the midline. Lift.

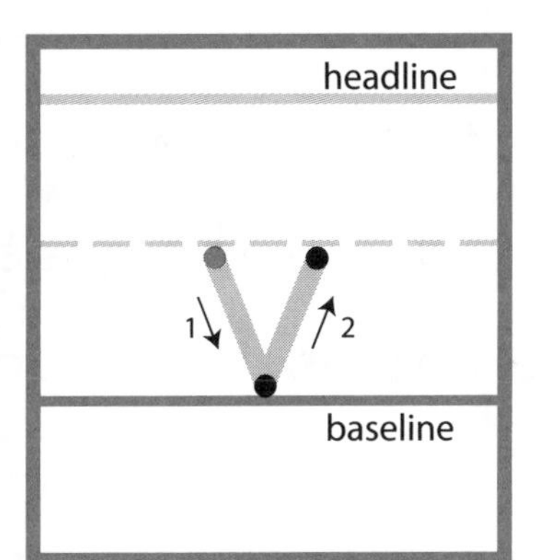

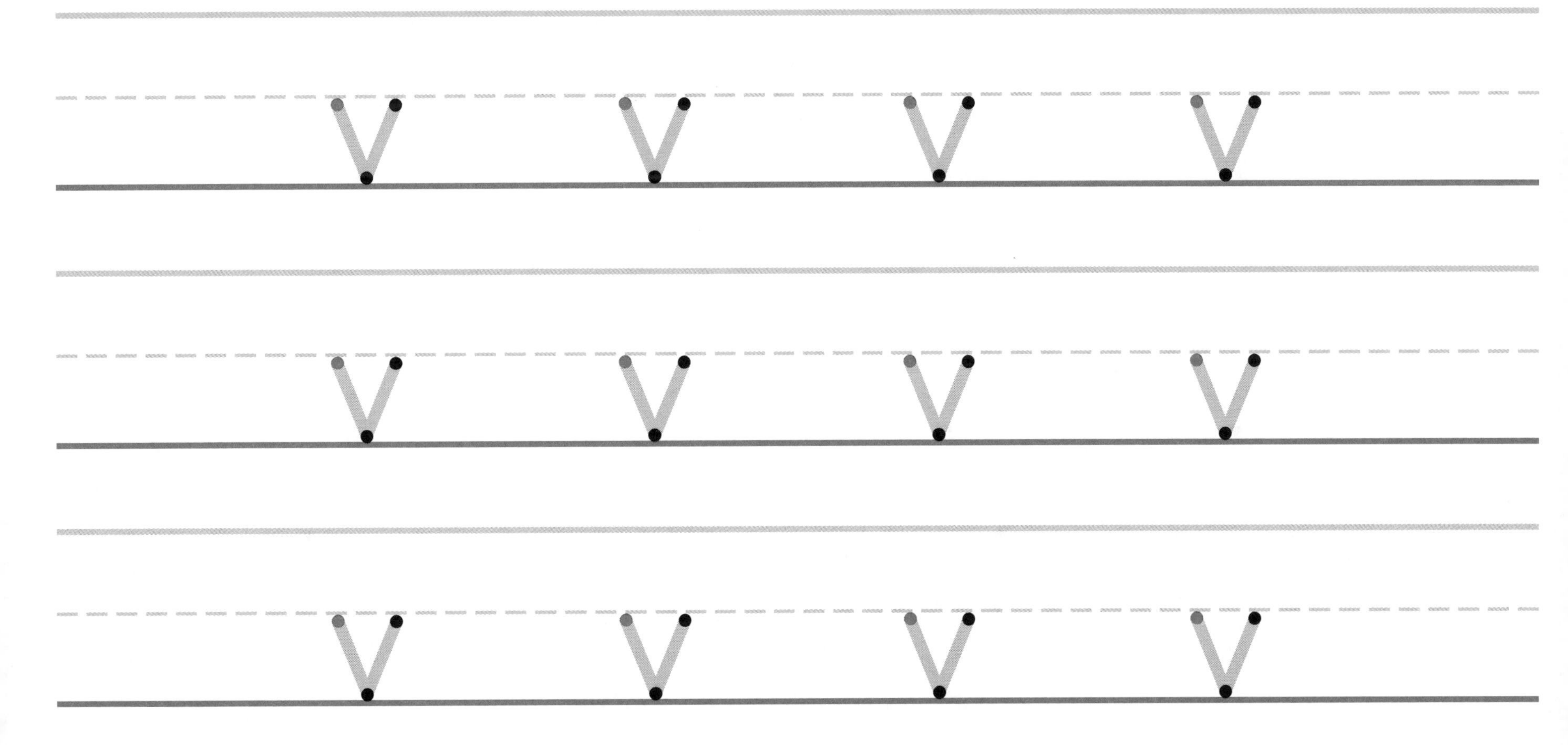

Touch the blue dot on the headline; slant right to the dot on the baseline. Pause; slant up right to the dot on the headline. Lift.

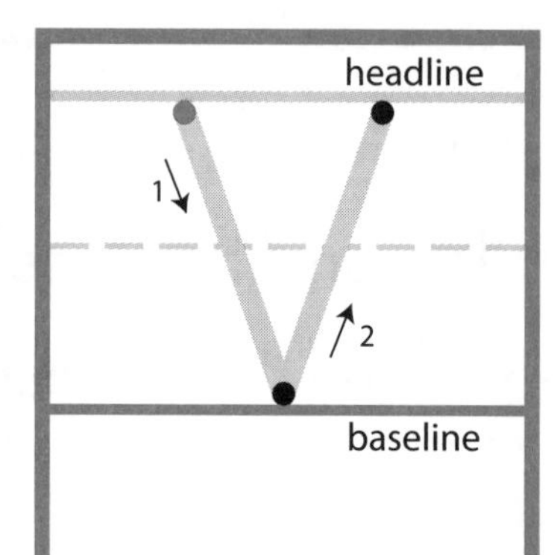

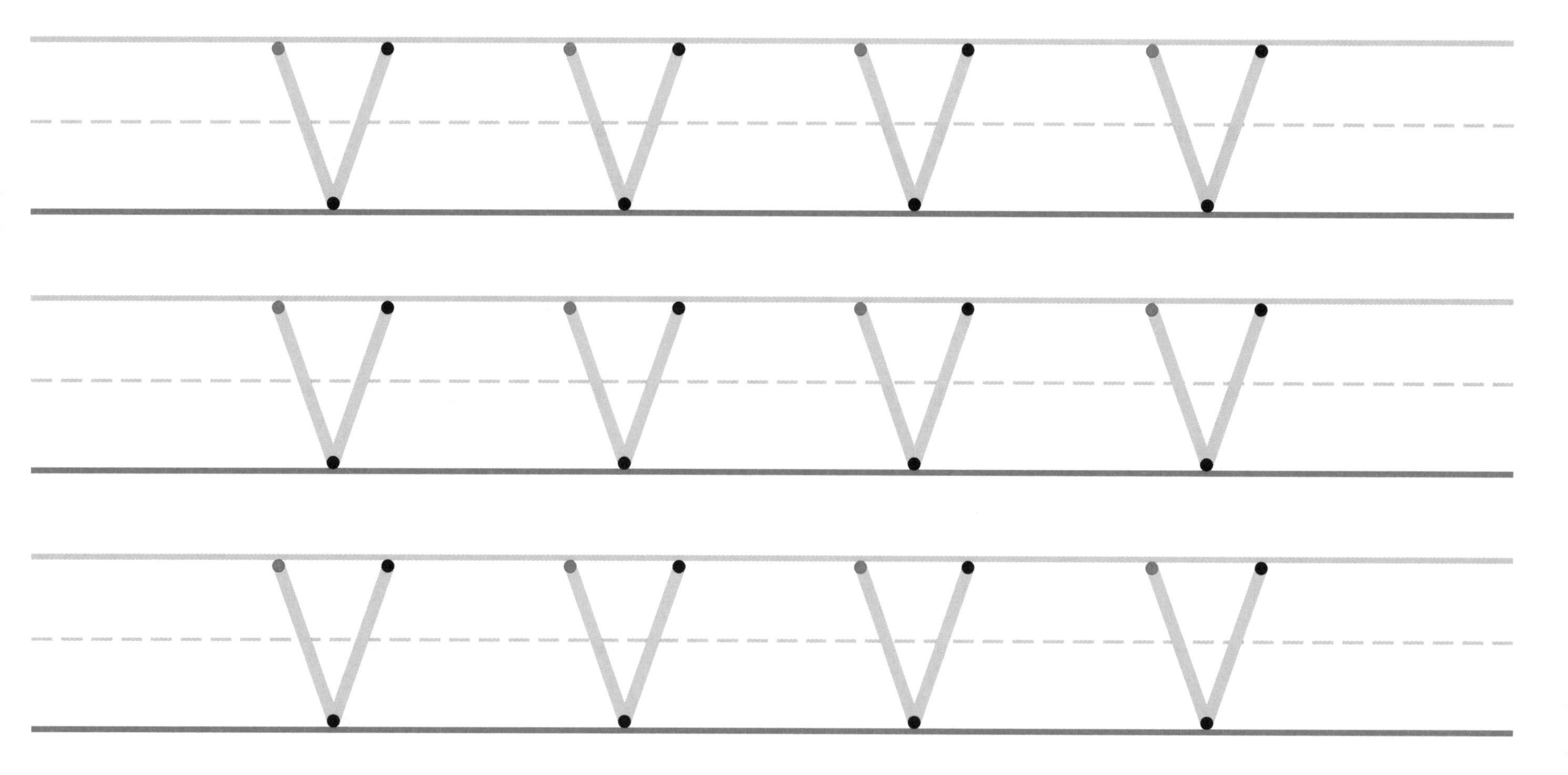

Today is Monday.

I see things that begin with the sound of v.

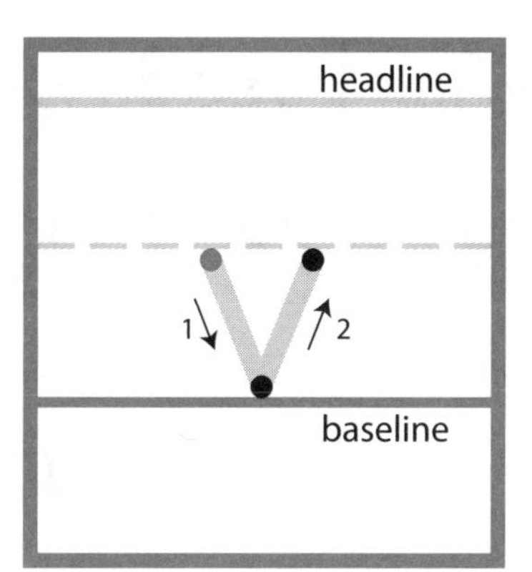

v v v v v v v

Attention Parent/Teacher: Using bright colored pencils, your child may draw pictures of today's items beginning with the sound of **v**. Emphasizing the sound of the letter, instruct your child to trace and write the letter. As your child writes, read the following Zaner-Bloser Stroke Descriptions: Touch the midline; slant right to the baseline. Slant up (right) to the midline.

Today is Tuesday.

I hear words that begin with the sound of v.

van vat

vet Val

v v v v v v v

Attention Parent/Teacher: Read the words to your child. Emphasizing the sound of the letter, instruct your child to trace and write the letter. As your child writes, read the following Zaner-Bloser Stroke Descriptions: Touch the midline; slant right to the baseline. Slant up (right) to the midline.

Today is Wednesday.
I taste things that begin with the sound of v.

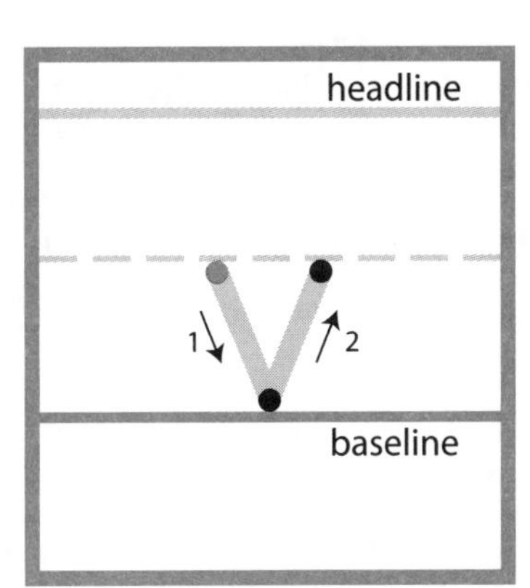

v v v v v v v

Attention Parent/Teacher: Using bright colored pencils, your child may draw pictures of today's items beginning with the sound of **v**. Emphasizing the sound of the letter, instruct your child to trace and write the letter. As your child writes, read the following Zaner-Bloser Stroke Descriptions: Touch the midline; slant right to the baseline. Slant up (right) to the midline.

Today is Thursday.

I smell things that begin with the sound of v.

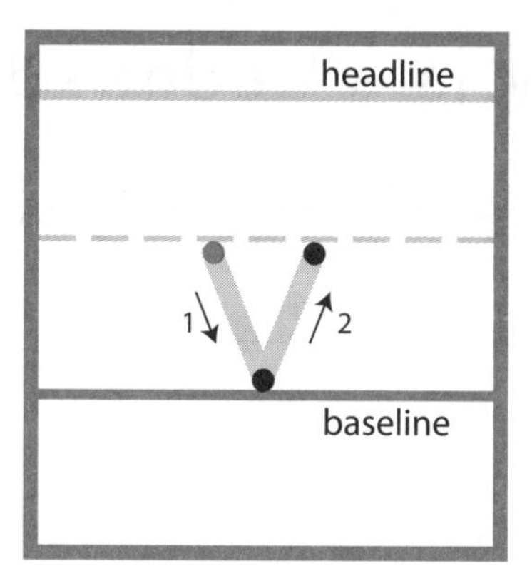

v v v v v v v

Attention Parent/Teacher: Using bright colored pencils, your child may draw pictures of today's items beginning with the sound of **v**. Emphasizing the sound of the letter, instruct your child to trace and write the letter. As your child writes, read the following Zaner-Bloser Stroke Descriptions: Touch the midline; slant right to the baseline. Slant up (right) to the midline.

Today is Friday.

I touch things that begin with the sound of v.

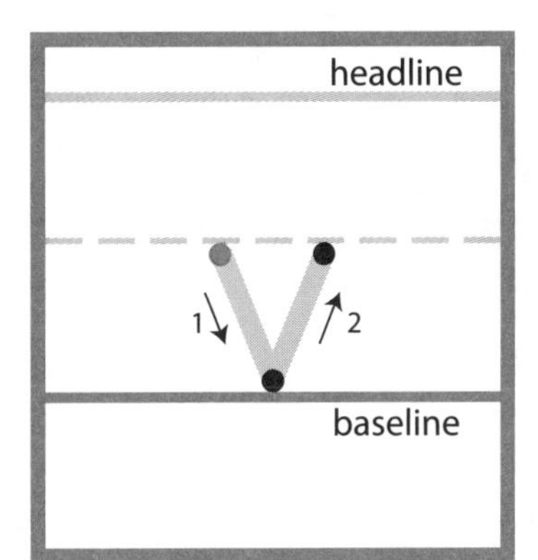

v v v v v v v

Attention Parent/Teacher: Using bright colored pencils, your child may draw pictures of today's items beginning with the sound of **v**. Emphasizing the sound of the letter, instruct your child to trace and write the letter. As your child writes, read the following Zaner-Bloser Stroke Descriptions: Touch the midline; slant right to the baseline. Slant up (right) to the midline.

Mother of mercy, day by day,
My love of thee grows more and more;
Thy gifts are strewn upon my way
Like sands upon the great seashore.

Touch the blue dot on the midline; slant right to the dot on the baseline. Pause; slant up right to the dot on the midline. Pause; slant right to the dot on the baseline. Pause; slant up right to the dot on the midline. Lift.

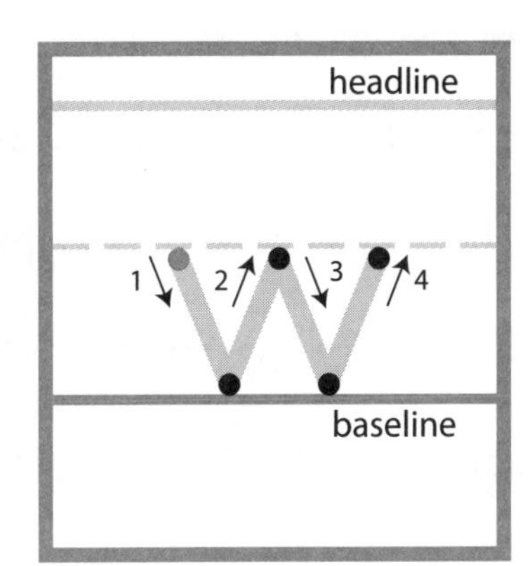

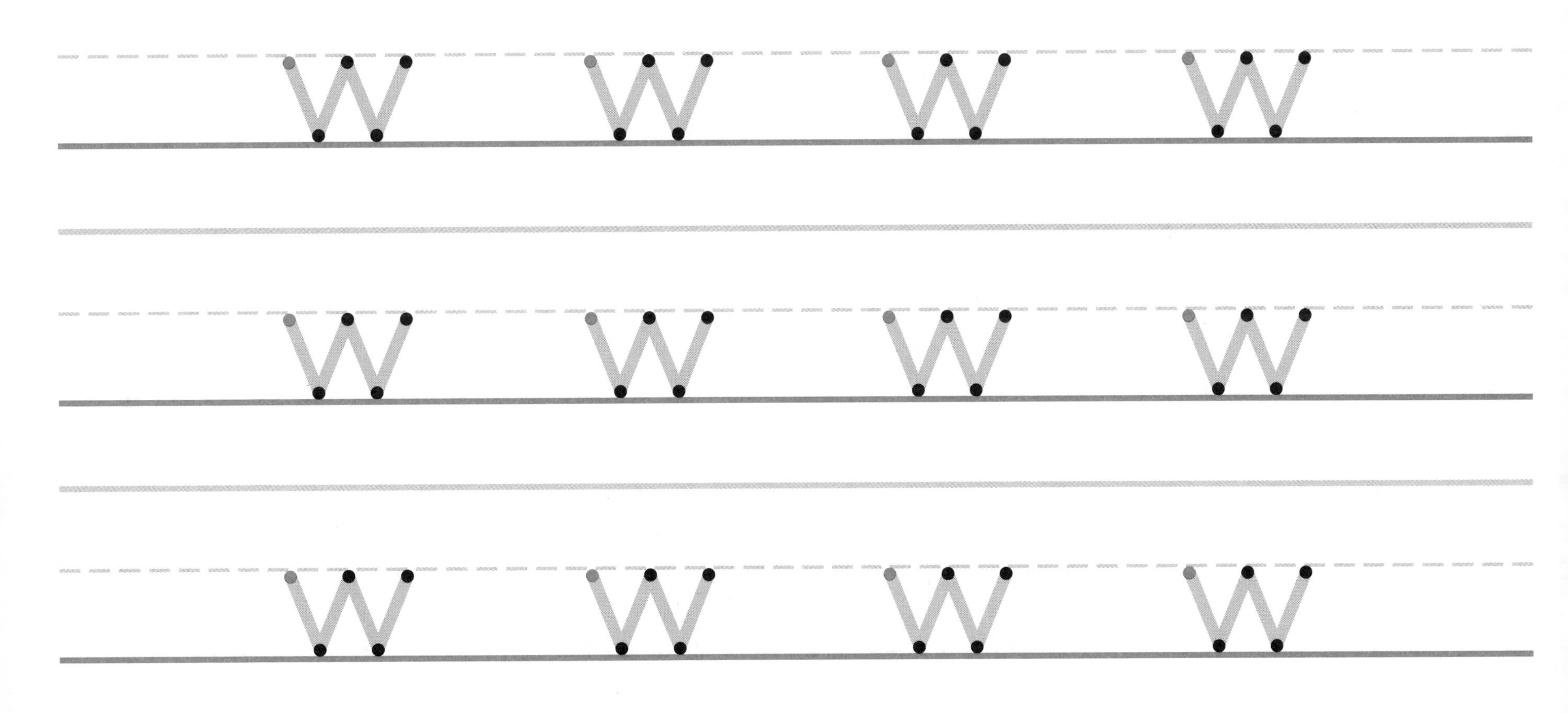

Touch the blue dot on the headline; slant right to the dot on the baseline. Pause; slant up right to the dot on the headline. Pause; slant right to the dot on the baseline. Pause; slant up right to the dot on the headline. Lift.

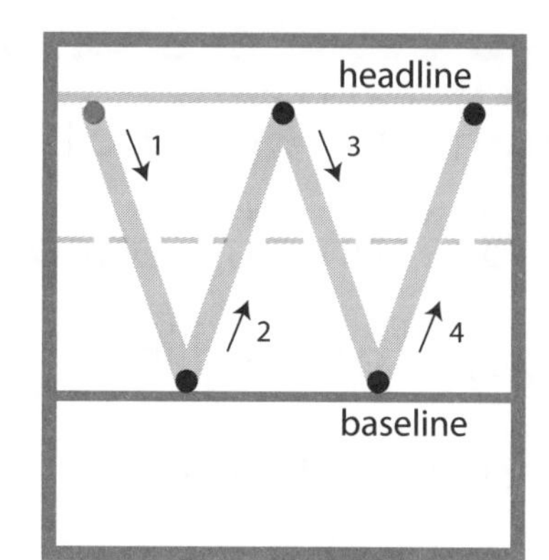

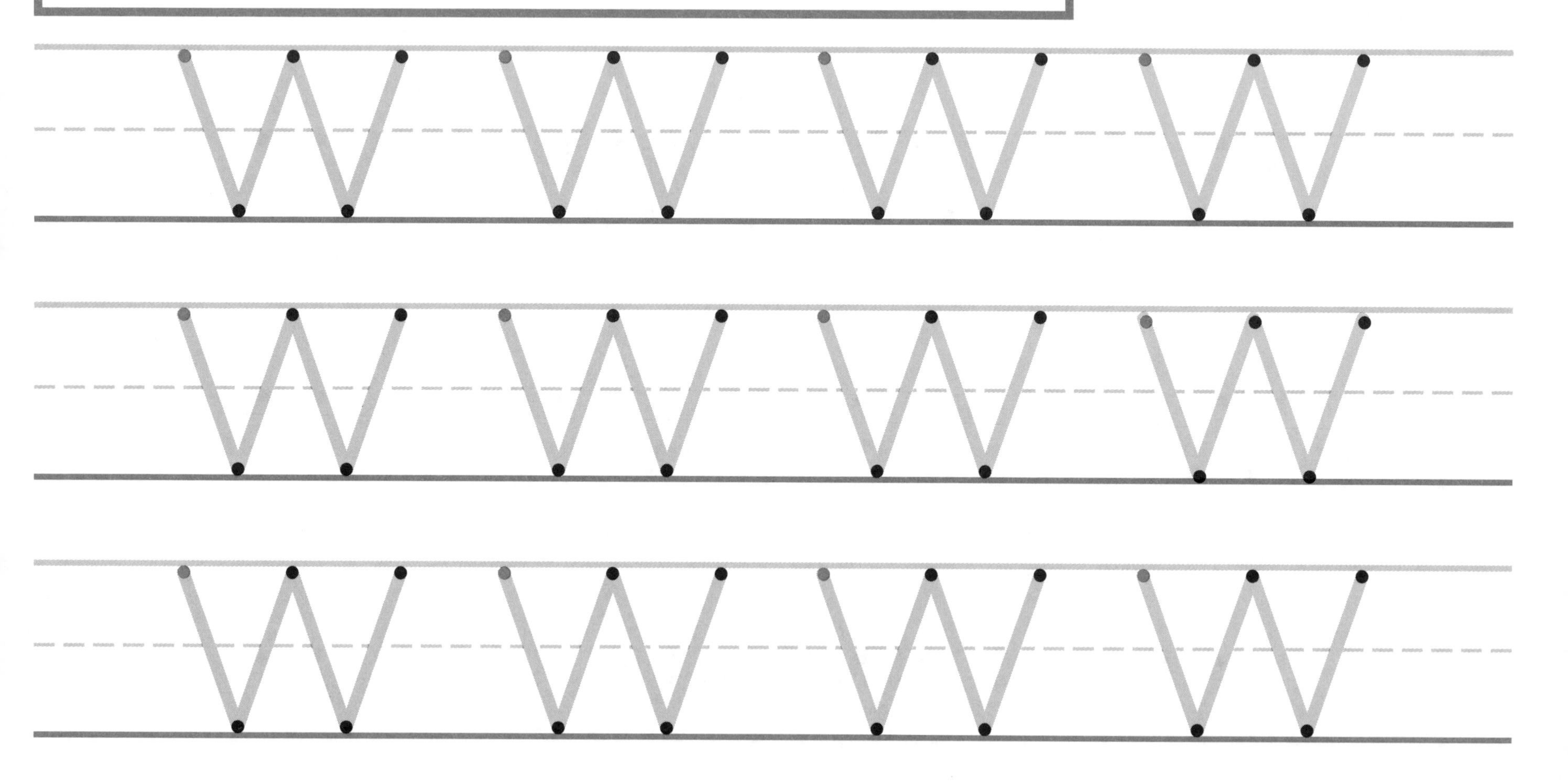

Today is Monday.
I see things that begin with the sound of w.

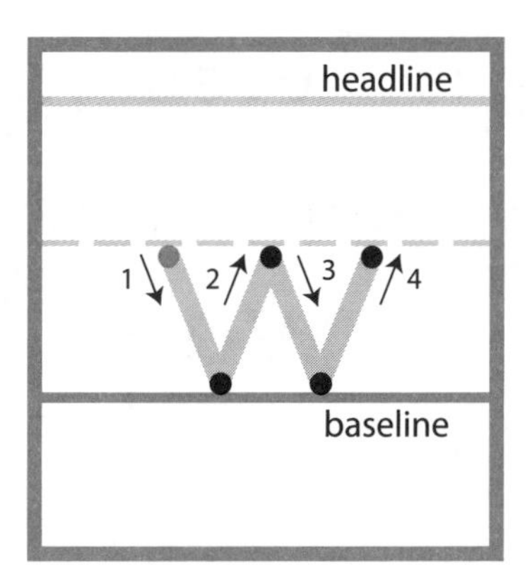

Attention Parent/Teacher: Using bright colored pencils, your child may draw pictures of today's items beginning with the sound of **w**. Emphasizing the sound of the letter, instruct your child to trace and write the letter. As your child writes, read the following Zaner-Bloser Stroke Descriptions: Touch the midline; slant right to the baseline. Slant up (right) to the midline. Slant right to the baseline. Slant up (right) to the midline.

Today is Tuesday.

I hear words that begin with the sound of w.

wag wax wet

web wed well

wick will win

w w w w w w

Attention Parent/Teacher: Read the words to your child. Emphasizing the sound of the letter, instruct your child to trace and write the letter. As your child writes, read the following Zaner-Bloser Stroke Descriptions: Touch the midline; slant right to the baseline. Slant up (right) to the midline. Slant right to the baseline. Slant up (right) to the midline.

Today is Wednesday.
I taste things that begin with the sound of w.

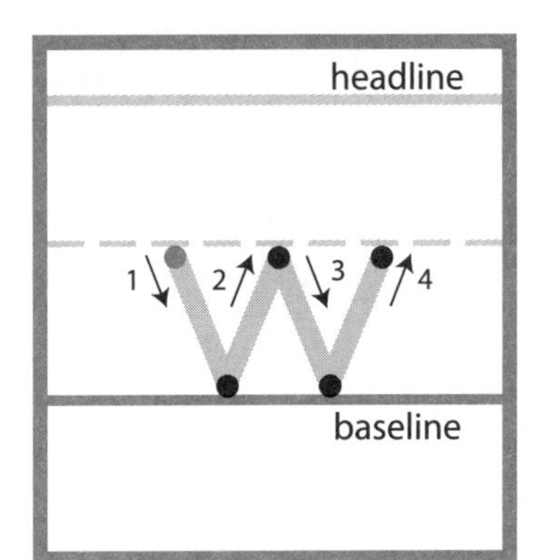

w w w w w w

Attention Parent/Teacher: Using bright colored pencils, your child may draw pictures of today's items beginning with the sound of **w**. Emphasizing the sound of the letter, instruct your child to trace and write the letter. As your child writes, read the following Zaner-Bloser Stroke Descriptions: Touch the midline; slant right to the baseline. Slant up (right) to the midline. Slant right to the baseline. Slant up (right) to the midline.

Today is Thursday.
I smell things that begin with the sound of w.

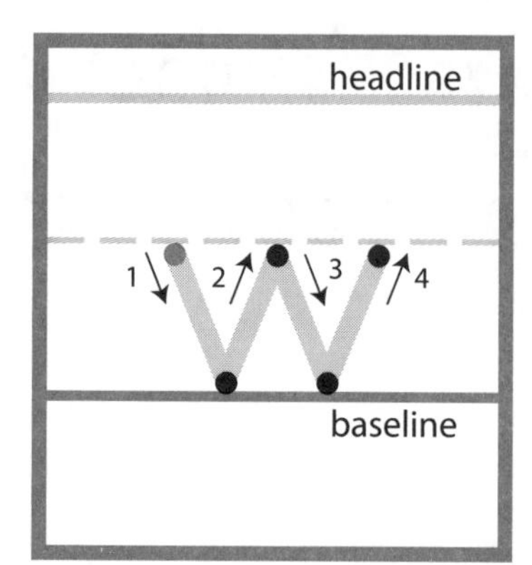

w w w w w w

Attention Parent/Teacher: Using bright colored pencils, your child may draw pictures of today's items beginning with the sound of **w**. Emphasizing the sound of the letter, instruct your child to trace and write the letter. As your child writes, read the following Zaner-Bloser Stroke Descriptions: Touch the midline; slant right to the baseline. Slant up (right) to the midline. Slant right to the baseline. Slant up (right) to the midline.

Today is Friday.
I touch things that begin with the sound of w.

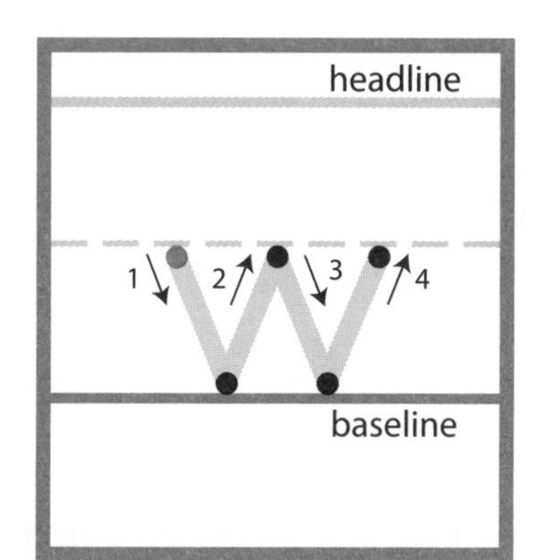

w w w w w w

Attention Parent/Teacher: Using bright colored pencils, your child may draw pictures of today's items beginning with the sound of **w**. Emphasizing the sound of the letter, instruct your child to trace and write the letter. As your child writes, read the following Zaner-Bloser Stroke Descriptions: Touch the midline; slant right to the baseline. Slant up (right) to the midline. Slant right to the baseline. Slant up (right) to the midline.

Though poverty and work and woe
The masters of my life may be,
When times are worst,
Who does not know
Darkness is light with love of thee?

1. Touch the blue dot on the midline; slant right to the dot on the baseline. Lift.
2. Move to the right and touch the dot on the midline; slant left to the dot on the baseline. Lift.

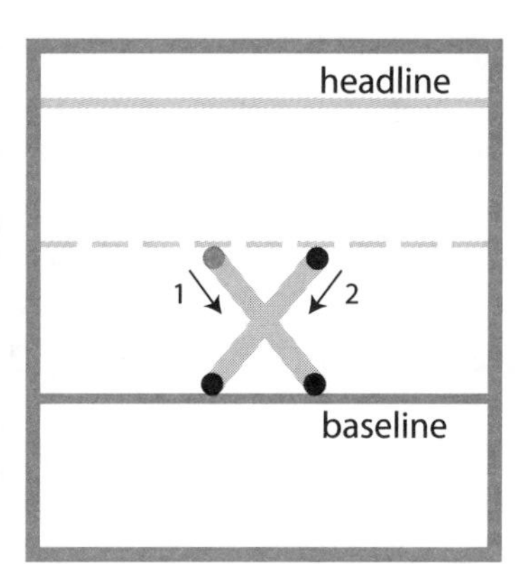

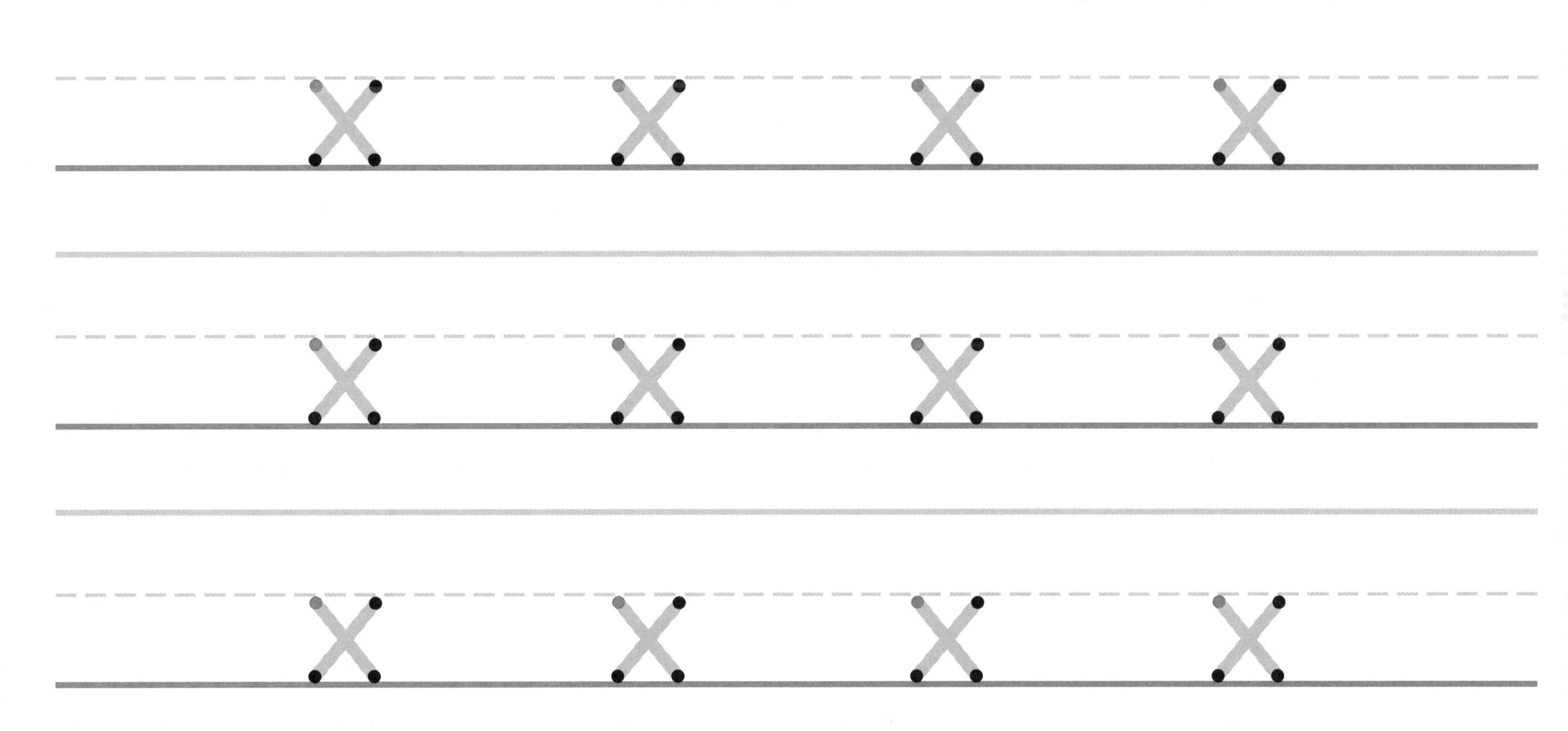

1. Touch the blue dot on the headline; slant right to the dot on the baseline. Lift.
2. Move to the right and touch the dot on the headline; slant left to the dot on the baseline, crossing near the midline. Lift.

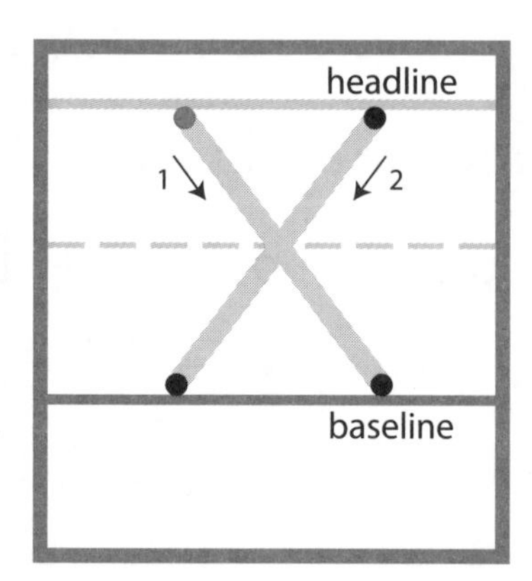

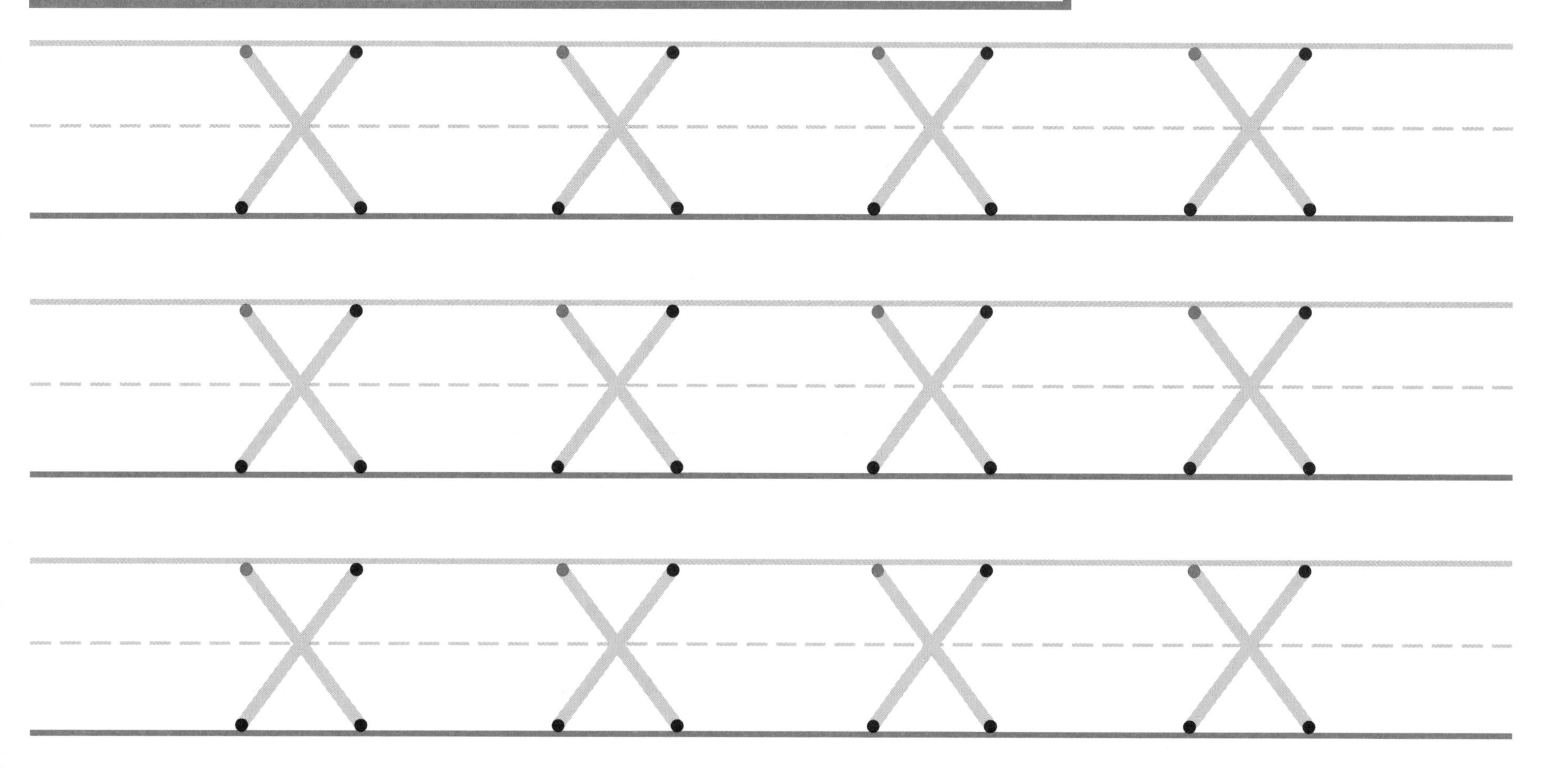

Today is Monday.

I see something that ends with the sound of x.

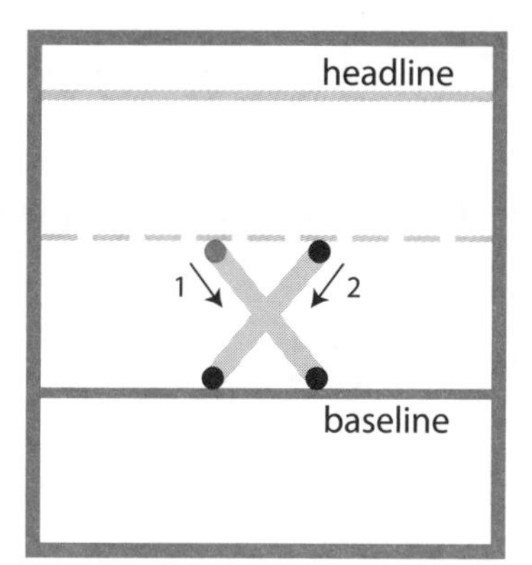

x x x x x x x

Attention Parent/Teacher: Using bright colored pencils, your child may draw pictures of today's items ending with the sound of **x**. Emphasizing the sound of the letter, instruct your child to trace and write the letter. As your child writes, read the following Zaner-Bloser Stroke Descriptions: Touch the midline; slant right to the baseline. Lift. Move to the right and touch the midline; slant left to the baseline.

Today is Tuesday.

I hear rhyming words that end with the sound of x.

ax	tax	wax
fix	mix	six
ox	box	fox

x x x x x x x

Attention Parent/Teacher: Read the rhyming words to your child. Emphasizing the sound of the letter, instruct your child to trace and write the letter. As your child writes, read the following Zaner-Bloser Stroke Descriptions: Touch the midline; slant right to the baseline. Lift. Move to the right and touch the midline; slant left to the baseline.

Today is Wednesday.

I taste something that ends with the sound of x.

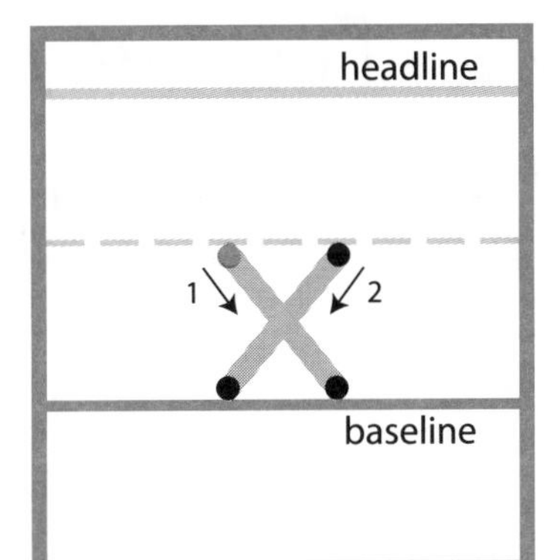

x x x x x x x

Attention Parent/Teacher: Cooking experience: Using a mix such as a cake mix or drink mix, emphasize the taste of the mix. Using bright colored pencils, your child may draw pictures of today's items ending with the sound of **x**. As your child writes, read the following Zaner-Bloser Stroke Descriptions: Touch the midline; slant right to the baseline. Lift. Move to the right and touch the midline; slant left to the baseline.

Today is Thursday.

I smell something that ends with the sound of x.

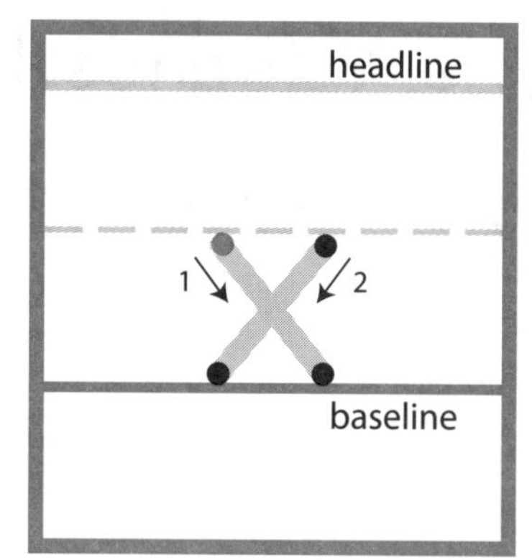

x x x x x x x

Attention Parent/Teacher: Using a mix such as a cake mix or drink mix, emphasize the smell of the mix. Using bright colored pencils, your child may draw pictures of today's items ending with the sound of **x**. As your child writes, read the following Zaner-Bloser Stroke Descriptions: Touch the midline; slant right to the baseline. Lift. Move to the right and touch the midline; slant left to the baseline.

Today is Friday.

I touch something that ends with the sound of x.

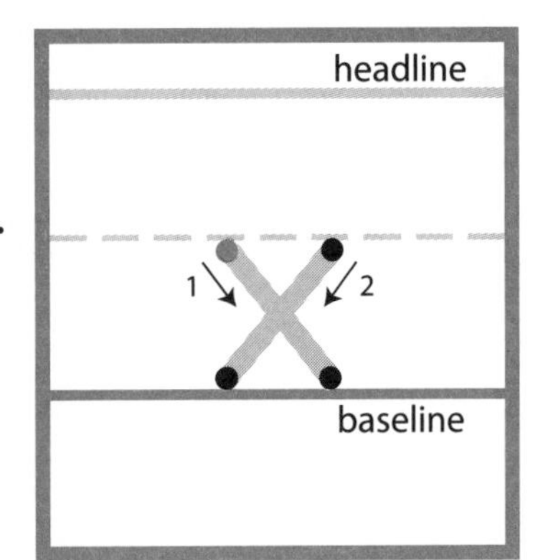

x x x x x x x

Attention Parent/Teacher: Allow your child to touch candle wax when it is hard and cool as well as when it is soft and warm. Using bright colored pencils, your child may draw pictures of today's items ending with the sound of **x**. As your child writes, read the following Zaner-Bloser Stroke Descriptions: Touch the midline; slant right to the baseline. Lift. Move to the right and touch the midline; slant left to the baseline.

But scornful men have coldly said
Thy love was leading me from God;
And yet in this I did but tread
The very path my Savior trod.

1. Touch the blue dot on the midline; slant right to the dot on the baseline. Lift.
2. Move to the right and touch the dot on the midline; slant left through the dot on the baseline to the dot on the next line. Lift.

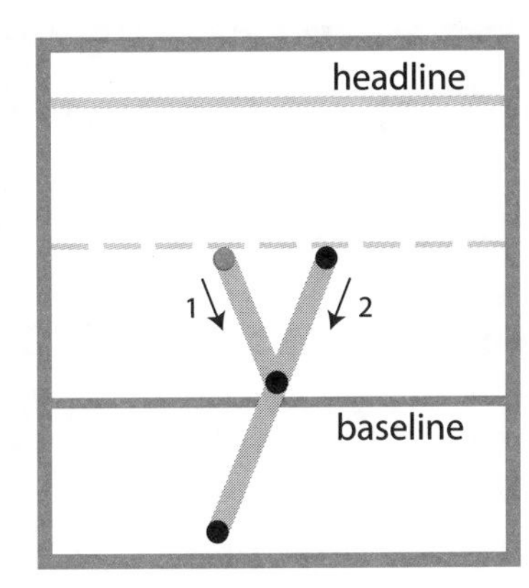

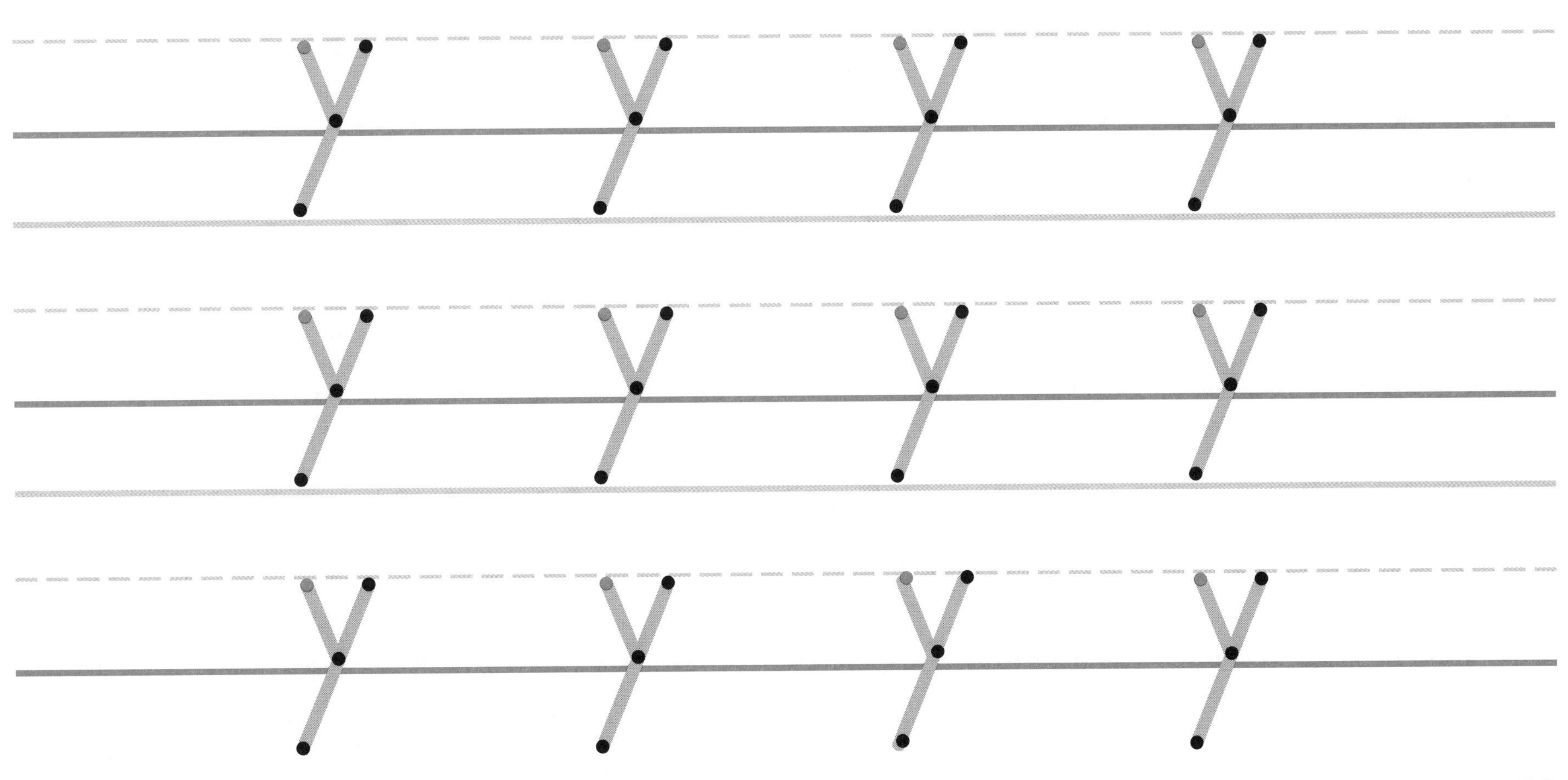

1. Touch the blue dot on the headline; slant right to the dot on the midline. Lift.
2. Move to the right and touch the dot on the headline; slant left to the dot on the midline. Pull down straight to the dot on the baseline. Lift.

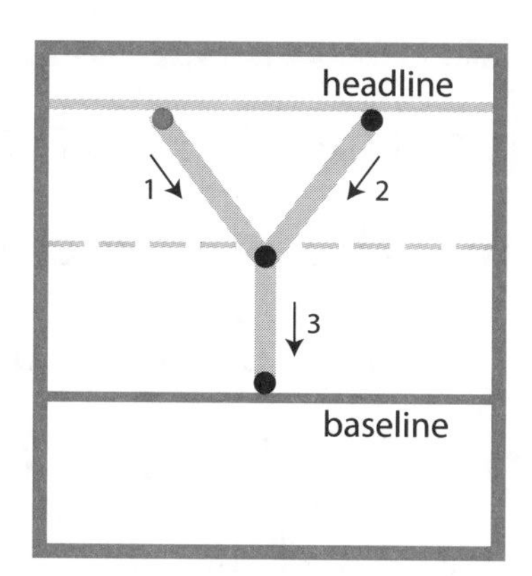

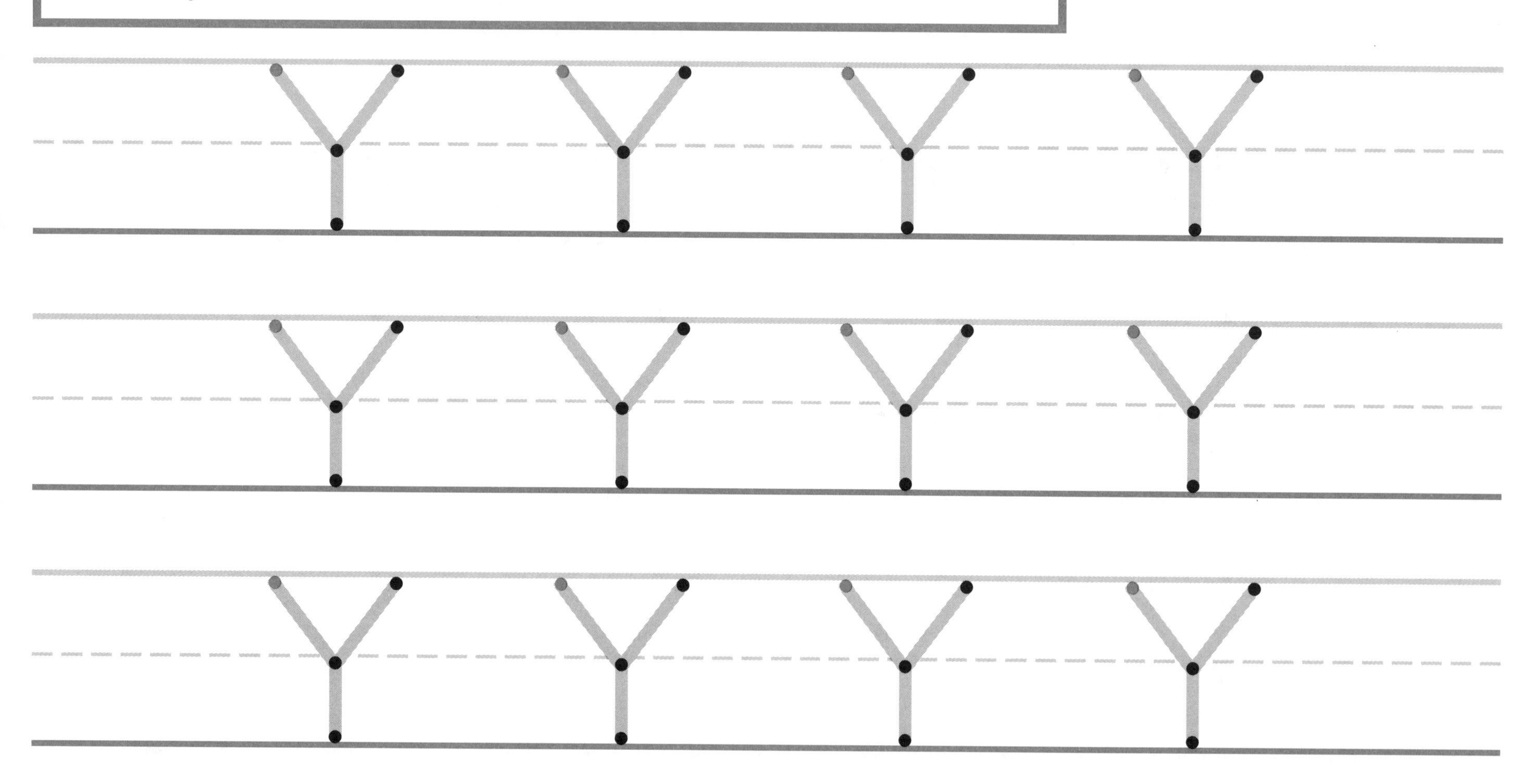

Today is Monday.

I see things that begin with the sound of y.

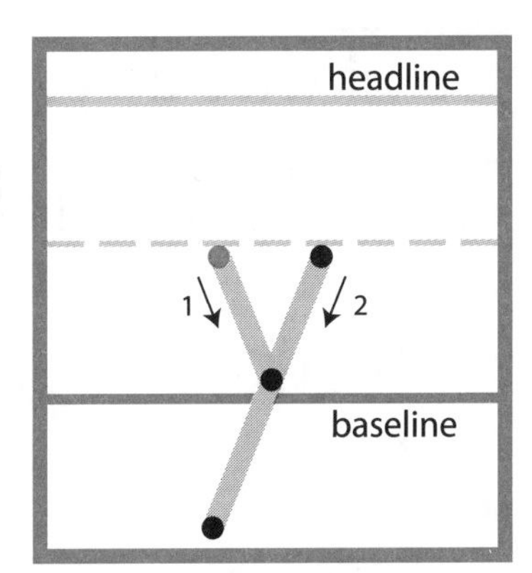

y y y y y y y

Attention Parent/Teacher: Using bright colored pencils, your child may draw pictures of today's items beginning with the sound of **y**. Emphasizing the sound of the letter, instruct your child to trace and write the letter. As your child writes, read the following Zaner-Bloser Stroke Descriptions: Touch the midline; slant right to the baseline. Lift. Move to the right and touch the midline; slant left through the baseline.

Today is Tuesday.

I hear words that begin with the sound of y.

yak	yell	yuk
yam	yes	yum
yap	yet	yo-yo

y y y y y y y

Attention Parent/Teacher: Read the words to your child. Emphasizing the sound of the letter, instruct your child to trace and write the letter. As your child writes, read the following Zaner-Bloser Stroke Descriptions: Touch the midline; slant right to the baseline. Lift. Move to the right and touch the midline; slant left through the baseline.

Today is Wednesday.
I taste things that begin with the sound of y.

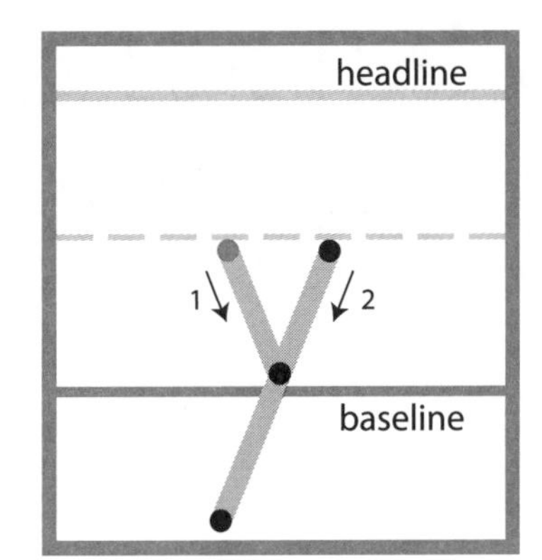

y y y y y y y

Attention Parent/Teacher: Using bright colored pencils, your child may draw pictures of today's items beginning with the sound of **y**. Emphasizing the sound of the letter, instruct your child to trace and write the letter. As your child writes, read the following Zaner-Bloser Stroke Descriptions: Touch the midline; slant right to the baseline. Lift. Move to the right and touch the midline; slant left through the baseline.

Today is Thursday.

I smell things that begin with the sound of y.

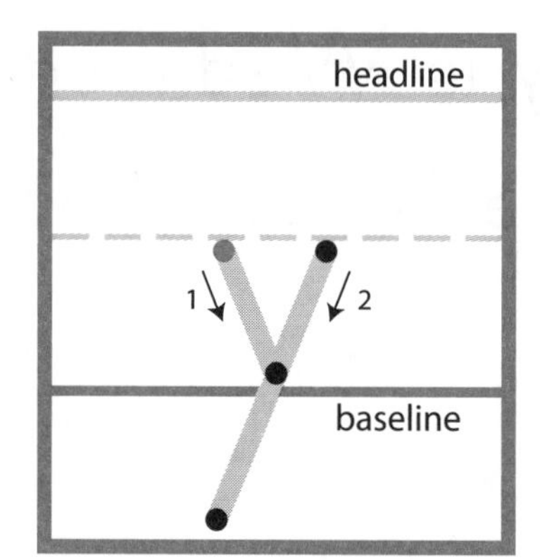

y y y y y y y

Attention Parent/Teacher: Using bright colored pencils, your child may draw pictures of today's items beginning with the sound of **y**. Emphasizing the sound of the letter, instruct your child to trace and write the letter. As your child writes, read the following Zaner-Bloser Stroke Descriptions: Touch the midline; slant right to the baseline. Lift. Move to the right and touch the midline; slant left through the baseline.

Today is Friday.

I touch things that begin with the sound of y.

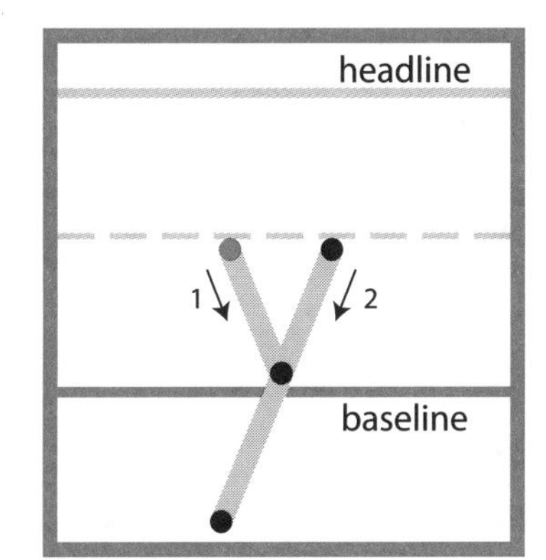

Attention Parent/Teacher: Using bright colored pencils, your child may draw pictures of today's items beginning with the sound of **y**. Emphasizing the sound of the letter, instruct your child to trace and write the letter. As your child writes, read the following Zaner-Bloser Stroke Descriptions: Touch the midline; slant right to the baseline. Lift. Move to the right and touch the midline; slant left through the baseline.

They know but little of thy worth
Who speak these heartless words to me,
For what did Jesus love on earth
One half so tenderly as thee?

Touch the blue dot on the headline; pull down straight to the dot on the baseline. Lift.

headline

1↓

baseline

Number One

Trace the number one on the lines.

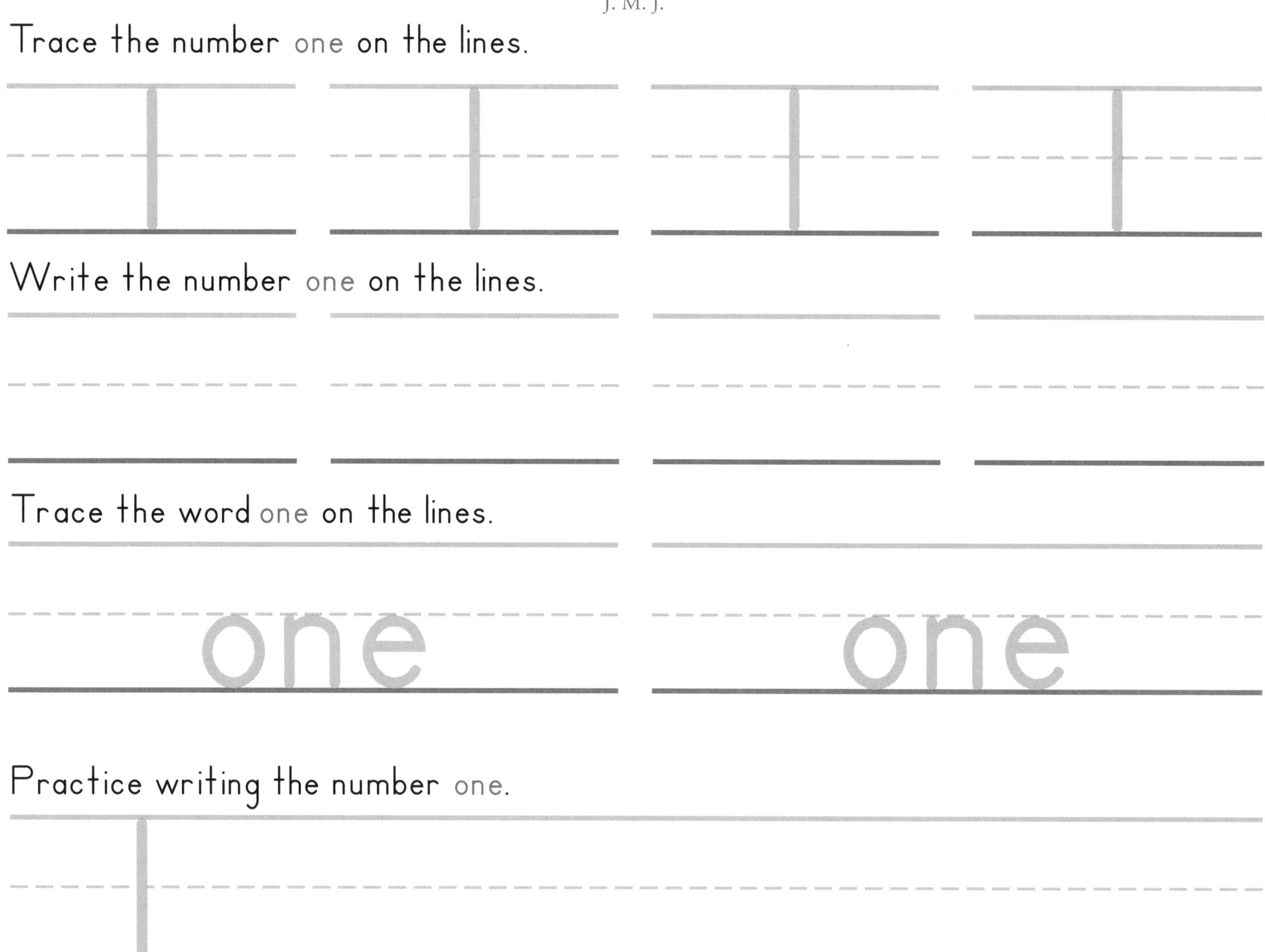

Write the number one on the lines.

Trace the word one on the lines.

Practice writing the number one.

Touch the blue dot below the headline; curve forward clockwise; slant left to the dot on the baseline. Pause; slide right to the dot. Lift.

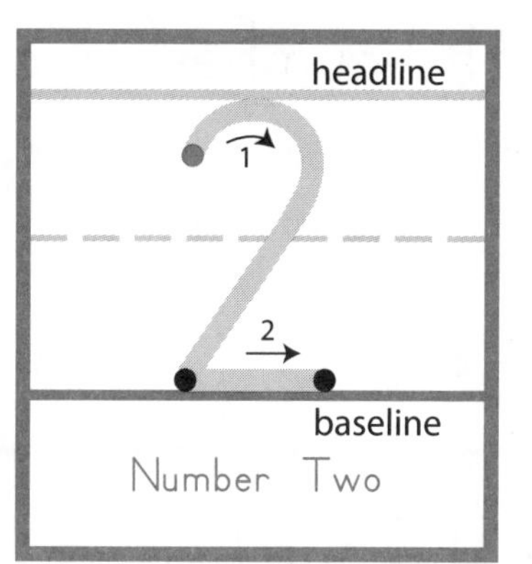

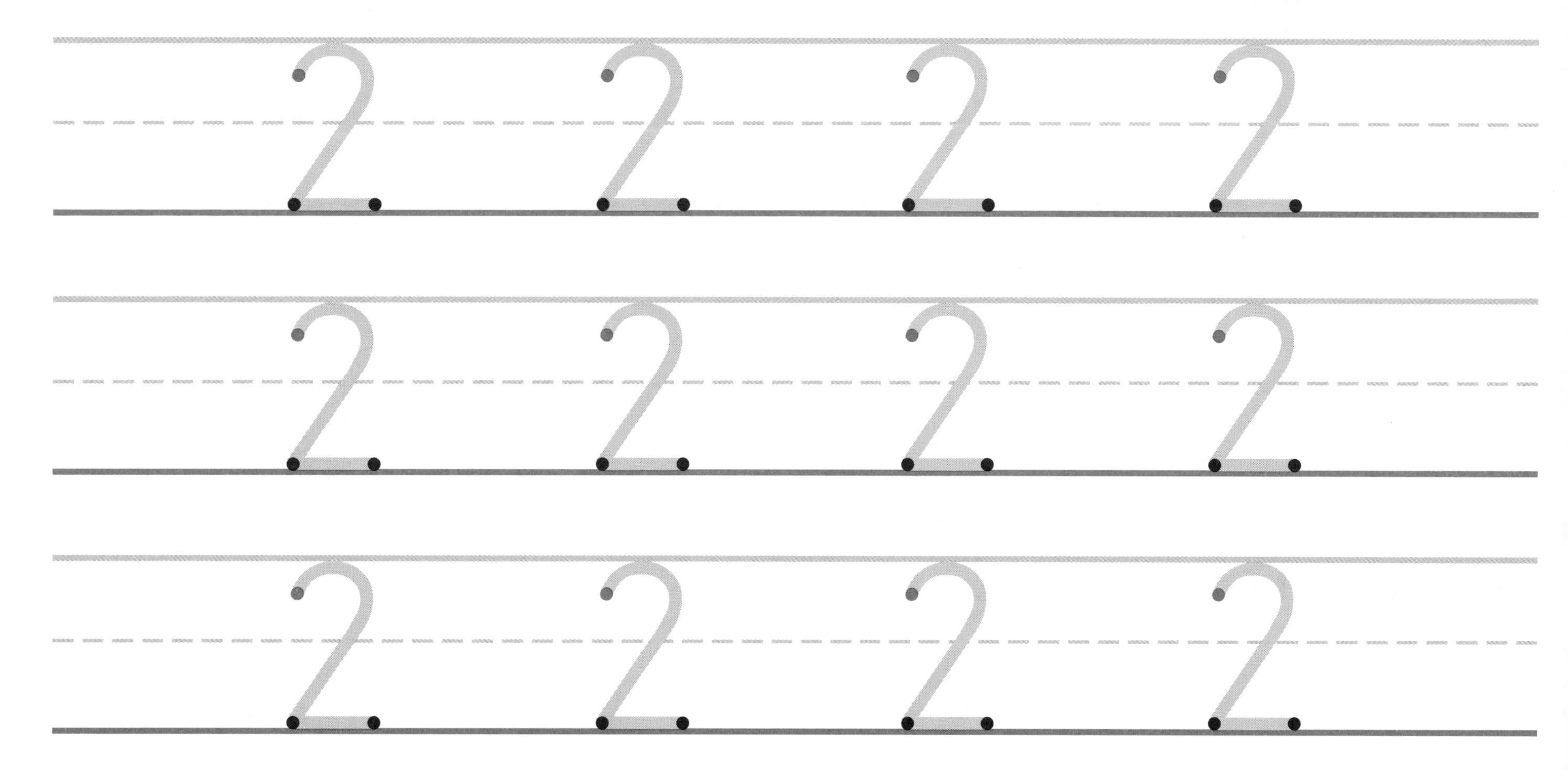

Trace the number two on the lines.

2 2 2 2

Write the number two on the lines.

Trace the word two on the lines.

two two

Practice writing the number two.

2

a b c d e f g h i j k l m n o p q r s t u v w x y z

Write the missing letters to complete the alphabet.

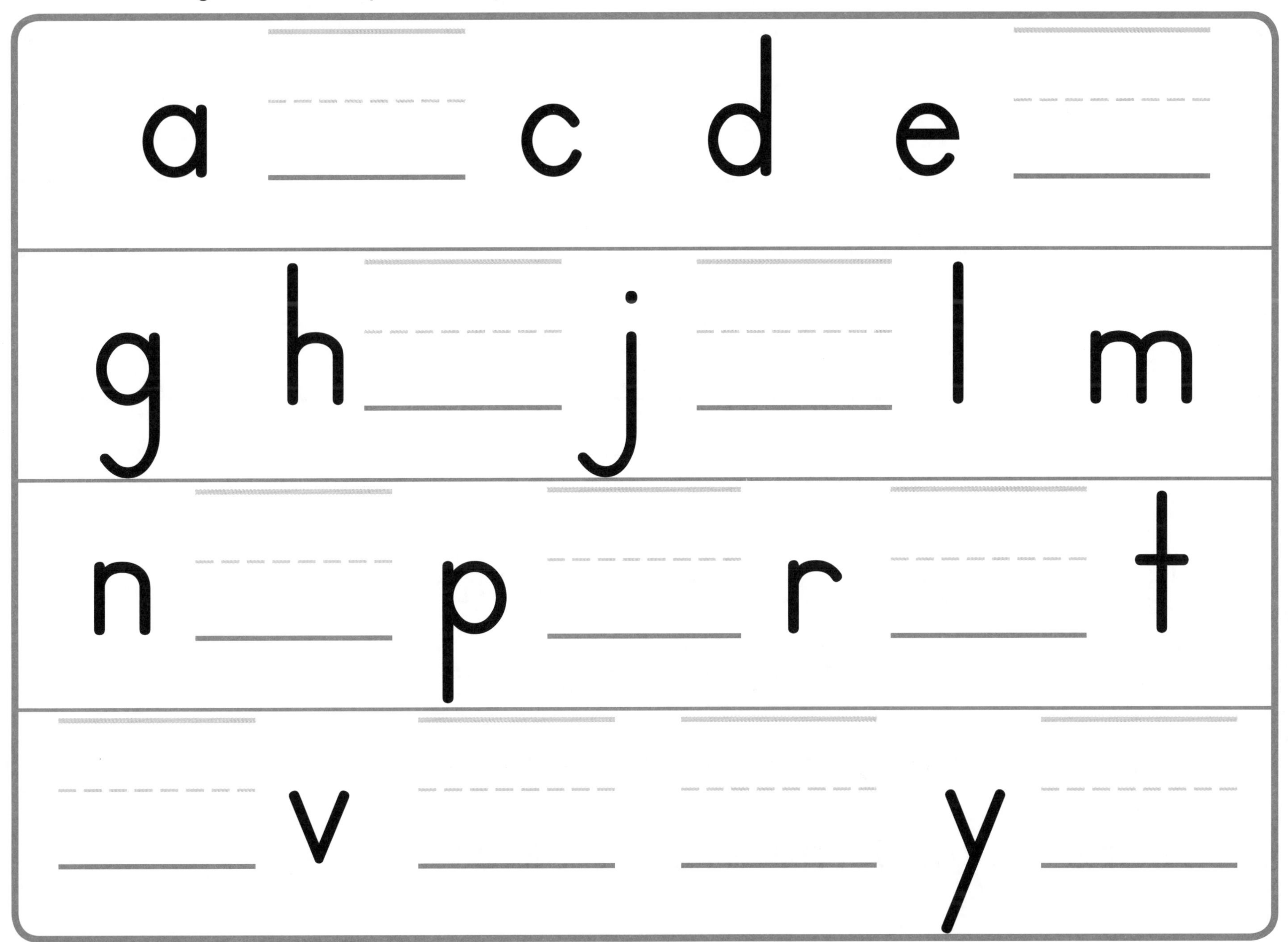

Hear thy child, gentlest Mother,
Prayerful heart to thee arise;
Hear me while my evening Ave
Soars beyond the starry skies.

Touch the blue dot below the headline; curve forward clockwise to the dot on the midline; curve forward clockwise, ending on the dot above the baseline. Lift.

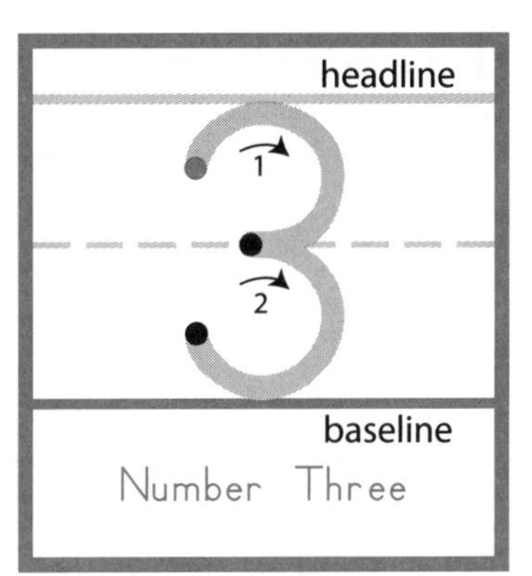

Trace the number three on the lines.

3 3 3 3

Write the number three on the lines.

Trace the word three on the lines.

three three

Practice writing the number three.

3

1. Touch the blue dot on the headline; pull down straight to the dot on the midline. Pause; slide right to the dot. Lift.
2. Move to the right and touch the dot on the headline; pull down straight to the dot on the baseline. Lift.

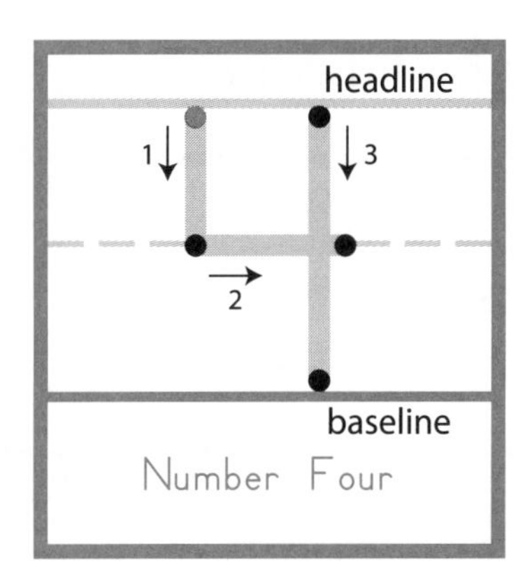

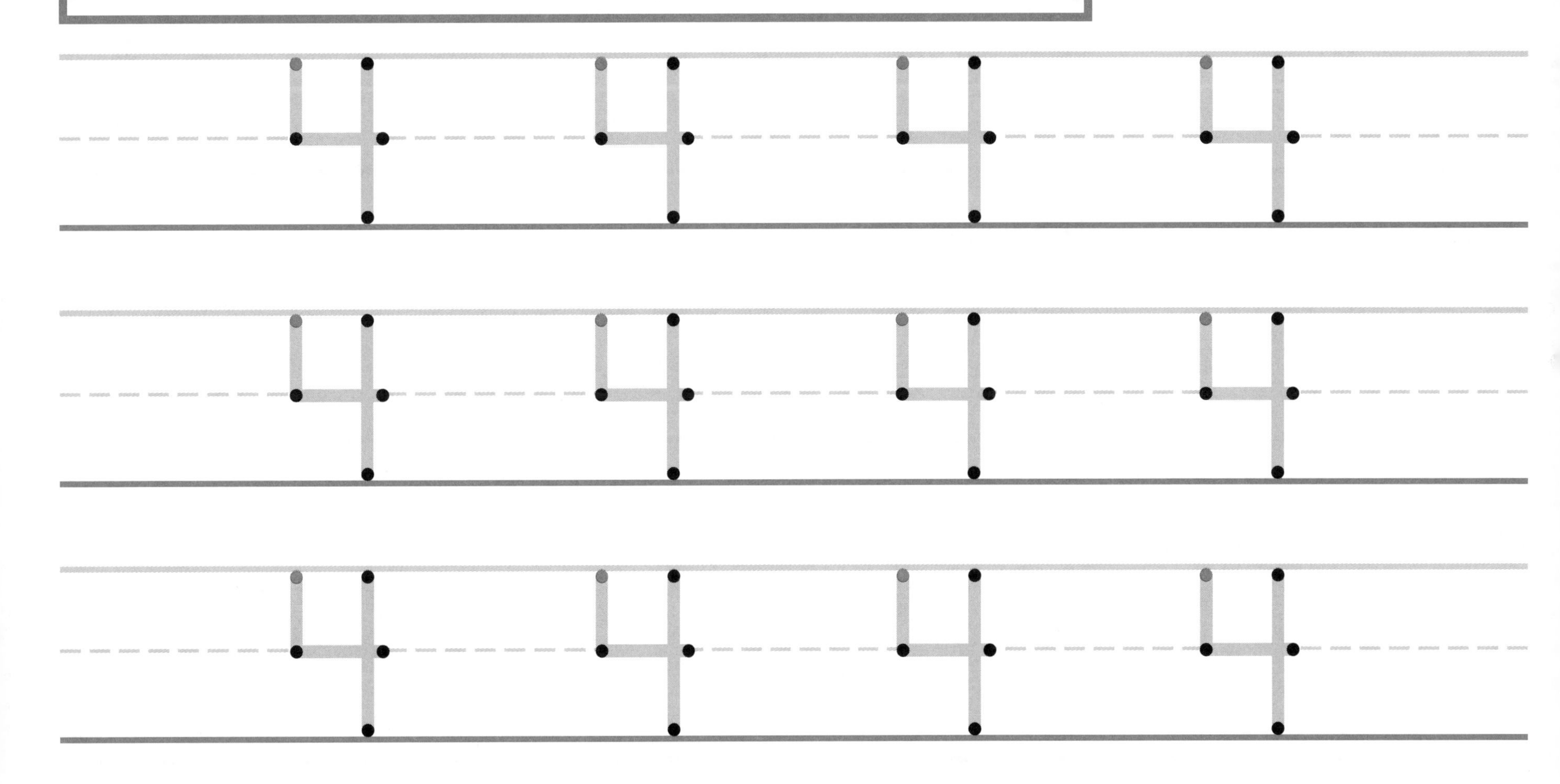

Trace the number four on the lines.

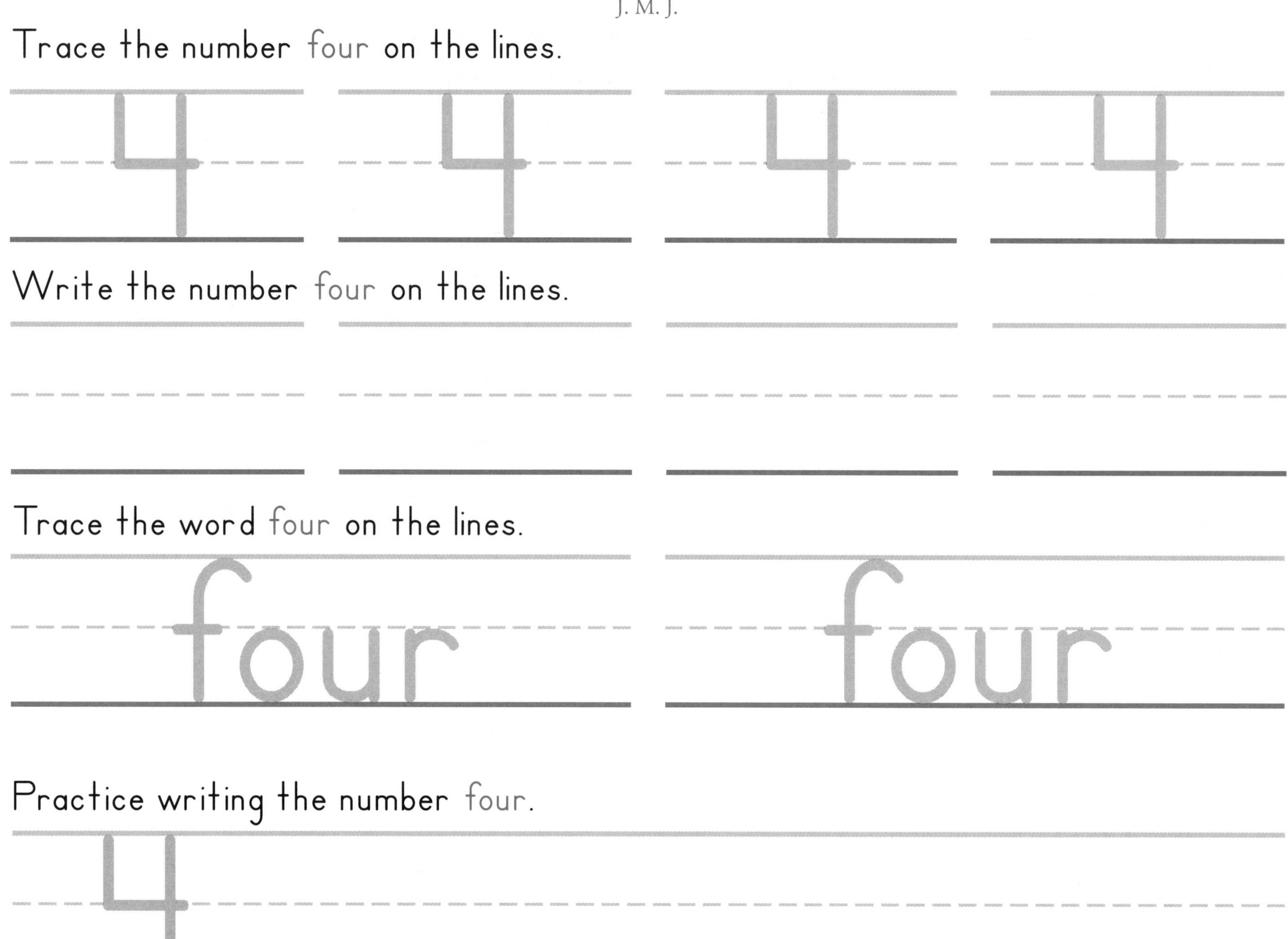

Write the number four on the lines.

Trace the word four on the lines.

Practice writing the number four.

a b c d e f g h i j k l m n o p q r s t u v w x y z

Write the missing letters to complete the alphabet.

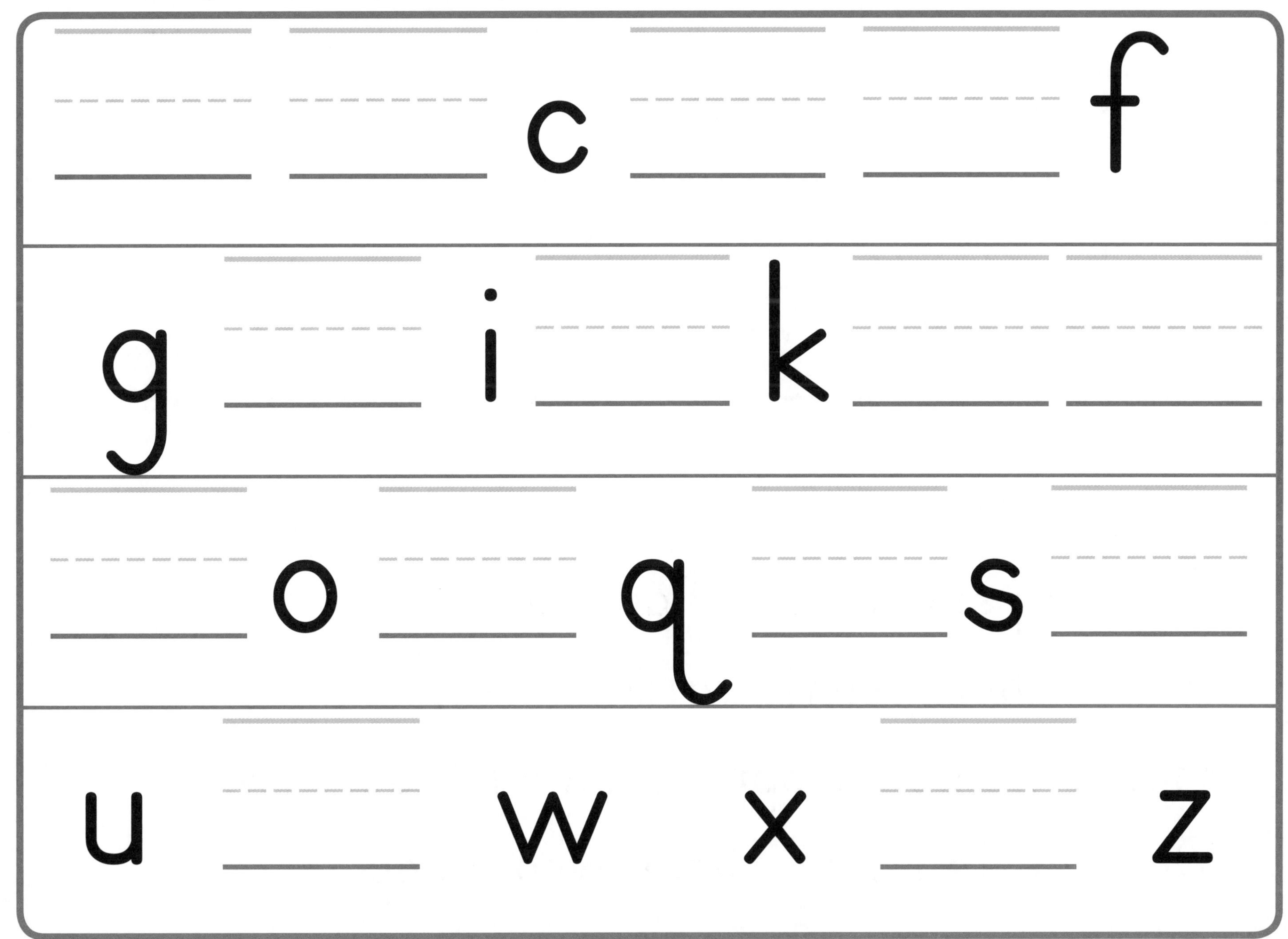

Darkling shadows fall around me,
Stars their silent watches keep;
Hush the heart oppressed with sorrow,
Dry the tears of those who weep.

1. Touch the blue dot on the headline; pull down straight to the dot on the midline. Pause; circle forward clockwise, ending on the dot above the baseline. Lift.
2. Touch the blue dot on the headline; slide right to the dot. Lift.

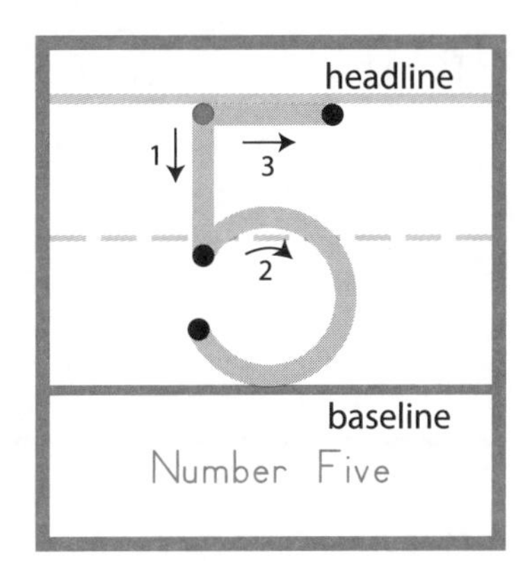

Trace the number five on the lines.

5 5 5 5

Write the number five on the lines.

Trace the word five on the lines.

five

Practice writing the number five.

5

Touch the blue dot on the headline; curve down to the dot on the baseline; curve up counterclockwise to the midline and around to close the circle on the dot on the midline. Lift.

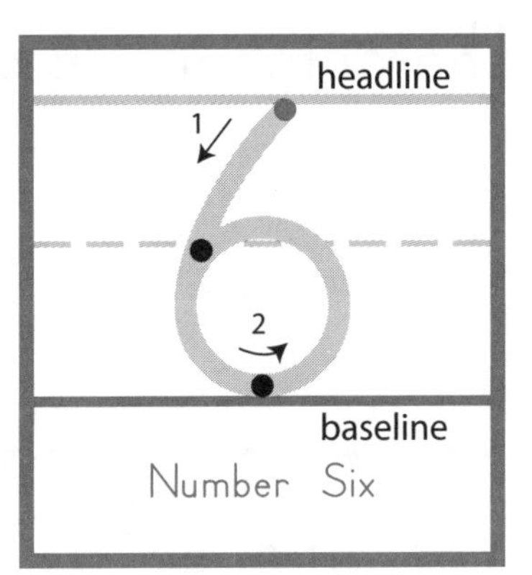

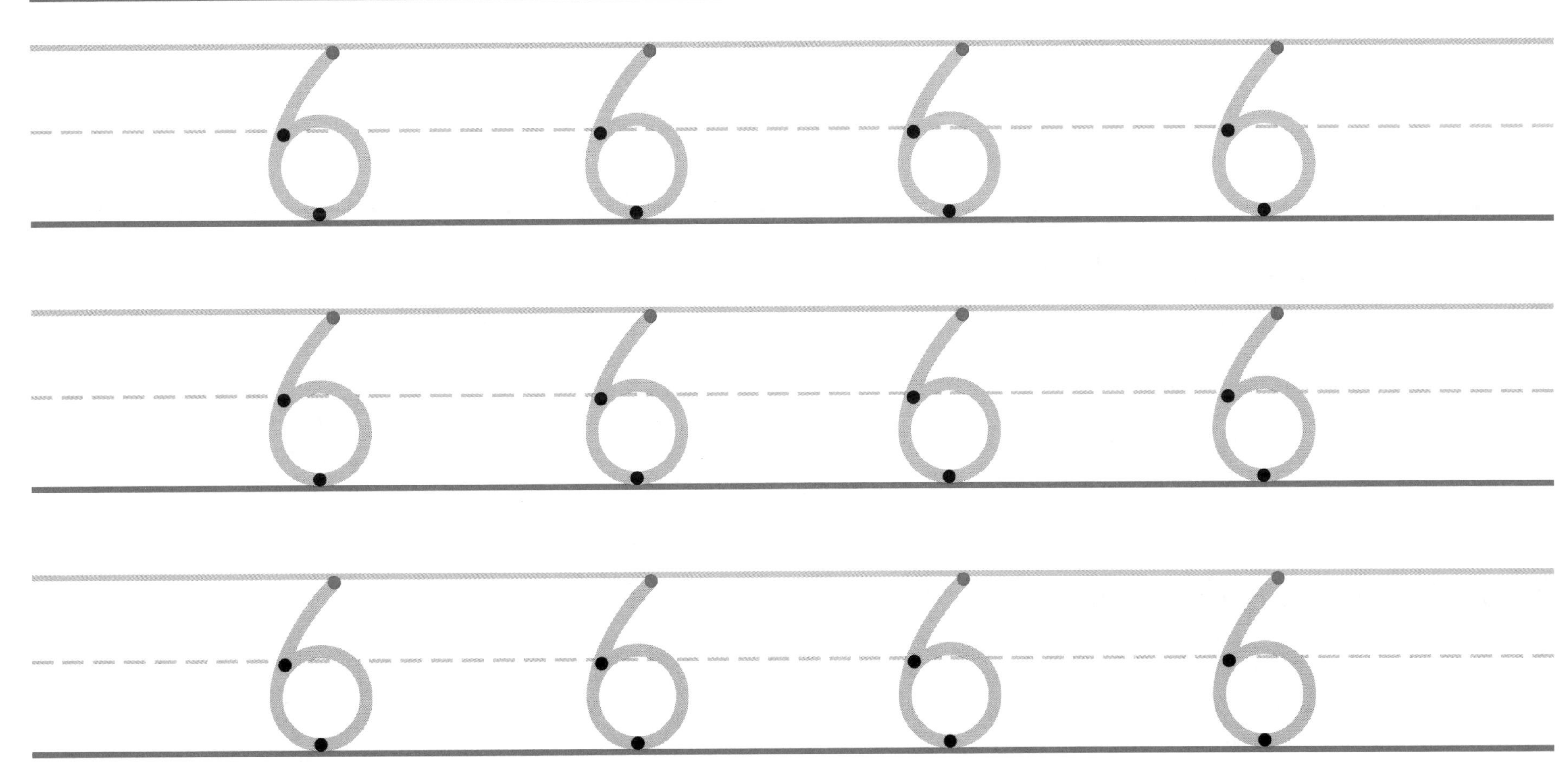

Trace the number six on the lines.

6 6 6 6

Write the number six on the lines.

Trace the word six on the lines.

six six

Practice writing the number six.

6

a b c d e f g h i j k l m n o p q r s t u v w x y z

Write the missing letters to complete the alphabet.

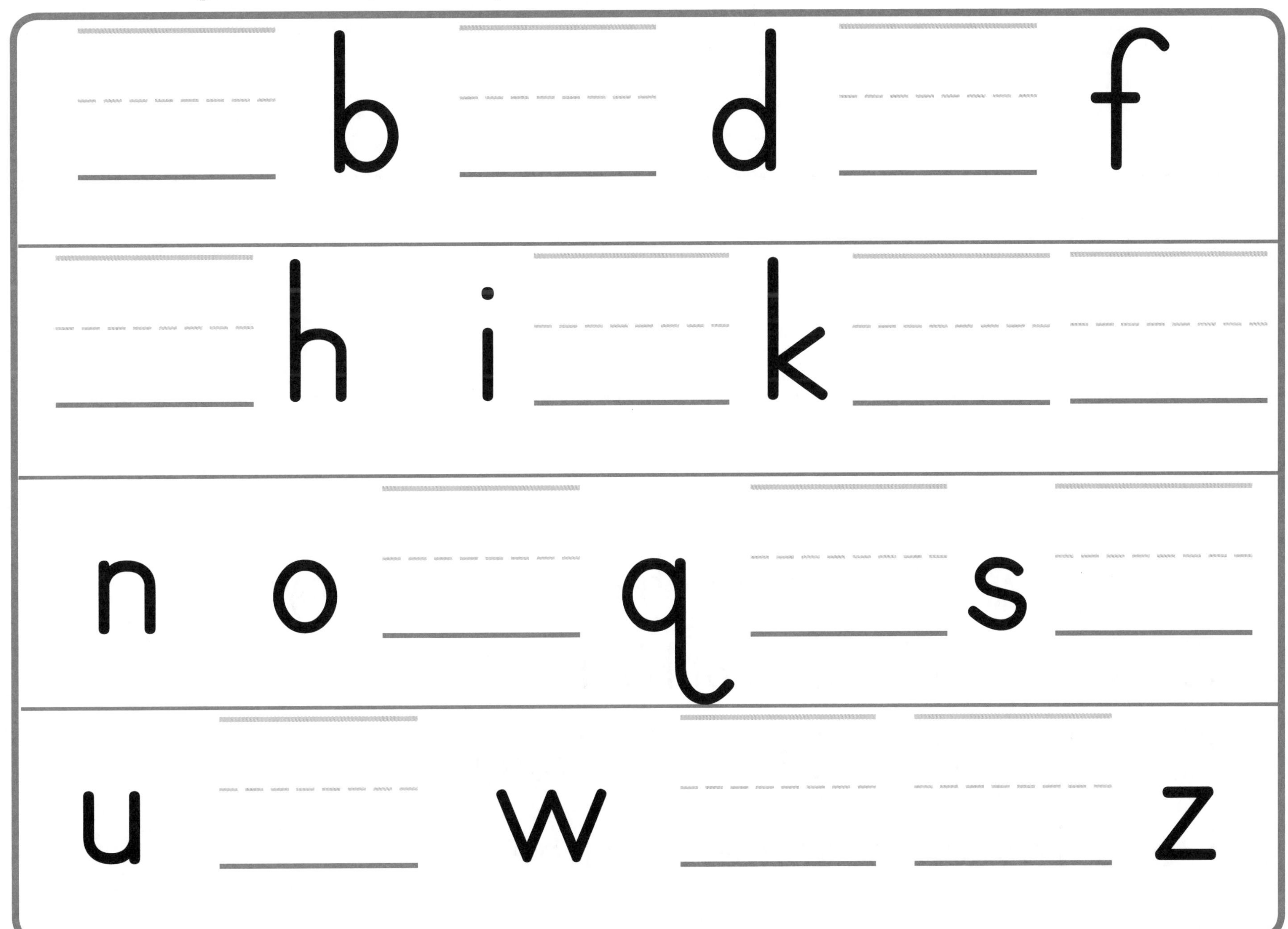

Hear, sweet Mother, hear the weary,
Borne upon life's troubled sea;
Gentle guiding Star of Ocean,
Lead thy child home to thee.

Touch the blue dot on the headline; slide right to the dot. Pause; slant left to the dot on the baseline. Lift.

headline

1

2

baseline

Number Seven

Trace the number seven on the lines.

7 7 7 7

Write the number seven on the lines.

Trace the word seven on the lines.

seven seven

Practice writing the number seven.

7

Touch the blue dot below the headline; curve back counterclockwise to the midline; curve forward clockwise, touching the dot on the baseline; curve up and slant up through the blue dot and to the dot on the headline. Lift.

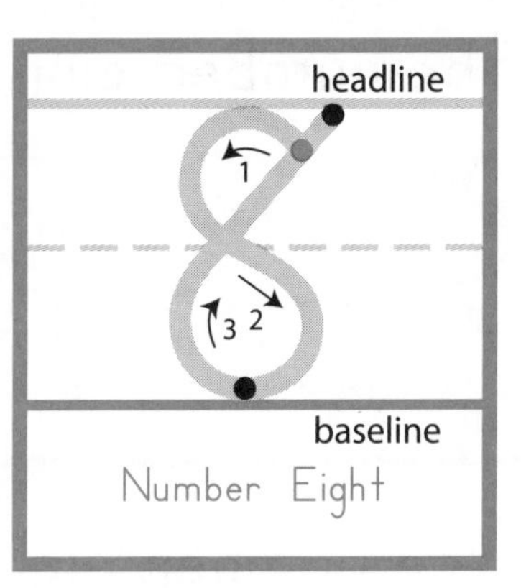

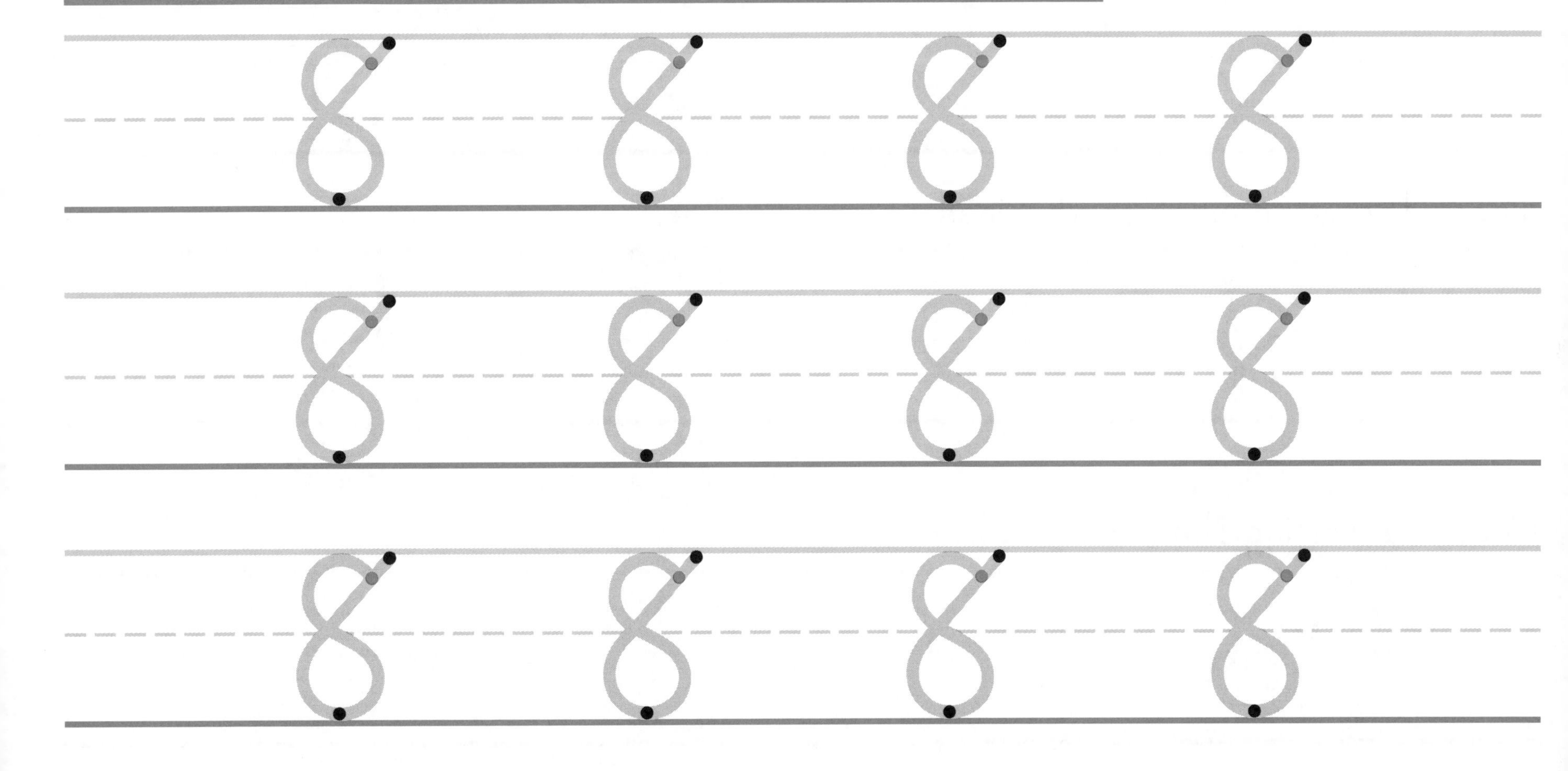

Trace the number eight on the lines.

8 8 8 8

Write the number eight on the lines.

Trace the word eight on the lines.

eight eight

Practice writing the number eight.

8

a b c d e f g h i j k l m n o p q r s t u v w x y z

Write the missing letters to complete the alphabet.

a b ___ d e ___

g ___ i j ___ l m

n ___ p ___ r s ___

u v ___ x y ___

Still watch over me, dearest Mother,
From thy beauteous throne above;
Guard me from all harm and danger,
'Neath thy sheltering wings of love.

Touch the blue dot below the headline; circle back counterclockwise all the way around and back to the blue dot. Pause; pull straight down to the dot on the baseline.

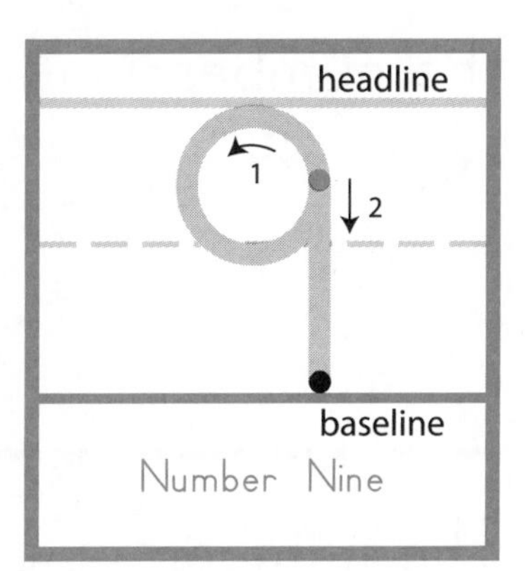

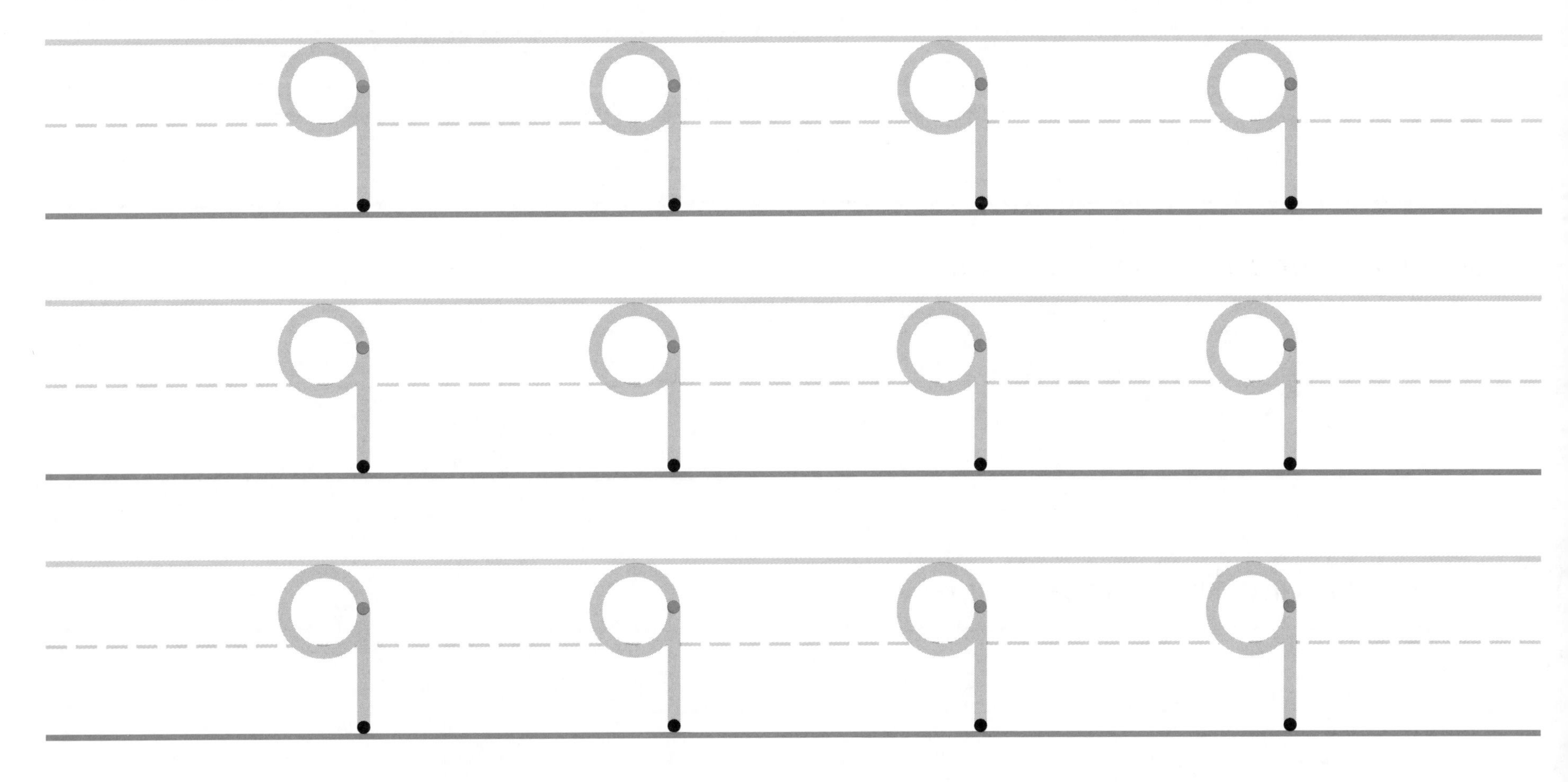

Trace the number nine on the lines.

9 9 9 9

Write the number nine on the lines.

Trace the word nine on the lines.

nine nine

Practice writing the number nine.

9

1. Touch the blue dot on the headline; pull down straight to the dot on the baseline. Lift.
2. Touch the blue dot on the headline; curve down counterclockwise to the dot on the baseline; curve up to the blue dot on the headline. Lift.

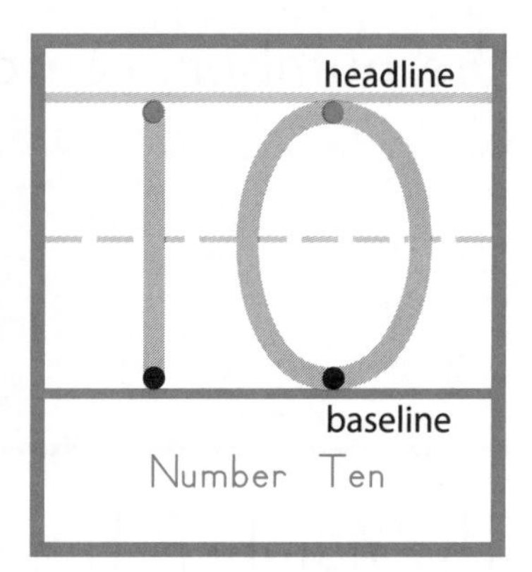

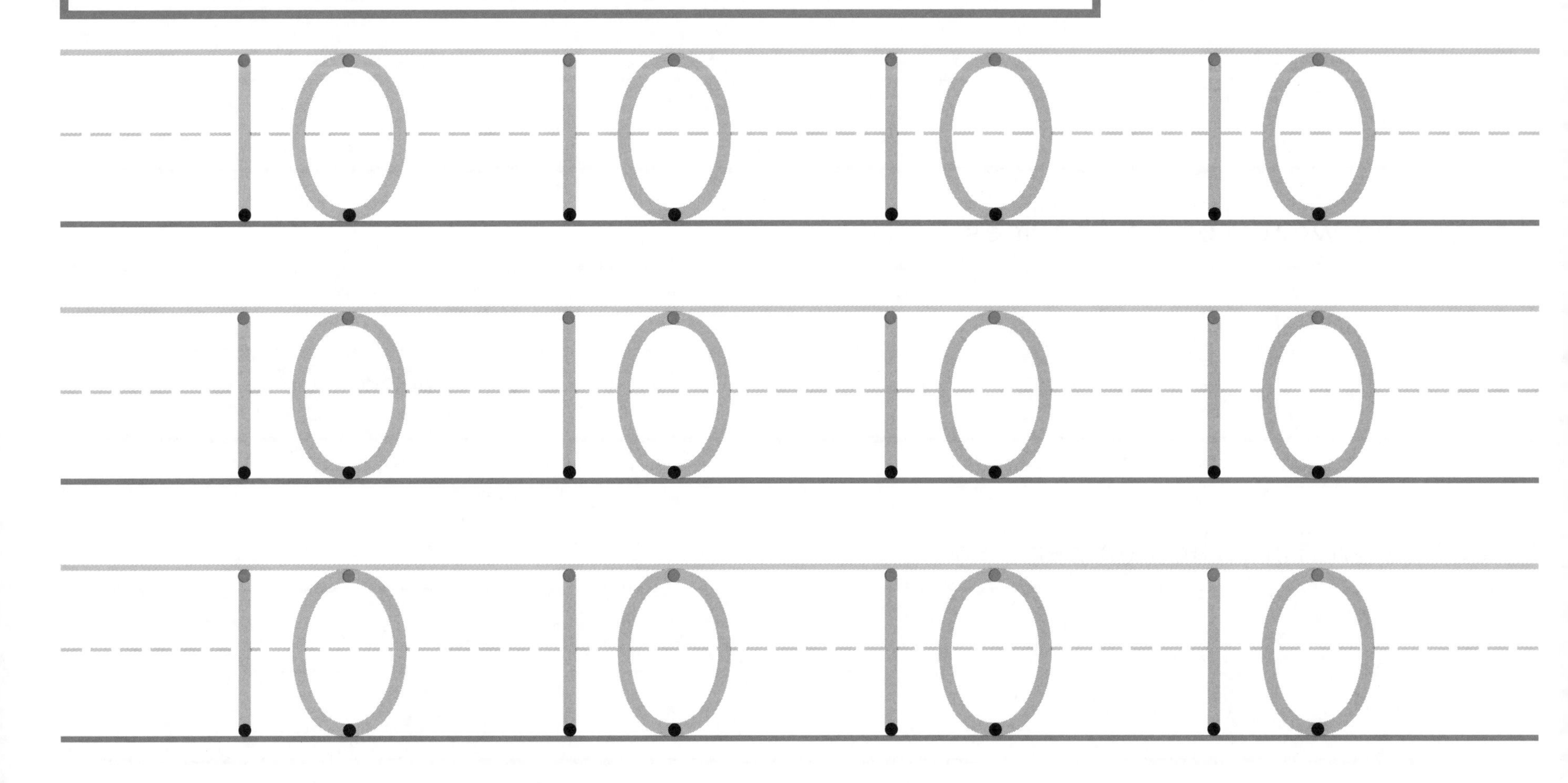

Trace the number ten on the lines.

10 10 10 10

Write the number ten on the lines.

Trace the word ten on the lines.

ten ten

Practice writing the number ten.

10

Hail Mary, full of grace,
The Lord is with thee.
Blessed art thou among women,
And blessed is the Fruit of thy womb, Jesus.

Holy Mary, Mother of God,
Pray for us sinners,
Now and at the hour of our death.
Amen.